Logic Circuits

Third Edition

Also by Noel Morris:
Control Engineering
Industrial Electronics
Advanced Industrial Electronics

Logic Circuits

Third Edition

Noel M. Morris
Principal Lecturer
North Staffordshire Polytechnic

McGRAW-HILL Book Company (UK) Limited

London · New York · St Louis · San Francisco · Auckland · Bogotá
Guatamela · Hamburg · Johannesburg · Lisbon · Madrid · Mexico
Montreal · New Delhi · Panama · Paris · San Juan · São Paulo
Singapore · Sydney · Tokyo · Toronto

Published by
McGraw-Hill Book Company (UK) Limited
Maidenhead · Berkshire · England

British Library Cataloguing in Publication Data

Morris, Noel M.
  Logic circuits—3rd ed.
  1. Logic circuits
  I. Title
  621.3815'37   TK7868.L6

  ISBN 0-07-084672-3

Library of Congress Cataloging in Publication Data

Morris, Noel Malcolm.
  Logic circuits.

  Bibliography: p.
  Includes index.
  1. Logic circuits.   2. Digital electronics.
  3. Microprocessors.   I. Title.
  TK7868.L6M67 1983   621.3819'5835   82-25874
  ISBN 0-07-084672-3

12345CP8543

Printed and bound in Great Britain

Preface

The sweeping changes that have taken place in the field of digital electronics in recent years have made a revision of the book necessary. This edition of the book provides coverage not only of static logic circuits, logic families, integrated circuits, counters, memories, and shift registers, but also of the ubiquitous microprocessor. This book provides coverage of vital aspects of digital electronics in a wide range of courses including undergraduate courses and TEC certificate, higher certificate, and diploma courses. It will be of value not only to undergraduates and postgraduates in many fields of science and engineering but also to the reader studying related subjects. The book will also be useful to established engineers who need an introduction to the rapidly expanding field of digital electronics, and to the reader studying on his own.

The arrangement not only of the chapters in this edition but also of the content of the chapters has been altered to emphasize the importance of microprocessor-based systems. The book has been thoroughly revised, new material has been added, and dated material removed.

To aid the understanding of logical problems, a systematic approach has been used, commencing with an introduction to the fundamentals of logic with emphasis on mapping techniques. In the second chapter, the process of converting logical equations into electronic hardware is described, together with techniques for the minimization of logic networks.

Chapters 3 and 4 are devoted to a study of a wide variety of semiconductor circuits and integrated circuit logic families. The latter includes TTL, I^{2}L, ECL, and MOS gates together with an introduction to interfacing methods. Programmable logic arrays and uncommited logic arrays are also covered.

In this edition the scope of the chapter on flip-flops and data storage has been broadened to include information and circuits of integrated circuit memories.

Chapter 7 covers the design of synchronous counters, shift registers, and code convertors; the use of programmable logic arrays and ROMs as code convertors is also described. This chapter also deals with parallel adders and subtractors, together with a hardware multiplying circuit.

Chapter 8 introduces microprocessors and microcomputers, and deals with the architecture of a typical microprocessor, its three-bus system, its memory map, and address decoding. The register structure of popular central processing units is described. A vital feature of any microprocessor is its instruction set and addressing modes. In Chapter 9, ten addressing modes used by a variety of microprocessors are described in detail, and their use is described. The instruction set of one of the most popular central processing units — the 6502 — is outlined, together with illustrative examples.

The final chapter covers assembly language programming and applications of microcomputers. The chapter commences with basic operations such as data transfer between locations in the memory and proceeds to outline arithmetic operations, input/output routines (including the use of programmable input/output ports), and driving light-emitting diodes and liquid crystal displays (including multiplexed displays). The work on input/output routines is extended to cover simple waveform generation, digital-to-analogue conversion, and analogue-to-digital conversion. A range of analogue-to-digital converters is described, including the high speed 'flash' convertor. The basis of peripheral handshake methods is outlined, together with stack operations, subroutines, interrupts, and direct memory access. The chapter is completed by an introduction to the IEEE-488 and IEC-625 instrument interface bus.

I would like to thank the manufacturers of the logic circuit and microprocessor products mentioned in the book, whose assistance was freely given. I am also indebted to colleagues at the North Staffordshire Polytechnic for the comments I have received from time to time, special thanks being due to Mr S. Rakowski, M.Sc. Thanks are due once more to the McGraw-Hill editorial and production staff for maintaining the quality of the book.

I am also greatly indebted to my wife for her help, assistance, and encouragement during the preparation of the book.

N. M. Morris

Contents

1. Fundamentals of logic

It is ironical to reflect that the foundation of modern logic theory has lain dormant for many years before being utilized in practice. The basis of logic as we now know it was set down in the nineteenth century by Boole, De Morgan, and others. Many generations were to pass before technologists began to realize the implications of these theories, and even longer for the fabrication techniques for the construction of 'logical' devices to be perfected.

1.1 Traditional logic

Traditional logic can be illustrated by considering groups of people, shown in Fig. 1.1. The whole population of any town, country, or continent can be split up into many distinct groups; three are shown in the figure. The selection of the groups is quite arbitrary, but every person falls into one or more of the categories shown. If he does not, he does not exist.

Thus a man is either a sailor (S) or a non-sailor ($\bar{S}$). The bar over the S signifies *negation*, or *logical inversion*, and is referred to as the logical NOT function. That is,

$$\bar{S} = \text{NOT } S$$

A man who is unmarried AND who is a sailor falls into the category $\overline{M}.S$. The 'dot' (.) is referred to as the logical AND function, or *connection*. This dot is frequently confused with the dot used to represent the arithmetic product function, but throughout this book it is used as the logical AND function. To make matters worse the AND operation is often described as the *logical product function*. Thus

$$\bar{M}.S = \text{a man who is unmarried AND is a sailor}$$

1

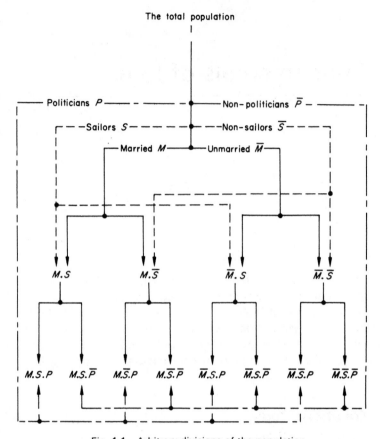

Fig. 1.1   Arbitrary divisions of the population

Whenever equality signs (=) are used in logical equations they refer to logical equality, which may not have the same meaning as arithmetic equality.

For each group of people there are two possible divisions. Thus the whole population can be split into married people (M) and unmarried people ($\bar{M}$). Alternatively, the population can be split into sailors (S) and non-sailors ($\bar{S}$), or into politicians (P) and non-politicians ($\bar{P}$). When the intersections of any two groups are considered there are 2^2 combinations. For instance, between groups M and S these combinations are $M.S$, $M.\bar{S}$, $\bar{M}.S$, and $\bar{M}.\bar{S}$. The number of intersections doubles each time an additional group is introduced. With three groups it is 2^3, shown in Fig. 1.1, and for n groups it is 2^n. In all cases the grand total of all the intersections cannot exceed the total population, which is therefore referred to as the whole or unity (1).

1.2 The Venn diagram

The condition for one division of the population, discussed in Sec. 1.1, is shown diagrammatically in the Venn diagram in Fig. 1.2(a). The whole population is represented by the square, while those who are married are within the circle. Unmarried people are represented on the diagram by the area outside the circle, but within the square. The diagram can also be shown in rectangular form, as in Fig. 1.2(b).

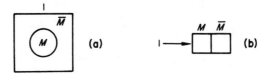

Fig. 1.2   Division of the population into married and unmarried people by (a) the Venn diagram and (b) a rectangular form of diagram

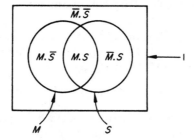

Fig. 1.3   Intersection of two groups of people on the Venn diagram

All possible intersections of two groups are shown in Fig. 1.3. All who are married lie within the left-hand circle, while all sailors are encompassed by the right-hand circle. Thus circle M contains both married non-sailors $(M . \bar{S})$ and married sailors $(M . S)$. The S circle contains married sailors $(M . S)$ and unmarried sailors $(\bar{M} . S)$. The area outside the circles is all that which is NOT within the two circles, i.e., unmarried non-sailors $(\bar{M} . \bar{S})$.

The union of divisions of the population can also be investigated by the Venn diagram. Thus if we are interested in people who are married OR who are sailors, we find them within the shaded area in Fig. 1.4(a). People in the shaded area fall into the category $(M + S)$. The 'plus' is referred to as the logical OR function,* and should not be confused with the arithmetical addition sign. The OR function is sometimes referred to as the *logical sum function*. Thus in

* Sometimes a V or U symbol is used to represent the logical OR function (see also Chapter 2).

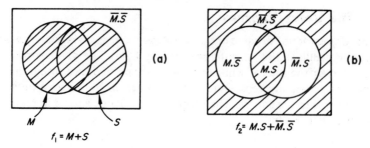

Fig. 1.4   The union of two sections of the population

Fig. 1.4(a) the total function is

$$f_1 = \text{married people OR sailors} = M + S$$

Since the shaded parts of the diagram cover the areas represented by $M.\bar{S}$, $M.S$, and $\bar{M}.S$, it is clear that

$$f_1 = M + S = M.\bar{S} + M.S + \bar{M}.S$$

In this way it is possible to construct logical equations and to formulate logical proofs using the Venn diagram.

It is obvious from Fig. 1.4(a) that, since we are interested in people within the circles, we are NOT interested in the people outside the circles but who are within the square, i.e., NOT $\bar{M}.\bar{S}$. Hence

$$M + S = \overline{\bar{M}.\bar{S}}$$

In Fig. 1.4(b) the shaded areas cover people who are unmarried non-sailors ($\bar{M}.\bar{S}$) OR who are married sailors ($M.S$); hence

$$f_2 = \overline{M.\bar{S}} + M.S$$

The unshaded area in Fig. 1.4(b) is NOT f_2; hence

$$\bar{f}_2 = \bar{M}.S + M.\bar{S}$$

From the expressions for f_2 and $\bar{f}_2$ it follows that

$$f_2 = \bar{M}.\bar{S} + M.S = \overline{\bar{M}.S + M.\bar{S}}$$

1.3   The Karnaugh map

As the number of groups of people considered increases, the Venn diagram becomes progressively more complex. Figure 1.5 illustrates the effect on the diagram of considering politicians (P) in addition to married people and

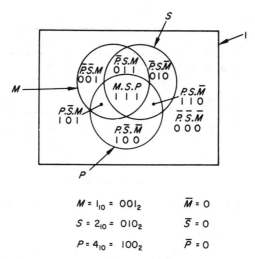

$$M = 1_{10} = 001_2 \qquad \bar{M} = 0$$

$$S = 2_{10} = 010_2 \qquad \bar{S} = 0$$

$$P = 4_{10} = 100_2 \qquad \bar{P} = 0$$

Fig. 1.5   Venn diagram for three groups of people within the total population

sailors. In all there are eight areas on the diagram, corresponding to the eight results obtained in Fig. 1.1.

By allocating numbers in binary order to each group of people, each area on the diagram can be identified uniquely. By giving M the value 1_{10} (001_2), S the value 2_{10} (010_2), and P the value 4_{10} (100_2), the area defined as $P.S.M$ has the value 7_{10} (111_2). Similarly $\bar{P}$, $\bar{S}$, and $\bar{M}$ are all given the value zero, and the area $\bar{P}.\bar{S}.\bar{M}$ has the value zero while $P.S.\bar{M}$ has the value 6_{10} (110_2).

Some simplification is effected by arranging the groups in a rectangular form, as shown in Fig. 1.6. All cells in the lower row are M, while cells in the upper row are $\bar{M}$. Similarly all cells in the second and third columns are P, while those in the first and fourth columns are $\bar{P}$. The first two columns are defined as $\bar{S}$, while the third and fourth columns are S. This allows all possible intersections of M, S, and P to be shown on the diagram. This form of diagram is known as a *Veitch*[1] or *Karnaugh*[2] map.

Individual cells are defined in Fig. 1.6 either in terms of the alphabetical characters along the edges of the map or in terms of the binary groups of digits along the edges. Veitch maps use alphabetical characters to define the cells, while the cells on the Karnaugh map are defined in terms of the binary values of variables P, S, and M. The Veitch version is particularly useful when dealing with logical expressions of the type in Sec. 1.4, and the Karnaugh version is more useful when transferring data from truth tables (see Chapter 2). The name Karnaugh map is used throughout this book to describe both Veitch and Karnaugh maps.

Karnaugh maps for two and four variables are shown in Fig. 1.7(a) and (b) respectively. The fourth group C contains those who possess a car, giving 16 possible intersections in all, ranging from $C.P.S.M$ to $\bar{C}.\bar{P}.\bar{S}.\bar{M}$.

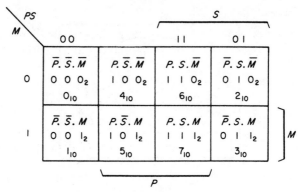

Fig. 1.6   Veitch and Karnaugh representation of Fig. 1.5

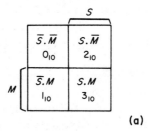

(a)

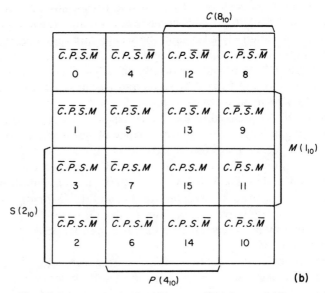

Fig. 1.7   Karnaugh map for (a) two and (b) four variables

1.4 Function mapping

Mapping is a graphical method of representing logical equations. It finds wide use in proving theorems and in the design of logical networks. Consider the equations

$$f_1 = A \cdot \bar{B}$$
$$f_2 = A \cdot \bar{B} \cdot \bar{C} \cdot \bar{D}$$

The statement $f_1 = A \cdot \bar{B}$ implies that f_1 is a function of the two variables A and B, which exists ($f_1 = 1$) only when A AND (NOT B) occur simultaneously; otherwise the function does not exist ($f_1 = 0$). The function f_1 is therefore mapped as shown in Fig. 1.8(a). Function f_2 is mapped in Fig. 1.8(b).

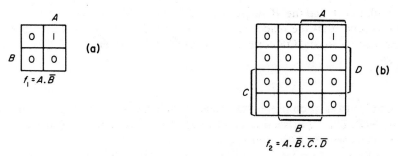

Fig. 1.8 Karnaugh maps for (a) $f_1 = A \cdot \bar{B}$ and (b) $f_2 = A \cdot \bar{B} \cdot \bar{C} \cdot \bar{D}$

It is also possible to obtain the logical product or sum of a number of Karnaugh maps, a common method in logical proofs. An example of the product of Karnaugh maps is given in Fig. 1.9. In Fig. 1.9 variables A and B are mapped independently, and the values of corresponding cells in each map are multiplied together to give the final function $f = A \cdot B$. For cell $\bar{A} \cdot B$ (lower left-hand cell), in the 'A' map, the value is '0', while in the 'B' map it is '1'. The value shown in the '$A \cdot B$' map is $0 \cdot 1 = 0$. Other cells are dealt with in this manner.

An example of the logical sum of Karnaugh maps is given in Fig. 1.10. Provided that one of the two values in corresponding cells is zero, the logical

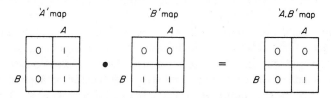

Fig. 1.9 Karnaugh map showing the logical product $A \cdot B$

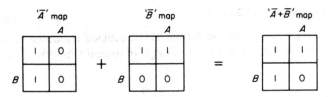

Fig. 1.10   The logical sum of two Karnaugh maps

sum follows normal arithmetic processes; thus

$$0+0=0$$
$$0+1=1$$
$$1+0=1$$

In both the 'A' and the 'B' maps, cell $\overline{A}.\overline{B}$ in Fig. 1.10 is marked with a '1'. It is at this point that the reader is reminded that the 'plus' sign is used here to represent the logical OR connective. Where this sum occurs, the following rule holds:

$$1+1=1$$

A simple justification of this statement follows. Consider the logical equation $X + Y = Z$. Thus Z exists if X OR Y exists. By the same token Z also exists if both variables exist simultaneously.

Applying these rules sequentially to equivalent cells of the two left-hand maps in Fig. 1.10 gives the right-hand map.

1.5   Adjacent cells on the Karnaugh map

Cells which are adjacent on a Karnaugh map differ by only one binary digit or *bit* (the weights of the digits being ignored) if the pure binary equivalent of the decimal notation in Fig. 1.7 is used. A four-variable map is shown in Fig. 1.11(a). Cell $A.B.\overline{C}.D$ contains three 1's, while those on either side have either two or four 1's. Cells at the top and bottom are adjacent in this sense, e.g., cells $\overline{A}.\overline{B}.\overline{C}.\overline{D}$ and $\overline{A}.\overline{B}.C.\overline{D}$.

Further inspection of the map shows that the four left-hand cells are adjacent to the four right-hand cells, according to the notation developed above, e.g., cells $\overline{A}.\overline{B}.\overline{C}.\overline{D}$ and $A.\overline{B}.\overline{C}.\overline{D}$.

For simplicity, the Karnaugh map is sometimes drawn in the manner shown in Fig. 1.11(b). The variables A and B have the binary combinations shown along the top, and variables C and D have the binary combinations shown on the left-hand side of the map. Thus, cell $A.B.\overline{C}.D$ has the binary value 1101 and is located at the point $AB=11$, $CD=01$. Cells $\overline{A}.\overline{B}.\overline{C}.\overline{D}$ (0000), $A.\overline{B}.\overline{C}.\overline{D}$ (1000), and $\overline{A}.\overline{B}.C.\overline{D}$ (0010) are located as shown.

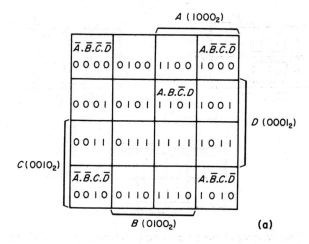

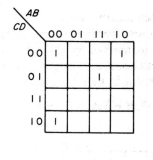

(b)

Fig. 1.11   The concept of adjacent cells is shown in map (a). Map (b) shows an alternative way of displaying the cell code combinations

Provided that cells are adjacent they may be grouped together. An example is shown in Fig. 1.12. Since each cell can be defined independently, the logical representation of the map is

$$f = A.B.C + A.B.\bar{C} + \bar{A}.B.\bar{C} + \bar{A}.B.C$$

Adjacent pairs of cells can now be grouped. In Fig. 1.12(a) pairs of cells in the horizontal plane are grouped, giving

$$f = B.C + B.\bar{C}$$

Grouping pairs of cells in the vertical plane, Fig. 1.12(b), gives

$$f = A.B + \bar{A}.B$$

Alternatively, all four adjacent cells may be grouped as in Fig. 1.12(c) when

$$f = B$$

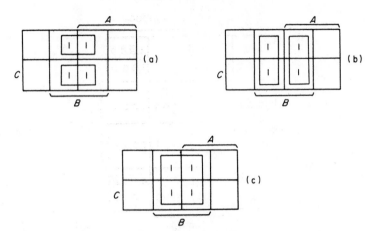

Fig. 1.12   Three methods of grouping adjacent cells are shown in (a), (b), and (c)

The number of cells grouped together must be in binary order, i.e., 1, 2, 4, 8, etc. In deducing logical equations from the Karnaugh map, it is essential that all the terms in the equation are marked by a '1', other cells being left blank or marked with a '0'. If three adjacent cells appear on the map, then they are grouped as two pairs, illustrated in Fig. 1.13, where

$$f = A.B + B.C = B.(A+C)$$

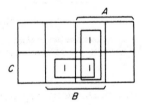

Fig. 1.13   Three adjacent cells are combined by grouping two pairs of adjacent cells

1.6   Don't care and can't happen conditions

It often happens in logical problems that certain combinations of the variables cannot be permitted to occur. Such a state is a *redundant* one and is sometimes known as a *can't happen* condition. In some cases certain states are permitted to occur, but their existence does not affect the solution. This is a *don't care* condition and is also redundant.

In a binary code known as the 8421 BCD code, the combinations 1010, 1011, 1100, 1101, and 1111 are forbidden combinations of bits. If D represents the least significant digit (2^0), C represents the digit 2^1, etc., then the forbidden

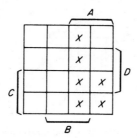

Fig. 1.14 The method of representing redundant states on the Karnaugh map

combinations are $A . \bar{B} . C . \bar{D}, A . \bar{B} . C . D, A . B . \bar{C} . \bar{D}, A . B . \bar{C} . D, A . B . C . \bar{D}$, and $A . B . C . D$ respectively. Each of these is plotted on the Karnaugh map in Fig. 1.14 by an X. Since these combinations 'can't happen', it is feasible to include them in loops on the Karnaugh map without affecting the accuracy of the resulting equations.

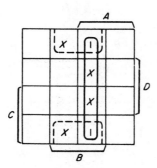

Fig. 1.15 Problem simplification can be achieved by utilizing redundant states

In Fig. 1.15 the function defined is $f = A . B . \bar{C} . \bar{D} + A . B . C . \bar{D}$, together with 'can't happen' conditions $A . B . D$ and $\bar{A} . B . \bar{D}$. By including the redundant pair $A . B . D$, four cells are grouped as shown by the full line, reducing the equation to $f = A . B$. Alternatively using the redundant pair $\bar{A} . B . \bar{D}$, the cells grouped by the dotted lines define the expression $f = B . \bar{D}$. Both groupings are equivalent with the redundant conditions given.

1.7 Complementing on the Karnaugh map

A function f is represented on the Karnaugh map by a series of 1's, and it is clear that $\bar{f}$ is represented by the cells fitted with 0's. An example is shown in Fig. 1.16 for $f = A . B + A . C$. The complement of the function is obtained by grouping cells marked with 0's in accordance with the rules laid down in this

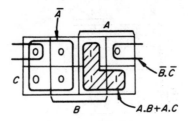

Fig. 1.16   Complementing by grouping the 0's on the map

chapter. With the grouping shown in Fig. 1.16,

$$\bar{f} = \bar{A} + \bar{B}.\bar{C}$$

This technique can be used to define a group of 1's by saying that they are NOT the 0's. In Fig. 1.17, the four 1's in the corner cells are defined by saying that they are not the 0's, viz.:

$$f = \overline{B + D}$$

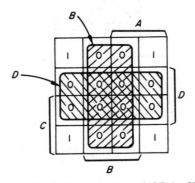

Fig. 1.17   Defining the 1's as NOT the 0's

It is left for the reader to show that the corner cells are also defined by the relationship $f = \bar{B}.\bar{D}$.

Example 1.1: Draw the Karnaugh map of the function

$$f = \bar{D}(\bar{A}[\bar{C} + \bar{B}.C] + A[\bar{C} + \bar{B}.C]) + B.\bar{C}.D$$

Simplify using the procedures outlined in this chapter.

Solution: The expression is first expanded as follows:

$$f = \bar{A}.\bar{C}.\bar{D} + A.\bar{C}.\bar{D} + B.\bar{C}.D + \bar{A}.\bar{B}.C.\bar{D} + A.\bar{B}.C.\bar{D}$$

The expanded terms are mapped in Fig. 1.18 and adjacent 1's are grouped

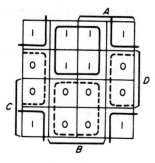

Fig. 1.18

together in the simplest form possible, giving two solutions:

$$f = \bar{B}.\bar{D} + B.\bar{C}$$
$$= \overline{(B+D)} + B.\bar{C}$$

Alternatively, the 0's in Fig. 1.18 are defined by $B.C + \bar{B}.D$; hence

$$f = \overline{B.C + \bar{B}.D}$$

Many problems have several minimal solutions, all being equally correct. In Example 1.1 three solutions were obtained. A network designer defines the *minimal* solution as one which gives the minimum number of circuit elements together with the minimum number of interconnections between the elements. Each solution obtained by the procedures outlined does not give the same number of interconnections.

The process of minimization of logical expressions by the map method is reduced to the following steps:

1. Expand the original function to give logical product or sum terms.
2. Map each term on the Karnaugh map by a series of 1's.
3. Group the 1's into the largest blocks of cells possible (in binary groups).
4. Write down the sum of the logical expressions obtained.

In step 3, the 0's could be grouped to give the complement of the final expression.

The advent of integrated electronic circuit technology has reduced the relative importance of minimization techniques, since complex circuits are obtainable in encapsulated form. Minimization techniques generally concentrate on producing circuits with the minimum number of integrated circuit packages, together with the minimum number of interconnections between them.

1.8 Maps for more than four variables

A map for two variables is obtained by putting two one-variable maps side by side, giving four cells in all. A three-variable map comprises two two-variable or four one-variable maps side by side. A square array of two three-variable or four two-variable maps gives a four-variable map.

The logical extension, for five variables, is to place two four-variable maps side by side, as shown in Fig. 1.19. The cell marked with a '1' in the E half is

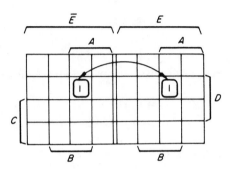

Fig. 1.19 One method of showing adjacency on a five-variable map

$A . B . \bar{C} . D . E$ and that in the $\bar{E}$ half is $A . B . \bar{C} . D . \bar{E}$. Giving the letters binary values, with A as the most significant digit, the cells have the values 11011 and 11010 respectively. Since the two numbers differ by only one binary digit, they are adjacent in accordance with the definition in Sec. 1.5. If the $\bar{E}$ map is placed below the E map, then cells next to one another in the vertical plane are adjacent. In any one plane the normal rules of adjacency apply. An example is shown in Fig. 1.20 in which selected adjacent groups of cells are indicated.

The basic idea can be extended to give a six-variable map, which is two five-variable or four four-variable maps placed side by side in a square array. Adjacency between cells can be deduced by considering each equivalent four-

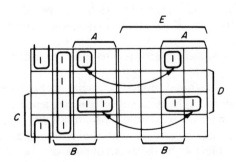

Fig. 1.20 Groups of adjacent cells on a five-variable map

variable map to be stacked one above the other. As in previous cases, adjacent cells must occur in multiples of two before they can be grouped together.

Usage of the map method becomes difficult when more than four variables are involved. One novel method for extending their use up to eight variables is described in Ref. 3. Alternative minimization techniques[4,5] include algebraic and tabular methods. These have the advantage that many more variables than four can be dealt with, but they lack the essential simplicity of map methods.

1.9   Generating unit-distance codes on the Karnaugh map

Unit-distance codes can readily be mapped on the Karnaugh diagram. A feature of unit-distance codes is that they change by only one binary digit for each consecutive group of code numbers. On the Karnaugh map this corresponds to the movement from one cell to an adjacent cell for a change from one code group to another. This is illustrated in Fig. 1.21 for a five-bit Gray code, where A is the most significant digit. The code commences at cell

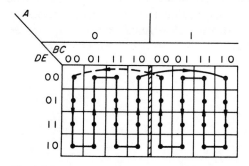

Fig. 1.21   Karnaugh map for a five-bit Gray code

00000 and moves through each adjacent cell in the $A = 0$ matrix, until it reaches cell $ABCDE = 01000$, when it transfers to the adjacent cell 11000 in the $A = 1$ matrix. The code follows the inverse pattern through this matrix, to the cell 10000, when it can either transfer to the start of the code (if it has a maximum of five bits) or it can enter the next matrix if there are six or more bits in the code. A four-bit code is generated if the pattern returns from cell 1000, on the $A = 0$ map, to cell 0000 on the same map.

It is evident that many forms of code can be generated by this technique. A code which utilizes all the cells in a given matrix is known as a *complete cyclic code*, one example being shown in Fig. 1.22(a). A code which does not use all the cells in the matrix is an *incomplete cyclic code*, one example being the unit-distance decimal code in Fig. 1.22(b). Other forms of code can be traced out on the Karnaugh map.

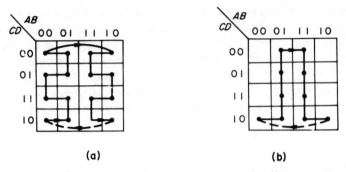

Fig. 1.22   Two forms of unti-distance code

1.10   Theorems and laws of logic

The truth of many logical statements is self-evident, while that of other statements may not be so clear. Providing that the statement is accurate, it is possible to test its truth using the ideas developed in this chapter.

Using the binary notation, we say that a statement is true, i.e., the function exists, if it has the logical value '1'. If it is untrue, or does not exist, then it has the value '0'. The Karnaugh map can be used to prove logical theorems. Examples are shown in Fig. 1.23(a) and (b), which correspond to Theorems 1 and 2 below:

Theorem 1:	$A + 0 = A$
Theorem 2:	$A \cdot 0 = 0$
Theorem 3:	$A + 1 = 1$
Theorem 4:	$A \cdot 1 = A$
Theorem 5:	$A + A = A$
Theorem 6:	$A \cdot A = A$
Theorem 7:	$A + \bar{A} = 1$
Theorem 8:	$A \cdot \bar{A} = 0$
Theorem 9:	$\bar{\bar{A}} = A$

Certain laws are self-evident from the logical equations. Examples of these are the commutative and associative laws.

$$\begin{array}{|c|c|}\hline 0 & 1 \\\hline\end{array} \; + \; \begin{array}{|c|c|}\hline 0 & 0 \\\hline\end{array} \; = \; \begin{array}{|c|c|}\hline 0 & 1 \\\hline\end{array} \quad \text{(a)}$$

$$\begin{array}{|c|c|}\hline 0 & 1 \\\hline\end{array} \; \cdot \; \begin{array}{|c|c|}\hline 0 & 0 \\\hline\end{array} \; = \; \begin{array}{|c|c|}\hline 0 & 0 \\\hline\end{array} \quad \text{(b)}$$

Fig. 1.23   Proof of Theorems 1 and 2 are shown in (a) and (b) respectively

Commutative law

$$A + B = B + A$$
$$A.B = B.A$$

Associative law

$$A + B + C = (A + B) + C = A + (B + C)$$
$$A.B.C = (A.B).C = A.(B.C)$$

Other theorems require further investigation, the distributive law being an example.

Distributive law

$$A + (B.C.D. \cdots) = (A + B).(A + C).(A + D). \cdots$$
$$A.(B + C + D + \cdots) = A.B + A.C + A.D + \cdots$$

The second statement of the distributive law is self-evident, but the first statement requires further investigation. Its justification can be shown on a Karnaugh map, using the above techniques.

One of the most powerful tools in engineering applications is De Morgan's theorem, given below.

De Morgan's theorem

$$\overline{A + B + C + \cdots} = \bar{A}.\bar{B}.\bar{C}. \cdots \tag{1.1}$$
$$\overline{A.B.C. \cdots} = \bar{A} + \bar{B} + \bar{C} + \cdots \tag{1.2}$$

Equations (1.1) and (1.2) are proved, for two variables A and B, using Karnaugh maps in Fig. 1.24(a) and (b) respectively.

An illustrative example of the use of De Morgan's theorem is taken from Sec. 1.7 in which the complement of the logical statement $A.B + A$ is required.

$$f = A.B + A.C = A(B + C) \tag{1.3}$$

or

$$\bar{f} = \overline{A.(B + C)}$$

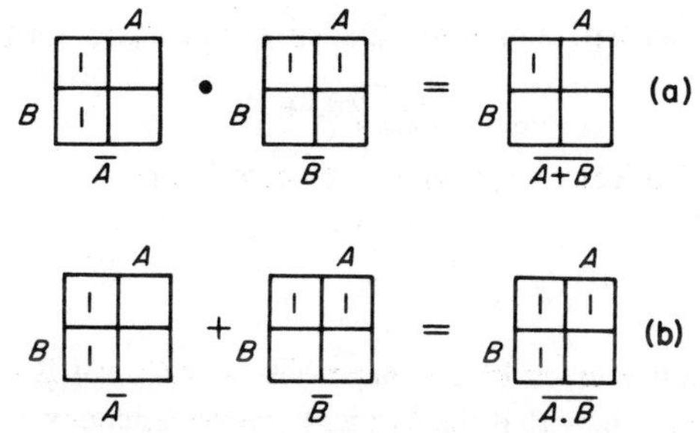

Fig. 1.24   Proof of the two forms of De Morgan's theorem for two variables

Applying Eq. (1.2), with $(B+C)$ treated as a single term,

$$\bar{f} = \overline{A} + \overline{(B+C)}$$

Application of Eq. (1.1) to the right-hand term yields

$$\bar{f} = \bar{A} + \bar{B}.\bar{C} \tag{1.4}$$

De Morgan's theorem is expressed in general terms as follows. *The logical complement of a function is obtained by (1) logically inverting each term in the expression and (2) by replacing the 'dots' with the 'plusses', and vice versa.*
For example, if

$$f = (A.\bar{B}.C) + (C.[A+\bar{D}]) + (E)$$

then $\qquad \bar{f} = (\overline{A} + B + \overline{C}).(\overline{C} + [\overline{A}.D]).(\overline{E})$

It is advisable to collect each group of letters inside brackets to avoid mistakes. The brackets are not affected by the complementing process.

1.11 Canonical forms of expression

There are two normal or *canonical* forms of logical expression, namely *minterms* (terms which are ANDed) and *maxterms* (terms which are ORed). For example, the following Boolean expression is written entirely in minterm form:

$$f_1 = \bar{A}.\bar{B}.C + \bar{A}.B.C + A.B.C$$

The above expression is known as the *sum of products* (S of P) form. The following expression is written entirely in terms of maxterms:

$$f_2 = (A + B + \bar{C}).(A + \bar{B} + \bar{C}).(\bar{A} + \bar{B} + \bar{C})$$

It is also known as the *product of sums* (P of S) form of expression.
The above expressions can also be represented by means of decimal (or octal) values, using a 4, 2, 1 weighting for A, B, and C respectively as follows:

$$f_1 = \sum(1, 3, 7)$$

where the sigma symbol denotes the sum of products form. Also

$$f_2 = \prod(6, 4, 0)$$

where capital π denotes the product of sums form.

Problems

1.1   Plot Karnaugh maps of the functions $\overline{A.B.C}$, $\overline{A} + \overline{B} + \overline{C}$, $\overline{A + B + C}$, and $\overline{A}.\overline{B}.\overline{C}$. Hence show that the first and second functions are equivalent to one another, and that the third and fourth functions are equivalent to one another.

1.2 Write down the truth tables, and draw the Karnaugh maps of the following functions:

$$f_1 = A.B + \bar{A}.\bar{B} \qquad f_2 = A.\bar{B} + B.C$$
$$f_3 = A + A.B.C \qquad f_4 = A + B + \bar{A}.\bar{B}$$

1.3 Using the Karnaugh map, devise unit-distance (a) octal, (b) decimal, and (c) duodecimal codes not given in this chapter.

1.4 Minimize the following, using symbolic logic and the Karnaugh map techniques:

(a) $W.\bar{Y}.\bar{Z} + W.\bar{X}.\bar{Z} + W.Y.Z + W.X.Z$

(b) $X.\bar{Y}.\bar{Z} + W.X.\bar{Y} + \bar{X}.\bar{Y}.Z + X.Y.\bar{Z}$

(c) $W.X.Y.Z + \bar{W}.X.Z + X.Y.Z + W.X.Y.\bar{Z} + W.\bar{X}.Z$

1.5 Minimize, using a Karnaugh map, the function

$$f = \bar{A}.\bar{B}.\bar{C} + \bar{B}.C.\bar{D} + \bar{A}.B.D + A.B.C.D + A.\bar{C}.D + A.B.\bar{C}.\bar{D}$$

Hence or otherwise show that it may be reduced to

$$f = \overline{B.\bar{D}} + \bar{B}.C.D$$

References

1. VEITCH, E. W., 'A chart method for simplifying truth functions', *Proc. Assoc. Comp. Mach.*, p. 127, May 1962.
2. KARNAUGH, M., 'The map method for synthesis of combinational logic circuits', *Commun. Electron.*, **9**, 11, 539, 1953.
3. DEAN, K. J. 'An extension of the use of Karnaugh maps in the minimization of logical functions', *J. Inst. Elect. Radio Engrs.*, **35**, 5, 294–296, 1968.
4. McCLUSKEY, E. J., 'Minimization of Boolean functions', *Bell Syst. Tech. J.*, **35**, 6, 1417, 1956.
5. PHISTER, M., *Logical Design of Digital Computers*, John Wiley, 1958.

2. Static logic networks

It is desirable, although not essential, to understand the operation of the actual logic devices used in the solution of problems. Since many electronic, magnetic, fluid, and other logic devices are now used, a general treatment using block diagrams is given before a detailed study of the devices employed is undertaken.

2.1 Symbolic representation

Many conventions are at present employed to represent logic devices. Those for NOT, AND, and OR gates are illustrated in Fig. 2.1; a range of other logic symbols are given in Appendix B.

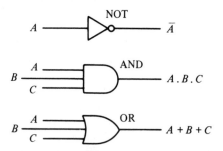

Fig. 2.1 Symbolic representation of NOT, AND, and OR gates

The term 'gate' is agricultural in origin since if a gate is open it is possible for livestock to pass freely through it. Logic elements are regarded as gates since there is flow of information when the gate is *open* and none when it is *closed* or *inhibited*.

20

2.2 Use of Karnaugh maps

It is useful to map functions in order to derive a block diagram of the logical network. An example is shown in Fig. 2.2 for the sum of two binary variables A

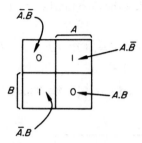

Fig. 2.2   Karnaugh map of the sum of two binary variables

Table 2.1
Truth table for the sum and carry functions of two binary variables

A	B	Sum S'	Carry C'
0	0	0	0
1	0	1	0
0	1	1	0
1	1	0	1

and B. Table 2.1 lists the four possible combinations of A and B, and it is observed from both Fig. 2.2 and Table 2.1 that a sum occurs when we have $A.\bar{B}$ OR $\bar{A}.B$. That is,

$$S' = A.\bar{B} + \bar{A}.B$$

The logical block diagram of this function is shown in Fig. 2.3, each term in the expression being generated separately. This circuit can also be used for the

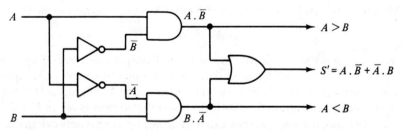

Fig. 2.3   Block diagram of a logic network giving the sum of two binary variables. The network can also be used as a comparator for two variables

comparison of two binary digits. If $A > B$ (i.e., $A = 1$, $B = 0$) the output from the upper AND gate is '1' while that from the lower AND gate is '0'. Similarly, if $A < B$ ($A = 0$, $B = 1$) the lower AND gate gives a '1' while the upper AND gate output is '0'.

De Morgan's theorem can be used in conjunction with Fig. 2.2 to yield other logic networks. It is clear that the area marked by 1's is NOT the area marked by 0's; hence

$$S' = \overline{A.\bar{B} + A.B} = (\overline{A.\bar{B}}) \cdot \overline{A.B} = (\bar{A} + \bar{B}).A.B$$
$$= (A + B).\overline{A.B}$$

This equation gives the network in Fig. 2.4. This circuit is more economic in

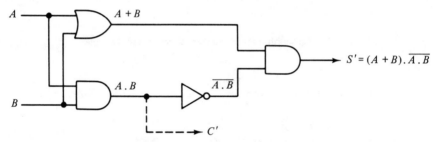

Fig. 2.4   Alternative block diagram of a network giving the sum of two binary variables

terms of the number of logic gates required compared with Fig. 2.3, and has an additional advantage which is described later in this section. De Morgan's theorem can be applied to the above equation again to give another network described by the function $(A + B) \cdot (\bar{A} + \bar{B})$.

The logic networks developed so far give an output when the two inputs are not equivalent, i.e., if $A = 1$, $B = 0$, OR $A = 0$, $B = 1$. These networks are known as NOT-EQUIVALENT or EXCLUSIVE-OR gates, the circuit representation being shown in Fig. 2.5(a). The not-equivalent operation is also known as MODULO-2 ADDITION and the symbol $\forall$ is used to express the function:

$$A \forall B = \bar{A} \cdot B + A \cdot \bar{B}$$

When a network with N inputs has to give a '1' output when an odd number of inputs have the value '1', a modulo-2 combination can be used. Examples of this are found in parity check networks and in feedback shift registers (Chapter 7). A schematic diagram for this form of combination is given in Fig. 2.5(b).

Equivalence between two bits can be detected by using a network that gives zero output when $A \not\equiv B$ and unity output when $A \equiv B$. This is satisfied by complementing or negating the output from a not-equivalent gate, as shown in

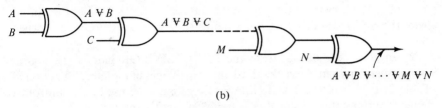

(a)

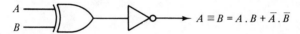

$$A \vee B \vee \cdots \vee M \vee N$$

(b)

Fig. 2.5   (a) Symbolic representation of the EXCLUSIVE-OR or NOT-EQUIVALENT gate.
(b) A network giving the EXCLUSIVE-OR function of *N* inputs

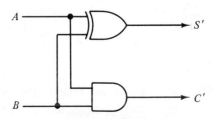

Fig. 2.6   Generating the EQUIVALENT function

Fig. 2.6. Alternatively, a new series of logic networks can be derived by noting that when $A \equiv B$ the logical equation to be solved is $\bar{A}.\bar{B} + A.B$. The reader should justify this equation and derive suitable block diagrams.

Table 2.1 shows that a carry occurs when inputs *A* AND *B* occur simultaneously. A block diagram for the complete addition of two bits is shown in Fig. 2.7, which requires one additional AND gate to be added to Fig. 2.3. A feature of the network in Fig. 2.4 is that the logical product $A.B$ is developed at an early point, shown as C'. Figure 2.4 thus provides both sum and carry digits without further modification.

Fig. 2.7   Block diagram of a network giving the sum-and-carry functions of two binary
variables

2.3 The EXCLUSIVE-OR gate as a buffer/invertor

If one of the inputs, say input B, of the EXCLUSIVE-OR gate in Fig. 2.5(a) is used as a 'control' signal, and input A is the input signal to the gate, then when $B=0$, the logic signal at the output of the gate is equal to the logic state of signal A. That is, when $B=0$, the gate acts as a buffer amplifier (this is verified in Table 2.1, where the reader will note that for the first two lines the output from the EXCLUSIVE-OR gate, given as sum S', is equal to input A when $B=0$).

When $B=1$, the output from the EXCLUSIVE-OR gate is the logical complement of input A (see the third and fourth lines of the sum S' function in Table 2.1). That is, the EXCLUSIVE-OR gate can be used as a controlled buffer/inverter gate. This facility is useful in many circuits.

The EXCLUSIVE-OR function is contained in the instruction set of every microprocessor, and a primary reason for including it is to enable the programmer to selectively logically invert certain of the bits in a binary word in the microprocessor.

2.4 The full-adder

The circuit described in Fig. 2.7 is called a *half-adder* since it provides the sum and carry outputs corresponding to the addition of two bits. In a practical calculation it is necessary to account for the carry bit generated by the previous calculation. The process of full addition of two bits and a 'carry in' C_I from the previous addition is given in Table 2.2. An output sum S_O is seen to

Table 2.2
Truth table for a full-adder

A	B	C_I	Output sum S_O	Output carry C_O
0	0	0	0	0
0	0	1	1	0
0	1	0	1	0
0	1	1	0	1
1	0	0	1	0
1	0	1	0	1
1	1	0	0	1
1	1	1	1	1

occur when an odd number of inputs are present, that is,

$$S_O = A \forall B \forall C_I$$

The output carry equation is derived from the truth table as follows:

$$C_O = \bar{A}.B.C_I + A.\bar{B}.C_I + A.B.\bar{C}_I + A.B.C_I$$
$$= C_I(\bar{A}.B + A.\bar{B}) + A.B(\bar{C}_I + C_I)$$
$$= C_I.S' + A.B = C_I.S' + C'$$

The equations for S_O and C_O are combined in Fig. 2.8 to give one form of *full-adder* circuit.

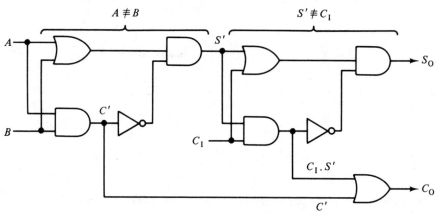

Fig. 2.8 One practical form of full-adder

2.5 NAND and NOR gates

Each element so far described performs only one function, e.g., the AND gate with given logic levels cannot be used to perform the NOT or OR functions. Two basic universal logic elements, the NOR and the NAND gates, are in common use today. Their functions are described in the following sections, and it will be shown that it is possible to construct any of the gates already described by suitable combinations of either type of universal logic element.

2.6 The NOR gate

The name NOR is derived from the logical statement

$$NOR = OR.NOT = \overline{OR}$$

That is, the NOR function is an inverted or negated OR function, illustrated in Fig. 2.9. The truth table for this function is developed in Table 2.3 for a two-input gate. It is seen that the output is zero if a '1' appears at either or both inputs and that the output is '1' only when both inputs are zero. This can be extended to an n-input NOR gate, since the output is '1' only when all the inputs are zero.

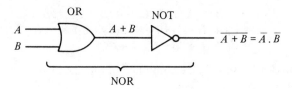

Fig. 2.9   Generating the NOR function using an OR and a NOT gate

Table 2.3
Truth table for a NOR gate with two inputs

| Inputs | | | Output |
A	B	$A+B$	$\overline{A+B}$
0	0	0	1
0	1	1	0
1	0	1	0
1	1	1	0

It is uneconomic to use two gates, an OR and a NOT gate, to perform the NOR function, but in practice two gates are not necessary. Many electronic logic devices perform the basic NOR function with greater economy than they can carry out the OR and AND functions. This is discussed in more detail in later chapters.

From De Morgan's theorem

$$\overline{A+B+C+\cdots} = \overline{A}.\overline{B}.\overline{C}.\cdots$$

It follows from this statement that if only input A exists (B, C, etc. $=0$), then the output is $\overline{A}$, i.e., a NOR gate with a single input performs the NOT function. This is illustrated in Fig. 2.10. The logical OR function is generated by

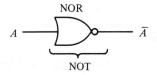

Fig. 2.10   The NOR gate with a single input acts as a NOT gate

complementing the output of the NOR gate since

$$A+B+C+\cdots = \overline{\overline{A+B+C+\cdots}}$$

This is shown in Fig. 2.11.

De Morgan's theorem allows the AND function to be realized with NOR

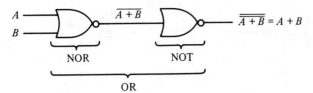

Fig. 2.11 Generating the OR function with NOR gates

gates since

$$\overline{A \cdot B} = \bar{A} + \bar{B}$$

or

$$A \cdot B = \overline{\bar{A} + \bar{B}}$$

The block diagram of the AND gate derived from NOR elements is shown in Fig. 2.12.

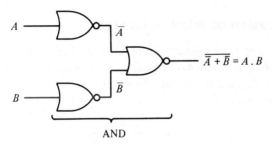

Fig. 2.12 The AND function of two variables is generated by three NOR gates

It may seem that any system built up of NOR gates will contain many more elements than are required using conventional discrete function gates, i.e., AND, OR, NOT gates. This is not necessarily so in practice since it is possible to eliminate many elements by inspection of the block diagram. One instance is shown in Fig. 2.13 where a single input A is applied to two cascaded NOR gates. Both gates can be eliminated since the output is equal to the input.

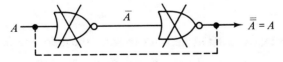

Fig. 2.13 Two cascaded NOR gates with single inputs are redundant

Another example is shown in Fig. 2.14(a), together with the simplified block diagram in Fig. 2.14(b). In Fig. 2.14(a) the output $\overline{A + B}$ from NOR 1 is complemented to $A + B$ by NOR 2. The final gate performs the NOR function

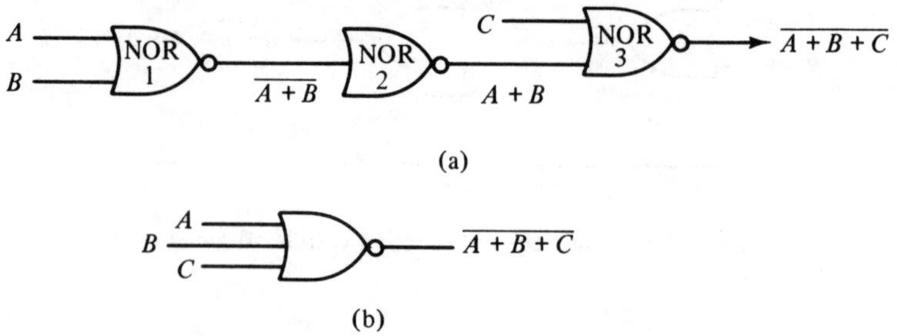

(a)

(b)

Fig. 2.14 The NOR network in (a) can be minimized to (b)

on the two inputs, giving an output of $A+B+C$. This output may be obtained from one NOR gate with inputs A, B, C as shown in Fig. 2.14(b).

2.7 Realization of NOR networks

If the statement of any problem can be expressed in the form of the logical product (AND) of a number of logical sums (ORs), then the OR and AND gates can be replaced directly with NOR gates.

This is illustrated in Fig. 2.15 for the function

$$f=(A+B).(C+D)$$

The logic block diagram using discrete function elements is shown in Fig. 2.15(a). Using the combinations described in Sec. 2.6, NOR equivalents of these elements are inserted, giving Fig. 2.15(b). Using the example of Fig. 2.13, four of the NOR gates are eliminated, giving the final configuration in Fig. 2.15(c). It is evident that the OR and AND gates in Fig. 2.15(a) can be replaced by NOR gates.

This method does not always produce minimal networks, i.e., containing the minimum number of logic elements, but has the element of simplicity. An example is given below to illustrate the technique.

Example 2.1: Devise a NOR network to solve the following problem:

$$f=(A+\bar{B}+D).(B+C+\bar{D}).(\bar{A}+B+\bar{D})$$

Solution: The block diagram of the network is shown in Fig. 2.16, seven NOR gates being required, three for the purpose of generating $\bar{A}$, $\bar{B}$, $\bar{D}$. Using discrete function elements, three NOT, three OR, and one AND gates would be needed.

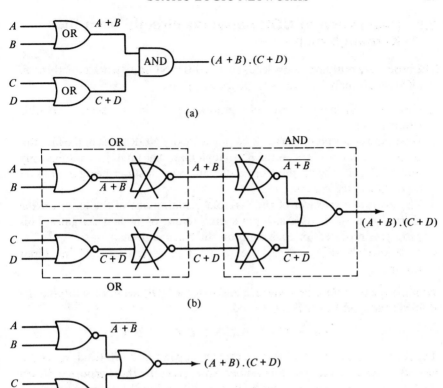

(a)

(b)

(c)

Fig. 2.15   The OR-AND network in (a) can be replaced by the NOR network in (b), which is minimized to the NOR network in (c)

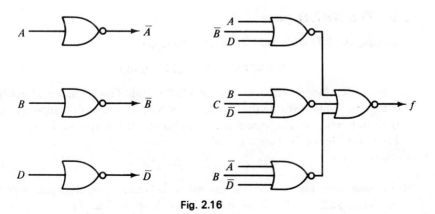

Fig. 2.16

2.8 Realization of NOR networks directly from the Karnaugh map

The procedure outlined below leads to a two-tier NOR network directly from the Karnaugh map. The steps to be followed are:

1. Draw the Karnaugh map and group the 0's in the largest possible combinations.
2. Draw a two-tier NOR network having as many NOR gates in the first tier as there are loops of 0's on the Karnaugh map. The final tier contains only one NOR gate, the output from each gate in the first tier being used as an input to the second tier gate.
3. The *logical complement* of the variables defining one of the loops on the Karnaugh map are used as input signals to one of the first tier gates. This process is repeated for each loop on the Karnaugh map.
4. Additional NOR gates may be required to invert some of the input variables.

To illustrate the above procedure, a design for a NOR network satisfying the Boolean function below is developed:

$$f = A.B.C + \bar{A}.B.\bar{C} + A.B.\bar{C} + \bar{A}.\bar{B}.C$$

The Karnaugh map for the function is drawn up in Fig. 2.17(a) and the 0's are looped in the most economical manner. Since there are three groups of 0's on the Karnaugh map, the two-tier NOR network in Fig. 2.17(b) contains three gates (G1–G3) in the first tier. Gate G1 in this tier is concerned with loop $A.\bar{B}$ on the Karnaugh map and, from rule 3 above, this gate has two input signals which are $\bar{A}$ and $\bar{\bar{B}} = B$. This procedure is repeated for gates G2 and G3 in the figure. Finally, inverters G5, G6, and G7 are introduced to generate the functions $\bar{A}$, $\bar{B}$, and $\bar{C}$ respectively.

2.9 The NAND gate

The name NAND is derived from the statement

$$NAND = AND.NOT = \overline{AND}$$

i.e., the NAND function is an inverted AND function. This is illustrated in Fig. 2.18 together with its truth table, Table 2.4. A NAND gate with N inputs gives a '0' output when all the inputs are '1'; otherwise the output is '1'.

From De Morgan's theorem

$$A.B.C.\cdots = \bar{A} + \bar{B} + \bar{C} + \cdots$$

If only one input line is used, the output is $\bar{A}$. That is, a NAND gate with a single input performs the NOT function, as shown in Fig. 2.19.

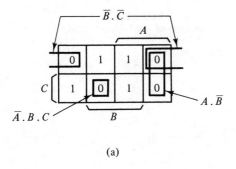

(a)

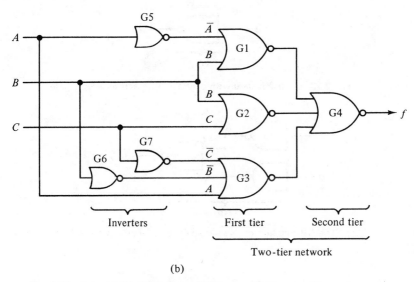

Inverters   First tier   Second tier

Two-tier network

(b)

Fig. 2.17 (a) and (b) Designing a NOR network from the Karnaugh map

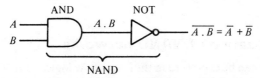

NAND

Fig. 2.18 Generating the NAND function using an AND and a NOT gate

De Morgan's theorem allows the OR gate to be realized:

$$\overline{A + B} = \bar{A} \cdot \bar{B}$$

or

$$A + B = \overline{\bar{A} \cdot \bar{B}}$$

The logical block diagram of this function is shown in Fig. 2.20.

As with the NOR gate, two cascaded NAND gates with a single input can

Table 2.4
Truth table of the NAND function

| Inputs | | | Output |
A	B	A·B	$\overline{A \cdot B}$
0	0	0	1
0	1	0	1
1	0	0	1
1	1	1	0

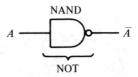

Fig. 2.19   A NAND gate with a single input acts as a NOT gate

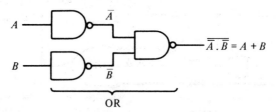

Fig. 2.20   The OR function of two variables is generated by three NAND gates

be eliminated, and a combination of NAND gates, similar to the NOR network in Fig. 2.14(a), can also be reduced to one NAND gate.

2.10   Realization of NAND networks

If the problem can be expressed in the form of the logical sum (OR) of a number of logical products (ANDs), then the OR and AND gates can be replaced directly with NAND elements.

Consider the function

$$f = A.B + C.D$$

The logic network to solve this equation using discrete function elements is shown in Fig. 2.21(a). These are replaced in Fig. 2.21(b) by the NAND equivalents. Eliminating four of the gates leaves the final logic diagram in Fig. 2.21(c).

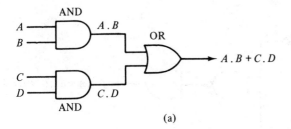

(a)

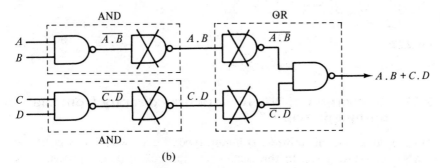

(b)

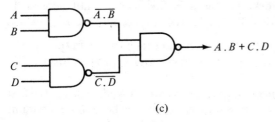

(c)

Fig. 2.21 The AND-OR network in (a) can be replaced by the NAND network in (b), which is minimized to the NAND network in (c)

Using this technique it is first necessary to manipulate the equation of the problem into the form of the logical sum of products. As an example consider the statement

$$f = (A+B).(C+D)$$

The function is first complemented to give

$$\bar{f} = \bar{A}.\bar{B} + \bar{C}.\bar{D}$$

or

$$f = \overline{\bar{A}.\bar{B} + \bar{C}.\bar{D}}$$

giving the NAND network in Fig. 2.22.

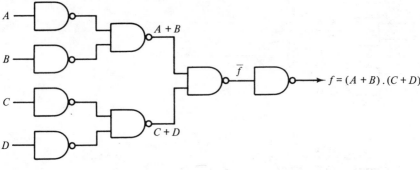

Fig. 2.22

2.11 Realization of NAND networks directly from the Karnaugh map

Modern logic systems utilize a common type of gate, which may either be NAND or NOR gates. In this section of the book, a design procedure is outlined which allows NAND networks to be designed directly from Karnaugh maps. The networks produced in this way are not necessarily minimal networks. The steps involved in the design procedure are listed below:

1. Draw the Karnaugh map of the function and group the 1's in the manner outlined earlier, each loop being expressed in a logical product form, i.e., in the form $A.B$, etc.
2. Draw a two-tier NAND network having as many NAND gates in the first tier as there are loops of 1's on the Karnaugh map. The final tier contains only one NAND gate, the output from each gate in the first tier being used as an input to the second tier gate.
3. The variables defining one of the loops of 1's on the Karnaugh map are used as input signals to one of the first-tier gates. This process is repeated for each loop on the Karnaugh map.
4. Additional NAND gates may be required to invert some of the input signals.

Consider the design of a NAND network which satisfies the logical equation

$$f = A.B.C + \bar{A}.B.\bar{C} + A.B.\bar{C} + \bar{A}.\bar{B}.C$$

The steps outlined above are illustrated in Fig. 2.23. First, the Karnaugh map for the function is drawn, see Fig. 2.23(a), in which the groups of cells $A.B$, $B.\bar{C}$, and $\bar{A}.\bar{B}.C$ are defined. A two-tier NAND network comprising gates G1–G4, inclusive, is drawn in Fig. 2.23(b). Gate G1 is taken in association with loop $A.B$ on the Karnaugh map, gate G2 in association with loop $B.\bar{C}$, and G3 in association with loop $\bar{A}.\bar{B}.C$. Accordingly, the two input lines of G1 are

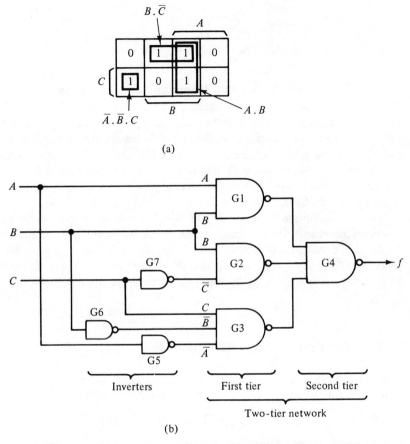

(a)

(b)

Fig. 2.23 (a) and (b) Designing a NAND network from the Karnaugh map

energized by signals A and B, the input lines of G2 are energized by signals B and $\bar{C}$, and signals $\bar{A}$, $\bar{B}$, and C are applied to G3. Three additional inverters — G5, G6, and G7 — are required to generate the functions $\bar{A}$, $\bar{B}$, and $\bar{C}$ respectively. Readers may find it instructive to verify that the circuit in Fig. 2.23(b) generates the original logic function.

2.12 The WIRED-OR connection or distributed logic

A useful feature of certain types of electronic gate is that their outputs may be wired directly together (see Fig. 2.24). Depending on the type of gate, this feature either causes a completely new logic function to be generated or leaves the function generated by the gates unchanged, but allows a greater number of input signals to be accommodated (this is known as increasing the *fan-in* of the

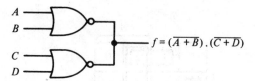

Fig. 2.24 The WIRED-OR connection of two NOR gates

gates). In general terms, it is possible to connect the outputs together in this way only if the output resistance of the gates is low when the output signal is at one of the logic levels (say logic '0') and is high when the complementary output signal is present (logic '1'). *Readers are cautioned that the WIRED-OR connection cannot be used with certain types of gate, such as conventional designs of TTL* (see Sec. 4.11).

Expressed in simple terms, the *WIRED-OR connection of a number of gates generates the logic AND function of the individual functions* of each of the gates. There is, of course, no objection to wiring together in this way gates which generate different types of logic function. For example, if the lower gate in Fig. 2.24 is replaced by a NAND gate, the function generated by the combination is $\overline{(A+B)} . \overline{A . B}$.

2.12.1 Distributed logic NOR networks

When two NOR gates are connected in the manner shown in Fig. 2.24, the expression for the logical output from the combination is

$$f = \overline{(A+B)} . \overline{(C+D)} = \bar{A} . \bar{B} . \bar{C} . \bar{D} = \overline{A+B+C+D}$$

That is, by connecting NOR gates together in this way the overall function is unchanged, but the circuit can accommodate a greater number of input signals than is possible in the case of a single gate, i.e., the fan-in of the system is greater than that of a single gate.

Note: The above expression is true in networks employing gates in which the output impedance is low for a '0' output and is high for a '1' output. If the reverse is the case, the resulting expression for the output is

$$f = \overline{(A+B)} + \overline{(C+D)}$$

Similarly for 2.12.2 below.

2.12.2 Distributed logic NAND networks

If the gates in Fig. 2.24 are replaced by two two-input NAND gates, the logical expression for the output is

$$f = \overline{(A \cdot B)} \cdot \overline{(C \cdot D)} - (\overline{A} + \overline{B}) \cdot (\overline{C} + \overline{D})$$

This is a new logic function which differs from the basic NAND function.

2.13 Realization of WIRED-OR NAND networks directly from the Karnaugh map

The WIRED-OR connection of NAND gates generates a new type of function which leads, in some cases, to circuit simplification. An algorithm for designing WIRED-OR networks is given below:

1. Draw the Karnaugh map for the function and group the 0's using the largest possible combinations.
2. Draw a WIRED-OR NAND network having as many NAND gates as there are loops on the Karnaugh map.
3. The input signals applied to a gate dealing with a specific loop on the Karnaugh map are given by the variables which define the loop on the map.
4. Additional NAND gates may be required to invert some input signals.

To illustrate the above procedure, a design is carried out for the Karnaugh map in Fig. 2.17(a). On that map, the loops joining the 0's were defined by the expressions $A \cdot \bar{B}$, $\bar{B} \cdot \bar{C}$, and $\bar{A} \cdot B \cdot C$. Rule 2 above indicates that, in this case, three NAND gates are required in the network, whose inputs (rule 3) are A and $\bar{B}$, $\bar{B}$ and $\bar{C}$, and $\bar{A}$ and B and C respectively. The resulting logic block diagram for this network is shown in Fig. 2.25. Additionally, three more NAND gates are required in order to generate the complements of variables A, B, and C.

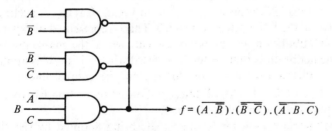

Fig. 2.25   Designing a WIRED-OR network

2.14 Three-state logic or tri-state logic

The output from a conventional logic gate can assume one of two possible logic states, namely logic '0' or logic '1'. Three-state gates or tri-state* gates have an additional control line (known as an *output enable* line) which, when

---

* Tri-state is a tradename adopted by the National Semiconductor Corporation of the United States.

activated by a suitable logic signal, connects the gate to the output pin of the chip; this enables the gate to perform its normal logical function. When the logical complement of the 'enabling' signal is applied to the output enable line, the connection between the gate and the output pin of the chip is open-circuited. That is, the output signal from the logic gate is effectively *disconnected* from the output pin of the chip. The basis of a two-input tri-state NAND gate is shown in Fig. 2.26.

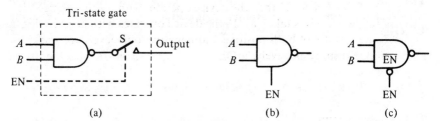

Fig. 2.26 (a) Simplified diagram of a three-state or tri-state NAND gate; (b) and (c) are circuit symbols (see text)

The output enable line, EN, in Fig. 2.26(a) controls the operation of switch S which connects the output of the NAND gate to the output pin of the chip. If the gate has an *active high* enable line, a logic '1' on the EN line results in S closing; the output from the tri-state gate may then be either logic '1' or logic '0', depending on the output from gate G1. If EN = 0, the contact of switch S is open and the output terminal of the chip is isolated from the output of gate G1. A circuit symbol representing this type of gate is shown in Fig. 2.26(b).

Some forms of tri-state gate have an *active low* output enable line (see the symbol in Fig. 2.26c); this is equivalent in Fig. 2.26(a) to connecting a NOT gate between the EN input and switch S. This is represented by positioning an inversion 'bubble' on the symbol of the gate where the enable line enters the gate. The net result is that switch S is closed when a logic '0' is applied to the output enable control line. For this reason, the control line is sometimes described as a NOT ENABLE line, symbolized by writing $\overline{EN}$ by the side of the output enable control connection.

The principle reason for tri-state logic being adopted by the electronics industry is that it allows many circuits to use a single wire or bus-bar for communication purposes. This practice is widely adopted in microprocessor-based systems (see also Chapter 8).

2.15 Logic signal levels

For most practical purposes it is convenient to think in terms of a true zero value, e.g., a zero value of voltage, current, pneumatic pressure, etc., as logical

'0' and a finite positive value for logical '1'. This is known as *positive logic notation*, since the more positive of the two levels is '1'. Many early semiconductor logic devices gave an output voltage which was either zero or a negative value. For convenience zero voltage was called logical '0' and the finite negative voltage was logical '1'. This is known as *negative logic notation* since the more negative voltage of the two logic levels is taken as the logical '1'.

Many devices used today have 'floating' levels, e.g., one of the levels in an electronic system may be + 5 V while the other may be − 4 V. If the higher of the two levels is taken as '1', then the device operates with positive logic. If the lower of the two levels is taken as '1', the device operates with negative logic. Illustrative examples of both positive and negative logic levels are shown in Fig. 2.27(a) and (b) respectively.

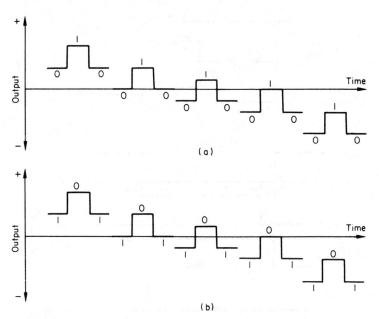

Fig. 2.27 Examples of (a) positive logic signal levels and (b) negative logic levels

It is convenient in some instances to use mixed logic. For example, the input logic could be positive logic while the output logic may be negative logic. That is, a finite signal at the input represents a '0'.

Conversion from positive logic to negative logic, and vice versa, can readily be carried out since

Positive logic = NOT negative logic
Negative logic = NOT positive logic

That is, either one is the logical component of the other. If the input to a NOT gate is '1' in positive logic, the output may be regarded as '0' in positive logic or '1' in negative logic.

2.16 Static hazards

In combinational logic the change of a single variable from '0' to '1', or '1' to '0', may cause a transient change in the output of a network when no change should exist. This is known as a *static hazard*.[1]

Two simple forms of static hazard are illustrated in Fig. 2.28. It is assumed in most logic devices that when $A = 1$, then $\bar{A} = 0$, and when $A = 0$, then $\bar{A} = 1$.

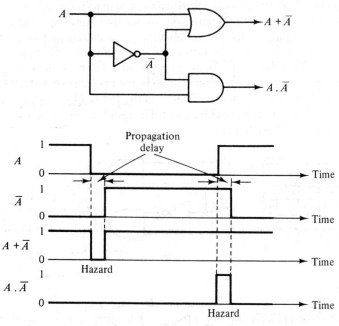

Fig. 2.28   Examples of static hazards

This is true under steady-state conditions, but during transition periods the condition $A = \bar{A} = 1$ or $A = \bar{A} = 0$ may exist, as shown in the figure. This is due to the time taken for the signal to propagate through the NOT gate. Only if the propagation time is zero does $A + \bar{A} = 1$ and $A . \bar{A} = 0$ at all times, eliminating the possibility of a static hazard in Fig. 2.28.

Due to the finite propagation time of practical gates, output $A + \bar{A}$ falls to zero for a short time and $A.\bar{A}$ assumes the value '1' for an instant. In many networks this is of no consequence, but if the output on the combinational logic feeds a circuit which counts pulses, the spurious pulses or 'glitches' produced by the static hazards may be counted in addition to the wanted pulses. This results in an inaccurate count.

It is possible to eliminate static hazards by including redundant gates in the network, but before these additional gates are included it should first be determined if the input conditions corresponding to the static hazard can occur. If this is not the case, then no static hazard occurs. Circuits can be designed to include known static hazards and still operate in a satisfactory manner.

A further example of a static hazard is considered here to illustrate the procedure for eliminating them. Consider the function

$$f = A.C + B.\bar{C}$$

Two networks are derived, using the Karnaugh map technique, in Fig. 2.29(a) and (b). Investigation of these networks shows that static hazards occur in both cases, but under different circumstances, as shown in Fig. 2.29(c). A hazard is said to exist when the input signal combinations change in such a way that they cause a change between adjacent cells in the Karnaugh map which are not grouped together. This is illustrated in Fig. 2.29(a) and (b) by the groups of cells connected by arrows. By linking these cells, as shown in Fig. 2.30(a) and (b), the hazards are eliminated. The resulting hazard-free networks are also shown in these figures.

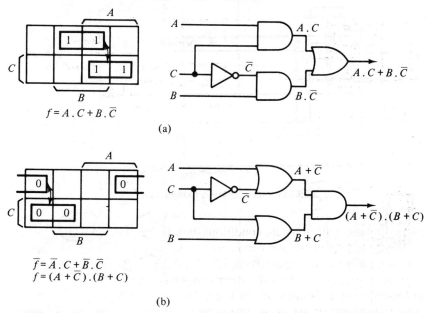

$$f = A.C + B.\bar{C}$$

(a)

$$\bar{f} = \bar{A}.C + \bar{B}.\bar{C}$$
$$f = (A + \bar{C}).(B + C)$$

(b)

Fig. 2.29 Static hazards exist if the input signals change in such a way that they cause a change between adjacent cells on the Karnaugh map which are not grouped together. This is shown in (a) and (b) by the groups of cells linked by arrows. The hazards are illustrated in (c)

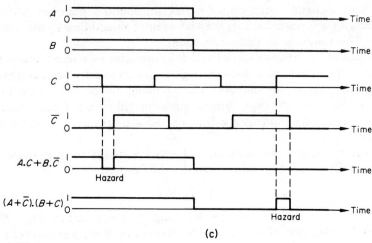

Fig. 2.29(c)

An illustration of a four-variable problem in which hazards may exist is shown in Fig. 2.31.

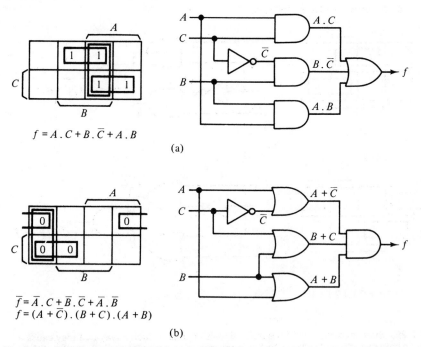

Fig. 2.30   The circuits in (a) and (b) are hazard-free versions of those in Fig. 2.29(a) and (b) respectively

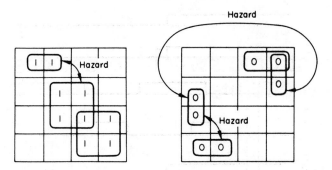

Fig. 2.31 Two four-variable problems in which static hazards may exist

Problems

2.1 With the aid of a truth table, deduce the logic equations for the sum and carry functions produced by the addition of two binary digits.

2.2 Draw a logic block diagram, using AND, OR, and NOT elements, which generate the functions deduced in problem 2.1.

2.3 Convert the network in problem 2.2 into (a) a NOR network and (b) a NAND network.

2.4 Develop the logic equation for the following truth table:

	Inputs		Output
A	B	C	f
0	0	0	0
0	0	1	1
0	1	0	1
0	1	1	0
1	0	0	0
1	0	1	1
1	1	0	1
1	1	1	0

Hence draw up a logic block diagram using AND, OR, and NOT elements.

2.5 Convert the network in problem 2.4 into (a) a NOR network and (b) a NAND network.

2.6 Devise minimal NOR and NAND networks for the functions

$$f_1 = \bar{A}.\bar{B}.\bar{C} + \bar{A}.B.C + A.\bar{B}.C + A.B.\bar{C}$$
$$f_2 = A.B.D + A.B.\bar{C} + A.\bar{B}.\bar{D} + \bar{B}.C.D$$

2.7 Show that a static hazard exists in the minimal network representing the function $\bar{A}.C + B.\bar{C}$. Devise minimal NOR and NAND equivalent networks, and investigate them for static hazards. If hazards exist, construct hazard-free networks.

References

1. HUFFMAN, D. A., 'The design and use of hazard-free switching networks', *J. Assoc. Comp. Mach.*, **4**, 1, 1957.

3. Electronic switching devices and circuits

3.1 Semiconductor terminology

A *semiconductor* is a material whose conductivity, at room temperature, is between that typical of conductors and insulators.[1] Germanium and silicon are the most commonly used semiconductor materials. Pure semiconductors become perfect insulators at absolute zero temperature and their conductivity rises with room temperature. This is known as *intrinsic conductivity* and is regarded as an imperfection in the material. By doping the pure semiconductor with a controlled amount of impurity (a few parts per million), another form of conductivity, known as *extrinsic conductivity*, is introduced.

The impurities introduced are referred to either as *p-type* or *n-type*. Semiconductors with a p-type impurity contain mobile positive charge carriers (known as *holes*), while the n-type impurity semiconductor contains mobile negative charge carriers (*electrons*). The electrical charge associated with the 'hole' and the electron are equal and opposite, and if a hole and an electron combine, the net electrical charge is zero.

Flow of current in an n-type material is largely due to the movement of electrons through it, and they are described as *majority charge carriers*. If positive charge carriers (holes) appear in an n-type semiconductor they also constitute flow of current, and are described as *minority charge carriers*. In a p-type material holes are the majority charge carriers and electrons are the minority charge carriers.

3.2 P-N junction diode

A p-n junction diode comprises a semiconductor crystal with both p- and n-type regions, the two being joined by molecular bonds, shown in Fig. 3.1(a), together with its circuit symbol, Fig. 3.1(b). It is found that current flow occurs

44

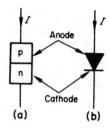

Fig. 3.1   (a) The basic physical arrangements of the p-n junction diode and (b) its circuit symbol

only when the p-type anode is positive with respect to the n-type cathode. In this state the diode is said to be *forward biased* and *forward conduction* takes place, the corresponding part of the characteristic being shown in Fig. 3.2.

When the anode is negative with respect to the cathode, the diode is said to be *reverse biased*, and only a minute leakage current flows. This is known as the *reverse blocking* state, when flow of current is blocked. A significant increase in reverse bias results in electrical breakdown of the diode, when it reverts to its second conducting state, known as *reverse conduction*. In semiconductor devices used as conventional diodes this usually results in a catastrophic failure, but diodes known as *Zener*, or *avalanche*, *diodes* are operated on the reverse breakdown region.

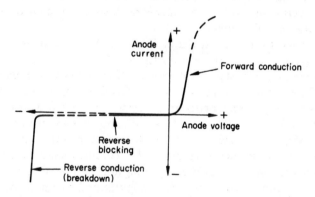

Fig. 3.2   Static characteristic of the p-n junction diode

3.3 Junction transistors

An n-p-n junction transistor is formed in a single semiconductor crystal, and has two n-regions and a p-region, as shown in Fig. 3.3(a). The n-p-n transistor is said to be a *bipolar* device since conduction is through two types of

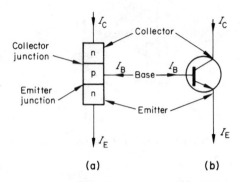

Fig. 3.3   The physical representation of an n-p-n transistor and (b) its circuit symbol

semiconductor material, and is carried by two types of charge carrier. The circuit symbol is given in Fig. 3.3(b), the arrow on the emitter giving the conventional direction of flow of current through the device, electron flow being in the opposite direction. The n-type *emitter* is the source of current carriers (electrons), which are divided between the *base* and *collector* regions. The name collector implies that it is the region at which most of the current carriers leaving the emitter are collected. The name base region dates back to the construction of early devices, and is regarded as the control electrode for the purposes of this book.

The p-n junction between the base and emitter regions is known as the *emitter junction*, and that between the base and collector regions as the *collector junction*. At first glance it appears that the simple equivalent electrical circuit of the transistor comprises two p-n junction diodes connected anode to anode. When the characteristics for the circuit in Fig. 3.4(a) are obtained, it is found that this is not the case. The circuit shown is known as the *common-emitter* configuration, since the emitter is common to both input (base-emitter) and output (collector-emitter) supplies. The common-emitter configuration is the mode most commonly used in switching applications. Other modes are the *common-base* and *common-collector* configurations. The principal advantage of the common-emitter configuration is the resulting high power gain.

The common-emitter *output characteristic*, in Fig. 3.4(b), is of great value to circuit designers. It shows the variation in collector current, I_C, with collector-emitter voltage, V_{CE}, and base current, I_B. With zero base current (base circuit disconnected), it is found that a small leakage current I_{CE0} flows between the collector and emitter. This leakage current lies between a few nanoamperes and a few microamperes. In this state the transistor is said to be 'off', in that it is approximately equivalent to a switch that is 'off' or 'open'.

By increasing I_B, at a constant value of V_{CE}, it is found that the collector current increases roughly in proportion to the base current, according to the relationship (neglecting leakage current)

$$I_C = h_{FE} I_B$$

A circuit diagram, known as the *equivalent circuit*, which embodies this fact is shown in Fig. 3.4(c). The constant current generator shunting the collector

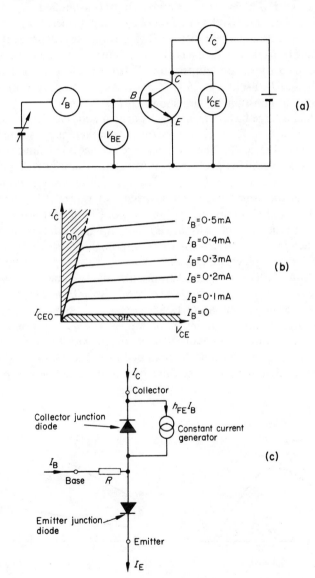

Fig. 3.4   (a) A circuit used to determine the output characteristic of an n-p-n transistor, (b) a typical output characteristic, and (c) a simplified equivalent circuit

diode generates the current $h_{FE}I_B$, and resistor R in the base line represents the ohmic resistance of the base region itself. Figure 3.4(c) is an equivalent circuit that is suitable for low frequencies, and is used here only to explain the circuit operation under steady-state conditions.

Parameter h_{FE} is the static value of the forward (signified by suffix F) current transfer ratio, I_C/I_B, in the common-emitter (signified by suffix E) configuration. The letter h refers to a set of hybrid parameters which are used to define the operation of the transistor. This parameter is dependent not only on the collector current at which it is measured but also on the value of V_{CE} and the semiconductor junction temperature T_j. It is therefore defined at a given value of V_{CE} and I_C, usually at 25°C. Typical curves giving variations in h_{FE} with I_C and T_j at constant V_{CE} are shown in Fig. 3.5.

By injecting a large base current, the transistor *saturates*, and is said to be *bottomed* or *turned-on*. The region of the output characteristic used in this state is labelled 'on' in Fig. 3.4(b). The problem here is what is the value of h_{FE} to be used in calculations? This problem is illustrated in more detail in Fig. 3.6. When V_{CE} is 1 V, the value of h_{FE}, for a base current of 1 mA, is $h_{FE} = 30$ mA/ 1 mA $= 30$. For the same value of base current, for values of V_{CE} of 0·5 V and 0·25 V, h_{VE} is 25 and 12.5 respectively. For a V_{CE} of 1 V, the transistor is not fully turned 'on', and the value of 30 for h_{FE} is clearly not applicable for a base drive of 1 mA. When $I_C = 25$ mA the transistor is approaching the ON state, but due to the spread of parameters other transistors of the same type may not saturate with $I_B = 1$ mA. To ensure that all transistors of the same type saturate, a working point of $V_{CE} = 0·25$ V, $I_C = 12·5$ mA, with a base current of 1 mA, should be aimed at, i.e., an h_{FE} of 12·5.

Manufacturers quote a number of values of h_{FE}, at points on the characteristics, at various values of collector current with V_{CE} constant, usually at 1 V. The true figure can only be obtained from the characteristics of the transistor to be used, but a suitable value may be obtained more rapidly from

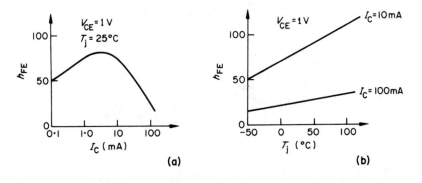

Fig. 3.5 Variation of h_{FE} with (a) I_C and (b) junction temperature

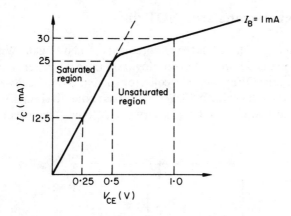

Fig. 3.6 Static characteristic of a transistor in the region of saturation

the data sheets as follows. The manufacturer specifies the maximum voltage existing across the transistor, $V_{CE(sat)}$, when it is in the saturated state with given collector and base currents. The value of h_{FE} to be used can be deduced from these figures. For example, if a silicon switching transistor has a specified $V_{CE(sat)}$ of 125 mV with $I_C = 10$ mA and $I_B = 1$ mA, the resulting figures of $h_{FE(sat)} = 10$ is a conservative figure for that type of transistor, and may be used in calculations. The parameter $h_{FE(sat)}$ is defined here as the static forward current ratio when the transistor is fully saturated. In general, the value of $h_{FE(sat)}$ is lower than the unsaturated value of h_{FE}, and is determined by the base current and the collector current (which is limited by external factors such as the value of the load resistance).

An alternative type of bipolar transistor, the p-n-p transistor, is also available. This comprises an n-region (the base) between two p-regions (the emitter and collector). With this type of device, negative collector and base potentials are used, otherwise the principle of operation is broadly similar to the n-p-n type.

The features of both types of transistor which make them suitable as switching devices are:

1. They are physically small and the power dissipation in both the ON and OFF states is low.
2. Their cost is low and the advent of integrated circuits has accelerated the reduction in cost per logical function.
3. The collector current in the saturated state is controlled by a much smaller base current ($I_B = I_C/h_{FE}$).

Their main disadvantages are:

1. The device is never truly OFF, since a small leakage current flows.
2. It can never be fully turned ON, since the saturation voltage $V_{CE(sat)}$ is finite.

3.4   Resistor-transistor NOT gate

The circuit in Fig. 3.7(a) fulfils the requirements of a NOT gate. When the base
is connected to the zero potential line (logic '0'), the base current is zero and the
transistor is in the OFF state. The collector current is practically zero and the
output potential is high (logic '1'). When the base potential is high (logic '1'), the
transistor is turned ON, and V_{CE} is very small (logic '0'), typically 0·2–0·5 V.

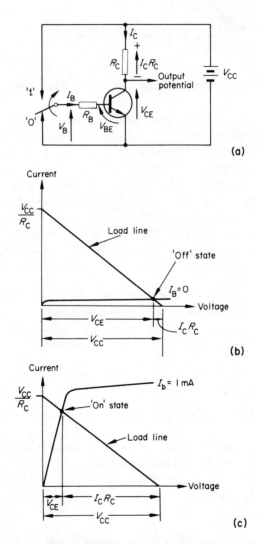

Fig. 3.7   (a) A simple resistor-transistor logic (RTL) NOT gate; (b) and (c) show the OFF
and ON states respectively of the transistor

The collector current in Fig. 3.7(a) can be evaluated by determining the conditions under which the following are satisfied simultaneously:

Current through the resistor = current through the transistor

$$V_{CC} = V_{CE} + I_C R_C$$

A precise mathematical solution can be obtained, but an easier and quicker method results from a simple graphical solution as follows. The collector potential is given by the equation

$$V_{CE} = V_{CC} - I_C R_C$$

$$I_C = \frac{V_{CC}}{R_C} - \frac{V_{CE}}{R_C}$$

This is the equation of a straight line of slope $-1/R_C$, terminating at points $V_{CE} = V_{CC}$ when $I_C = 0$ and $I_C = V_{CC}/R_C$ when $V_{CE} = 0$. The line is known as the *load line* and is shown in Fig. 3.7(b) and (c). The intersection of the load line with the appropriate output characteristic gives the point where the transistor and resistor currents are equal. The voltage across the transistor, V_{CE}, and across the resistor, $I_C R_C$, are then read off the output characteristic as shown.

When the switch in the base line connects the base to '0', $V_{CE} \simeq V_{CC}$ and $I_C \simeq 0$. When the input switch connects the base to the logic '1' level, when $V_B = V_{CC}$, a finite base current flows, given by

$$I_B = \frac{V_{CC} - V_{BE(sat)}}{R_B}$$

where $V_{BE(sat)}$ is the base-emitter voltage when the transistor is in the saturated state. $V_{BE(sat)}$ is small, compared with V_{CC}, and it may be neglected, giving

$$I_B \simeq \frac{V_{CC}}{R_B}$$

By applying adequate base current (referred to as base 'drive'), the transistor becomes saturated, and the collector potential falls to $V_{CE(sat)}$.

A simple design procedure for a transistor NOT gate is illustrated as follows. Consider transistor Q1 in Fig. 3.8(a), which has M similar circuits connected to its collector. The maximum value of M that Q1 can supply is known as the *fan-out* of the circuit. When the collector voltage of Q1 is 'high', the circuit provides base drive to transistors Q2, Q3, etc; consequently the drive circuit acts as a current source, and is described as a *current sourcing* logic gate. In general, bipolar logic circuits of the OR and NOR types are current sourcing gates. The worst operating state occurs when the input to Q1 is '0' and the maximum fan-out, M_{max}, is connected. In this case, the collector potential of Q1 is 'high', and it must be possible to draw sufficient current through R_C to drive all the connected gates into saturation. If the leakage current of Q1 can be neglected,

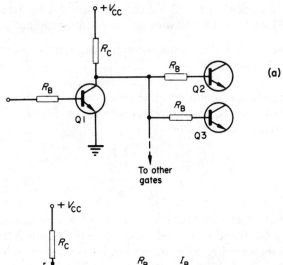

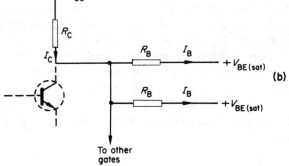

Fig. 3.8   Worst-case design of the NOT gate in Fig. 3.7 with a fan-out of *M*

the current through R_C when Q1 is OFF is

$$I_C = \frac{V_{CC} - V_{BE(sat)}}{R_C + R_B/M}$$

This operating condition is illustrated in Fig. 3.8(b). Neglecting $V_{BE(sat)}$, which is usually small compared with V_{CC}, the equation becomes

$$I_C \simeq \frac{V_{CC}}{R_C + R_B/M}$$

The base current supplied to each of the connected transistors Q2, Q3, etc., is

$$I_B = \frac{I_C}{M} = \frac{V_{CC}}{MR_C + R_B}$$

But $I_C = h_{FE(sat)}I_B$; therefore

$$I_B = \frac{I_C}{h_{FE(sat)}} = \frac{V_{CC}}{MR_C + R_B}$$

If $V_{CE(sat)}$ is small, then $I_C \simeq V_{CC}/R_C$ when the transistor is ON. Hence

$$\frac{V_{CC}}{R_C h_{FE(sat)}} = \frac{V_{CC}}{MR_C + R_B}$$

$$M = h_{FE(sat)} - \frac{R_B}{R_C}$$

Clearly M has a maximum value, with a given value of $h_{FE(sat)}$, when R_B/R_C is minimum. There are limits to the values of R_B and R_C that may be used, since a large value of R_C limits the current that may be drawn from the supply and a small value of R_B results in an excessive base current demand.

For a typical silicon switching transistor, $V_{CE(sat)} = 0.25$ V at a collector current of 10 mA and base current of 1 mA. Here $h_{FE(sat)}$ is 10, and if values of $R_B = R_C = 1$ kΩ, then $M_{max} = 10 - 1 = 9$, i.e., nine similar NOT gates may be connected to the collector of any transistor. The above calculations assumed that V_{CC} was constant, and the resistance values were not subject to variation in value. In practice, a tolerance must be allowed on these values, in addition to which h_{FE} will vary between transistors of the same type. Thus in the above case, if $h_{FE(sat)}$ lies between 9.5 and 12.5 and the resistors have a tolerance of 10 per cent, the worst case occurs when $h_{FE(sat)} = 9.5$, $R_B = 1.1$ kΩ, and $R_C = 0.9$ kΩ. This gives a new maximum theoretical fan-out of 8.28. Since an integral number of circuits only can be connected, the fan-out is reduced to eight.

3.5 Saturated operation of transistors

A transistor with an $h_{FE(sat)}$ of 10 may, typically, have a working h_{FE} in the unsaturated region of 50. The approximate equivalent circuit of an n-p-n transistor in the unsaturated region, with h_{FE} at a collector current of 5 mA ($I_B = 0.1$ mA) with a 1-kΩ collector load, is shown in Fig. 3.9(a). In the unsaturated region, the emitter diode is forward biased, and the constant current generator allows the collector current of 5 mA to flow in the load. The emitter current is $I_C + I_B = 5 + 0.1 = 5.1$ mA, resulting in a forward voltage drop of, say, 0.55 V across the emitter diode. The p.d. across the 1 kΩ load is 5 mA $\times$ 1 k$\Omega = 5$ V, and the collector potential is $10 - 5 = 5$ V. The collector diode has, therefore, a reverse bias of $5 - 0.55 = 4.45$ V across it. A further increase in base current results in an increase in collector current and a change in h_{FE}, here a reduction since the transistor is approaching saturation. The increased base and collector currents result in an increased emitter current and increased forward voltage drop in the emitter diode.

In Fig. 3.9(b), a base current of 0.47 mA results in an h_{FE} of 20, giving a collector current of 9.4 mA and an emitter current of 9.87 mA. The forward voltage drop across the emitter diode increases to 0.6 V as a result of this. Since 9.4 mA flows in the collector circuit, the p.d. across the 1-kΩ resistor is 9.4 V.

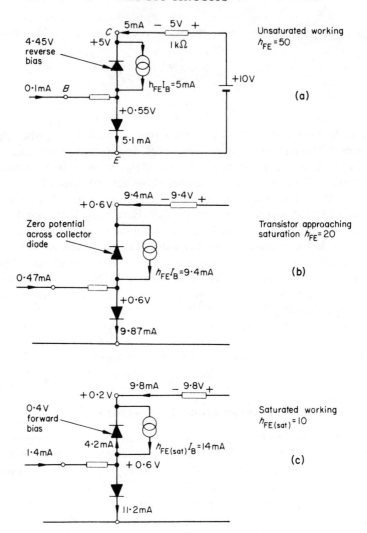

Fig. 3.9   Operating a junction transistor (a) in the unsaturated region, (b) on the verge of saturation, and (c) in the saturated region

That is, the collector potential is $10 - 9 \cdot 4 = 0 \cdot 6$ V. The reverse bias across the collector diode has now fallen to zero, and the transistor is on the verge of saturation.

Any further increase in base current results in a further reduction in the static forward current transfer ratio, illustrated in Fig. 3.9(c). Here $I_B = 1 \cdot 4$ mA and $h_{FE(sat)}$ is 10, resulting in a current of 14 mA through the constant current generator. Under these conditions the collector potential is of the order of

0·2 V; hence the current in the 1-kΩ resistor is $(10-0·2)/1 = 9·8$ mA. The difference between the external and internal collector currents $(14-9·8=4·2$ mA) circulates through the collector diode, which has now become forward biased. The effect of the forward bias on the collector diode is to reduce the collector potential below that of $V_{BE(sat)}$ (to 0·2 V in this case).

By using saturated transistors, one of the logical levels is practically equal to zero potential, while the other logical level can approach V_{CC}. The effective resistance between the collector and emitter in the saturated state is known as the *saturation resistance*, $r_{CE(sat)}$. In Fig. 3.9(c), $r_{CE(sat)} = 0·2$ V/9·8 mA $= 20·4$ Ω.

One problem of using the circuits in Figs 3.8 and 3.9 is that $V_{CE(sat)}$ rises, and $V_{BE(sat)}$ falls, with temperature. This means that a rise in temperature will reduce the margin by which one transistor in the ON state can hold a number of connected transistors in the OFF state. Offset against this is the fact that h_{FE} rises with temperature.

The principal advantage of saturated switching circuits is their simplicity. The main disadvantage is that the switching speed is reduced, since, during the switch-off period, the base region must be swept clear of base charges, which takes a finite time.

3.6 Transistor turn-on

The effect of a small change in base current on collector current can be measured at any given frequency. A graph of the small-signal forward current transfer ratio, h_{fe}, over a range of frequencies, to a logarithmic base, is shown in Fig. 3.10. The value of h_{fe} is constant over a wide range of frequency, falling off at the high-frequency end of the spectrum at the rate of approximately 20 dB/decade. At the low frequency end it assumes the value h_{FE}. It can be shown that at some frequency, ω,

$$h_{fe} = \frac{h_{FE}}{1 + j\omega/\omega_\beta}$$

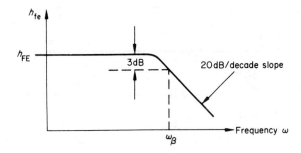

Fig. 3.10   Variation of h_{FE} with frequency

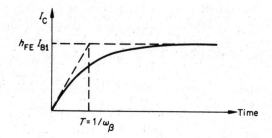

Fig. 3.11   Transient variation of I_C with a step change in base current

where $j = 1\underline{/90°}$ and ω_β is the 'corner' or 'cut-off' frequency, at which the gain is 3 dB below the low-frequency gain.

The transistor, in the common-emitter mode, thus displays the frequency response characteristic of a single time-lag network with a time-constant $T = 1/\omega_\beta$. It follows that, for a step change in base current from zero to I_B, the collector current I_C at any time t is given by

$$I_{C1} = h_{FE}I_{B1}(1 - e^{-t/T}) \qquad (3.1)$$

The general response of this equation is shown in graphical form in Fig. 3.11. An increased base drive results in a higher prospective value of collector current, as shown in Fig. 3.12. In practical circuits the collector current cannot exceed V_{CC}/R_C. Any prospective current above this value (known as *overdrive* current) must circulate through the internal collector diode of the transistor,

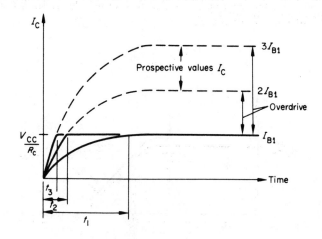

Fig. 3.12   Reduction in turn-on time with overdrive

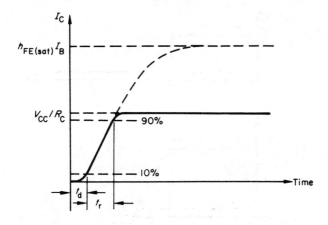

Fig. 3.13   Definition of turn-on delay t_d and rise-time t_r

and does not appear in the collector circuit. Overdrive directly results in a more rapid turn-on of the transistor, a reduction from t_1 to t_3 in Fig. 3.12, for an increase in base current by a factor of three.

The actual collector current waveform, for a step change in base current, is shown in Fig. 3.13. The *rise-time*, t_r, is defined as the time taken for the collector current to rise from 10 to 90 per cent of its final value. During this time the current rises along an exponential curve, as described above. At the instant of turn-on, base current begins to flow, but it takes a finite time for the current carriers to spread across the base region to initiate the turn-on mechanism. This delay is described as the *turn-on delay time*, t_d. The total time required to turn the transistor ON is known as the *turn-on time*, t_{on}, where

$$t_{on} = t_d + t_r$$

3.7 Transistor turn-off

When the transistor is saturated, both junctions are forward biased. The time taken for the overdrive current to be swept out of the collector junction, when turning the transistor OFF, is known as the *storage time*, t_s, shown in Fig. 3.14. When these current carriers have been swept out, I_C falls in an exponential manner. The *fall-time* or *turn-off transition*, t_f, of the collector current, is taken as the time for the current to fall from 90 to 10 per cent of the initial steady value. The total time required to turn the transistor OFF is known as the *turn-off time*, t_{off}, where

$$t_{off} = t_s + t_f$$

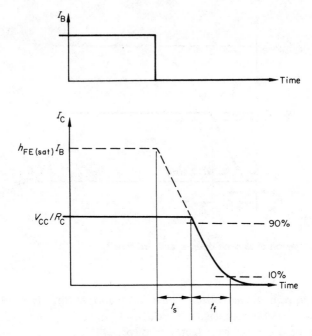

Fig. 3.14   Effect of overdrive on the turn-off time of the transistor

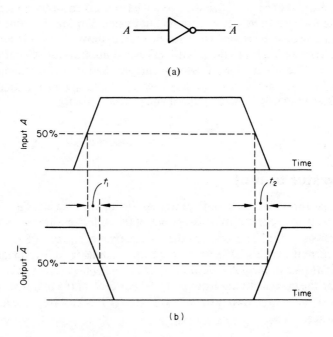

(a)

(b)

Fig. 3.15   Propagation delay of a gate

3.8   Propagation delay

A parameter used in specifying the switching performance of logic gates is the average time taken for the signal to propagate from the input to the output of the gate. This parameter is known as the *propagation delay*, t_{pd}, and is defined for the inverting gate in Fig. 3.15(a) in terms of the waveform diagrams in Fig. 3.15(b). The propagation delay is specified at the 50 per cent voltage levels of the input and output signals, and is given by

$$t_{pd} = (t_1 + t_2)/2$$

where t_1 and t_2 are defined in Fig. 3.15(b). The propagation delay depends on the type of logic circuit in use and on its loading, and may have a value less than one nanosecond in some electronic circuits.

3.9   Methods of reducing the switching time

It has been shown that a large base current is necessary to reduce the overall turn-on time, but it has the effect of prolonging the storage time. The simple circuit, shown in Fig. 3.16, improves the overall switching performance. When V_B is increased from zero, the capacitor draws a large charging current,

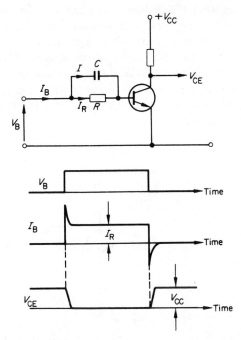

Fig. 3.16   Reduction of switching time by the use of an *R-C* circuit

ensuring that the base current is initially high. The transistor is rapidly forced into saturation by this artifice. When the capacitor becomes fully charged the base current falls to a value $I_R = (V_B - V_{BE(sat)})/R$. Providing that this value is sufficiently large to maintain the transistor in a state of saturation, the overdrive and hence storage time are reduced. The capacitor discharges rapidly when the input voltage is reduced to zero, drawing a reverse current from the base of the transistor. This ensures that the charge carriers in the base region are rapidly swept out when the applied voltage is reduced to zero.

So far the transistor has been regarded as a current-controlled device. In many switching applications, particularly those where capacitors are used to improve response time or as trigger devices, it is more convenient to regard the transistor as a *charge-controlled* device.[3,4] Charge control theory is based on the concept that the charge built up in the base region by minority carriers is the primary control mechanism.

An additional method of reducing the turn-off time is to use a bias supply, which reverse biases the emitter junction when the input voltage is zero. This arrangement is shown in Fig. 3.17. When V_B is zero the reverse bias applied to the base-emitter junction is approximately, neglecting the effect of the leakage current, $-V_{BB}R_1/(R_1 + R_2)$ V. The function of the bias circuit is to provide a transient reverse base overdrive current to discharge the base region.

One method of preventing the transistor being driven too hard into its saturated state is by means of the *antisaturation circuit* in Fig. 3.18. The onset of saturation occurs when the collector voltage falls below the base voltage. Diode D in Fig. 3.18 becomes forward biased after the onset of saturation, but before the transistor is heavily saturated, and diverts some of the excess base drive into the collector of the transistor. Since the diode only carries the excess base current, the storage time of the diode is much less than that of an overdriven transistor, so that the turn-off time of the circuit in Fig. 3.18 is less than that of the simple invertor circuit. A diode used in this mode is sometimes described as a *clamping diode*.

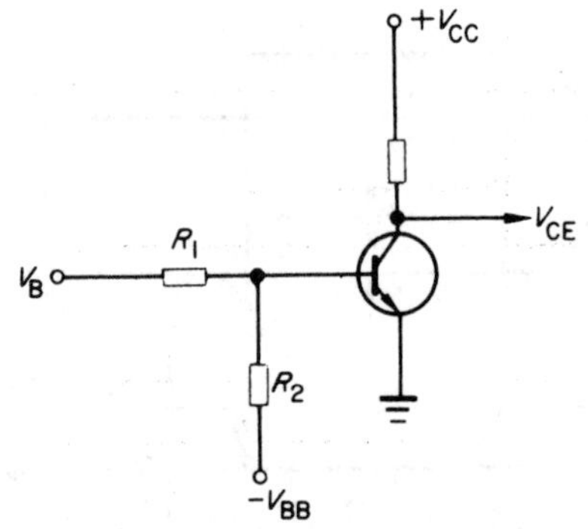

Fig. 3.17   A reverse bias applied to the base region reduces the turn-off time

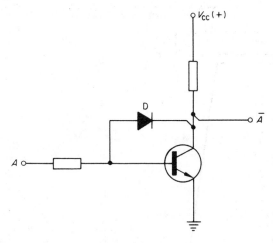

Fig. 3.18   Antisaturation diode (diode clamp)

Ideally, the clamping diode should have zero storage time, which is obtained in TTL gates by the use of Schottky diodes[1] (see also Chapter 4).

3.10   Noise immunity

The noise immunity of a logic gate is the electrical noise voltage it will withstand on any input line (or power supply line) without causing the output to register a change in voltage.

The d.c. noise margins are specified for an inverting gate in terms of its transfer characteristic (see Fig. 3.19). When the input signal is logic '0', the output voltage, V_a, corresponds to logic '1' level, and the device operates at point X on the characteristic. The noise margin which may be allowed on the input signal in this state is NM_0. When a logic '1' is applied to the input, the device operates at point Y on the characteristic, and the d.c. noise margin is NM_1. Should the values of voltage associated with the '0' and '1' logic levels differ from those shown, then the allowable noise margins change also. Manufacturers usually quote the statistically worst value of noise margin.

3.11   Diode-resistor gates

A positive logic diode-resistor OR gate is shown in Fig. 3.20. With both input lines at zero potential, the net e.m.f. acting in the circuit is zero, and the output potential is zero. If input line A is connected to $+E_s$ V (logic '1'), diode A is

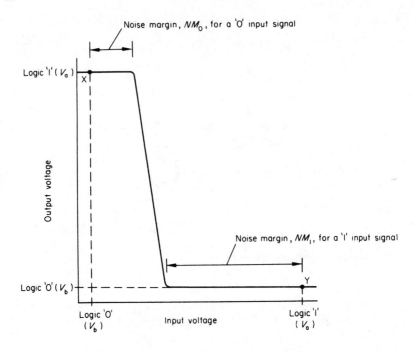

Fig. 3.19   Typical transfer characteristic of an inverting gate

forward biased and current flows through it and resistor R. Since the forward p.d. across the diode is small, the output voltage, V_o, is approximately equal to $+E_s$. Under this condition the anode of diode B is at zero potential and its cathode is at $+E_s$, i.e., it is reverse biased and no current flows through it. In diode-resistor OR logic the diode acts as a switch, which either connects the input directly to the output when the diode is forward biased or it isolates the input from the output when the diode is reverse biased.

When line A in Fig. 3.20 is at '0' and line B is at the '1' level, diode B conducts while diode A is reverse biased and the output voltage is again approximately

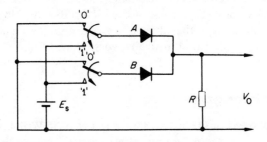

Fig. 3.20   Diode-resistor logic (DRL) OR gate

$+E_s$ V. When both A and B lines are at the '1' level, both diodes conduct and V_o is again approximately $+E_s$ V. The truth table for the circuit is given in Table 3.1.

Table 3.1
Truth tables for Figs 3.20 and 3.21

Input A	Input B	Output from Fig. 3.20	Output from Fig. 3.21
0	0	0	0
1	0	1	0
0	1	1	0
1	1	1	1

'1'=high potential, '0'=low potential.

A positive logic diode-resistor AND gate is shown in Fig. 3.21. If one or more of the input lines are at the '0' level (zero potential), those diodes are forward biased and conduct, irrespective of the signals applied to the other lines. The p.d. across the diodes, when conducting, depends on the current flowing and the construction of the diode. Generally the p.d. across the diode lies between 0·3 and 0·7 V, giving a potential at the output of the gate of this magnitude, which is taken as the logic '0' level.

Only when both input lines are at the '1' level does the output signal rise to logic '1', i.e., when $A = B = 1$.

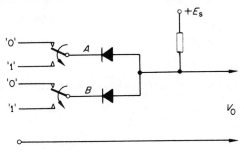

Fig. 3.21 Diode-resistor logic AND gate

3.12 Diode-transistor logic (DTL)

The positive logic NOR gate, Fig. 3.22(a), comprises a diode-resistor OR circuit followed by a transistor NOT gate, the NOR function being generated overall. The negative bias rail is used to reduce the turn-off time of the gate.

A positive logic diode-transistor NAND gate is shown in Fig. 3.22(b), comprising a diode-resistor AND gate followed by an inversion stage to give the NAND connective. In both circuits resistor R can be shunted by a capacitor to reduce the turn-on time of the gate. Antisaturation or clamping diodes can be used in conjunction with these circuits.

The circuit in Fig. 3.22(a) is sometimes referred to as current sourcing logic, since the gate acts as a current source to the inputs of the following stages when the transistor is in the OFF state. Figure 3.22(b) is also known as *current sinking* logic, since the transistor must absorb or 'sink' the current flowing in the diodes in connected gates when it is in the ON state.

To avoid the possibility of noise signals affecting the performance of these circuits, it is advisable to connect unused inputs on NOR gates to a 'low' (logic '0') signal and to connect unused inputs on NAND gates to a 'high' (logic '1') signal. Alternatively, unused inputs can be connected or 'strapped' to used inputs.

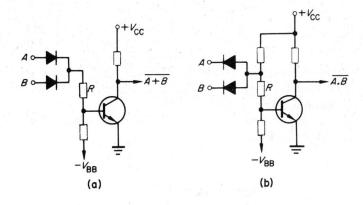

Fig. 3.22   Diode-transistor logic (DTL) (a) NOR gate and (b) NAND gate

3.13   Resistor-transistor *S-R* flip-flop

It is shown in Chapter 5 that two NOR gates can be used to construct a set-reset (*S-R*) memory. A resistor-transistor *S-R* version is shown in Fig. 3.23, comprising two NOR gates with direct feedback between them. A bias supply is used to reduce the turn-off time, and the feedback resistors are shunted by capacitors to reduce the switching time. The circuit in Fig. 3.23 is often referred to as a *S-R bistable* circuit since it has two stable states, corresponding to one or other of the transistors being in the ON state at any one time. In practice both transistors are ON simultaneously during the very short time that the output is changing state.

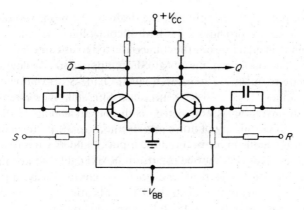

Fig. 3.23   The circuit diagram of an *S-R* flip-flop using resistor-transistor logic

3.14   Field-effect transistors

As the name of these devices suggests, an electrical field (rather than a current) is used to control the flow of current through them. There are two principal types of FET, namely:

1. The junction-gate FET (the JUGFET)
2. The insulated-gate FET (the IGFET or MOSFET)

The principal area of application of JUGFETs is in linear electronics, which is not of direct concern to us here. Their construction and operation is described in the literature.[1,5,6]

3.15   Insulated-gate field-effect transistors

The insulated-gate field-effect transistor forms the basis of many logic devices used in integrated circuit form (see also Chapter 4). Without it, the development of battery-operated pocket calculators would have been impossible.

A section through a basic element, the p-channel IGFET or MOSFET, is shown in Fig. 3.24(a). The source and the drain act as the respective electrodes at which the mobile charge carriers are injected into and extracted from the device. For reasons given later, only one type of charge carrier is involved in conveying current between the source and the drain which, in the case considered here, is the hole; since only one type of charge carrier is involved, these devices are sometimes described as *unipolar transistors*. Since, in Fig. 3.24(a), holes are used as charge carriers, the source electrode is connected to the positive pole of the supply and the drain to the negative pole. The gate region of the device provides a method of controlling the value of the drain current, and is insulated from the semiconducting substrate by a thin silicon oxide layer. The popular name of MOSFET applied to this device is derived from the gate-to-substrate structure (Metal-Oxide-Semiconductor FET).

In a p-channel device, two p^+-regions are diffused into an n-type substrate. Since the drain region is connected to the negative pole of the supply, a depletion region forms at the drain junction and, initially, the drain current is zero. The substrate is manufactured from low conductivity n-type silicon, so that only a relatively few mobile electrons are available. At normal values of ambient temperature, electrons and holes are continuously, but randomly, generated in the body of the substrate. The application of a negative potential to the gate electrode of the MOSFET causes the holes to be attracted to the metal-to-semiconductor interface beneath the gate electrode. At a gate potential known as the *threshold voltage*, V_T, a sufficient number of the thermally generated holes have collected in sufficient numbers on the underside of the oxide layer to form a conducting *channel* (known as an *induced channel* or as an *inversion channel*) between the source and the drain. Typical values of V_T lie in the range -2 to -5 V; devices which are manufactured using the silicon-gate process[1] have threshold voltages in the range $-1{\cdot}5$ to $-2{\cdot}0$ V. Increasing the value of the gate voltage, i.e., making it more negative with respect to the source electrode, attracts more holes to the interface, thereby increasing both the conductivity of the channel and the value of the drain current. The depth of the inversion channel formed in this way is typically a few angstrom units ($1 \text{ Å} = 10^{-10}$ m).

Since the value of the drain current is zero with zero gate voltage and, for gate voltages greater than V_T, is increased or enhanced, this type of device is known as an *enhancement-mode* MOSFET. A typical transfer characteristic or mutual characteristic for a p-channel enhancement-mode MOSFET is illustrated in Fig. 3.24(b). The circuit symbol for a device of this kind is shown in Fig. 3.24(c); the broken line between the source and drain electrodes indicates that, for zero gate voltage, no current flows between the two electrodes. In the symbol, the gate electrode is separated from the source-to-drain channel to indicate the electrical isolation between the two. The arrow pointing from the central part of the channel indicates the nature of the junction between the channel and the substrate; it points from the p-region (the channel) to the n-region (the substrate), i.e., it follows the diode convention.

Enhancement-mode MOSFETs can also be used to replace resistors in logic invertor circuits with some advantage since, for a given equivalent ohmic value, they require a much smaller area of the integrated circuit than does the resistor. This effectively either reduces the size (and cost) of a given logic gate, or allows a more complex logic circuit to be manufactured in the same physical space. An example of a MOSFET used in this way is given in Sec. 3.16.

Another type of MOSFET, the *depletion-mode* MOSFET, has the type of

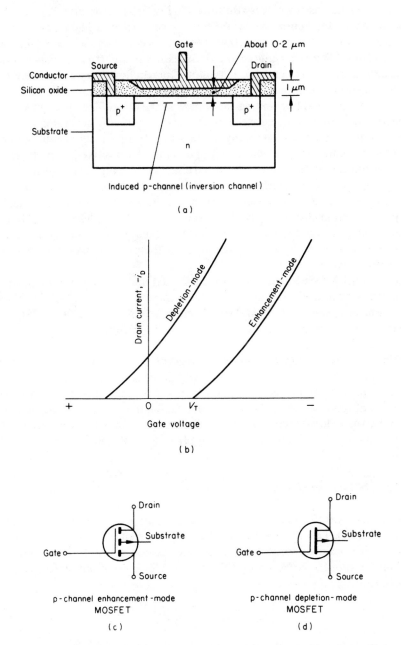

Fig. 3.24   (a) A section through a p-channel MOSFET, (b) typical transfer characteristics for p-channel devices, (c) circuit symbol for an enhancement-mode device, and (d) a circuit symbol for a depletion-mode device

mutual characteristic which is also shown in Fig. 3.24(b); the circuit symbol for a p-channel depletion-mode MOSFET is given in Fig. 3.24(d). This type of device, which is less common than the enhancement-mode device, has an *initial channel* of p-type semiconductor diffused into the structure between the source and the drain electrodes. This allows current flow to take place between these regions when the gate voltage is zero. This fact is illustrated in the circuit symbol by the solid line linking the source to the drain. The application of a negative potential to the gate electrode attracts thermally generated holes to the conducting channel, thereby increasing the drain current as before. However, in this type of device, the application of a positive potential to the gate region causes the holes in the initial channel to be repelled away from the oxide-semiconductor interface; this reduces the channel conductivity and the value of the drain current. Hence, in such an element it is possible to reduce or deplete the drain current below the zero bias value. Field-effect devices which have a finite drain current for zero gate voltage and whose value can be reduced or depleted by altering the value of the gate voltage are known as *depletion-mode* devices.

N-channel MOSFETs are also manufactured and are widely used in logic circuits. N-channel devices are used in conjunction with p-channel devices in the form of *complementary MOS* logic circuits (CMOS or COSMOS), one form of circuit being discussed in Sec. 3.16; in Chapter 4 a more general treatment is given.

Since the effective input circuit of the MOSFET is a capacitance shunted by a high value of resistance (typically $10^{12}\ \Omega$), the input time constant is such that their frequency response is not as good as that of bipolar transistors. However, the advantages of MOSFET circuits are such that they are widely used in logic circuits; these advantages include small size, low power consumption, high noise immunity, and a tolerance to supply voltage variations.

3.16   MOS NOT gates

Two types of MOS NOT gate are illustrated in Fig. 3.25. In the p-channel gate in Fig. 3.25(a), TR2 is so biased and constructed that it replaces the loading resistor in a conventional NOT gate. This circuit operates with a supply voltage of about -20 V and uses the negative logic notation; typical voltage levels are

$$\text{logic '1': } -11 \text{ to } -14 \text{ V}$$
$$\text{logic '0': } -2 \text{ to } -3 \text{ V}$$

The complementary MOS gate in Fig. 3.25(b) contains both p- and n-channel devices, both being switched by the input signal. That is, when TR3 is ON then TR4 is OFF, and vice versa. For this reason, TR4 is described as an *active load*. Consequently, the mean power consumption of the gate is only a few

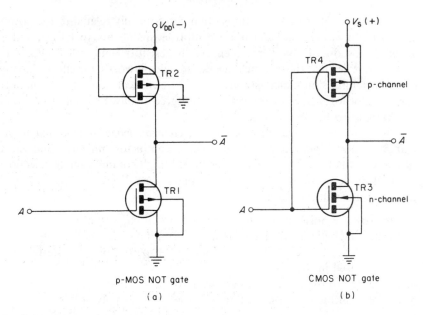

Fig. 3.25 (a) A p-channel MOS NOT gate and (b) a complementary MOS (CMOS) NOT gate

microwatts. CMOS logic uses a positive supply potential and the positive logic notation is used to describe its operation; the supply voltage can be in the range 3–15 V. When the input signal is logic '0', TR3 is OFF and TR4 is ON; in this state, the output line is coupled to the positive supply line. When the input signal is logic '1', TR3 is ON and TR4 is OFF; the output line is then coupled to ground. From the foregoing, the output resistance of the circuit is low (typically 500 Ω) for either level of output signal. With a 5 V supply, typical output voltages from a CMOS gate of the type shown are

$$\text{logic '1': } 4 \cdot 95 \text{ V}$$
$$\text{logic '0': } 0 \cdot 05 \text{ V}$$

This type of gate has a large noise margin and is typically $0 \cdot 45 \, V_s$, i.e., $2 \cdot 25$ V with a 5 V supply. Since the input impedance of this gate is very high, the input current has a very small value (typically 10 nA), giving each gate a theoretical fan-out in excess of 1000 at low operating frequencies (i.e., below about 10 kHz).

3.17 Noise in logic circuits

Noise is defined as all spurious signals, random and otherwise, that are not part of the input information. Noise is generally regarded as being either *narrowband* or *broadband*. Narrowband noise is low-frequency noise, typically in the range 10 Hz to 1 kHz, and is often harmonically related to the power supply frequency. Broadband noise comprises signals above 1 kHz, and is generally produced by thermal effects in resistors, and other effects in semiconductors and thermionic devices. In logic networks, the effect of many gates switching simultaneously gives rise to electrical noise. It is generally desirable for logic gates to possess a high degree of *noise immunity* to prevent inadvertent operation by noise signals.

Noise can be divided into two types, *common mode* and *normal mode*. Common mode signals appear between each conductor and earth, and many special circuits have been designed to have a high common mode rejection. Normal mode noise appears between conductors. There are five principal causes of noise in logic circuits:

1. Electrostatic noise, due to the effects of circuit capacitance.
2. Electromagnetic noise, due to magnetic coupling between circuits.
3. Thermal noise, due to the electrothermal properties of the materials and devices used in the circuits.
4. Noise due to the leakage of current across insulation.
5. Noise resulting from the variation in the power supply voltage.

The bias rail V_{BB} in Fig. 3.22 has the added advantage of increasing the noise rejection of those gates, as well as reducing the turn-off times. It is necessary for the noise voltage, at the input to the gate, to exceed the reverse bias applied to the transistor before the gate can be turned ON.

The forward conducting properties of diodes can also be utilized to increase noise rejection, as well as simplifying circuits. An example is shown in Fig. 3.26. By replacing resistor R in Fig. 3.22(b) with the diodes D1 and D2 in Fig. 3.26,

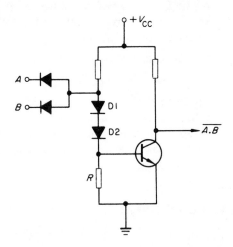

Fig. 3.26   Diodes D1 and D2 improve the noise immunity of the gate

the noise voltage at the input has to exceed the forward voltage drop of D1 and D2 before the transistor base potential begins to change. More diodes can be used if necessary. With this connection it is not necessary to use a negative bias supply since, with inputs A and B in the '0' state, the transistor base voltage is practically zero due to the forward conducting properties of D1 and D2. Resistor R in Fig. 3.26 provides a low impedance path for the charge carriers in the base region of the transistor when it is turned OFF. This resistor can be omitted if D1 and D2 are slow-recovery diodes, i.e., the transistor is capable of turning OFF at a faster rate than the diodes. In this event the charge carriers in the transistor base region, when the transistor is turned OFF, return to ground via D1, D2, and the input diodes. The latter arrangement is convenient in circuits using discrete components, but presents problems in monolithic circuit elements, since it is difficult to manufacture devices with different reverse recovery times in the same slice of silicon. Noise rejection can be further improved by replacing D1 and D2 by a Zener diode.

Problems

3.1 Given that the small-signal forward current transfer ratio h_{fe} of a transistor, at frequency ω, is given by

$$h_{fe} = \frac{h_{FE}}{1 + j\omega/\omega_\beta}$$

show that the expression for the collector current change, for a step change I_B in the base current, is

$$I_C = h_{FE} I_B (1 - e^{-t/T})$$

where

$$T = 1/\omega_\beta$$

3.2 In a resistor-transistor NOT gate, a transistor with an h_{FE} of 20 is used. The collector saturation current is 6 mA and the collector voltage is 'caught' at 2·5 V; under these conditions the base current is 0·3 mA. If a current of 0·1 mA is extracted from the base circuit by a constant current source, for 'speed-up' purposes, calculate the value of the resistor used in the input circuit.

3.3 Show that the NOR logic function is generated by connecting together the outputs of a number of NOT gates.

3.4 Describe the operation of a diode-transistor NOR element.

3.5 Compare diode-transistor logic with CMOS logic.

3.6 Draw a circuit diagram of a diode-transistor (a) AND gate and (b) OR gate. State whether positive or negative logic is used and explain the operation of the circuits. What logic functions are performed in each case if the logic levels are inverted?

References

1. MORRIS, N. M., *Semiconductor Devices*, Macmillan, 1976.
2. MORRIS, N. M., *Control Engineering*, 3rd. edn. McGraw-Hill, 1983.
3. BEAUFOY, R., and J. J. SPARKES, 'The junction transistor as a charge controlled device', *ATE Journal*, **13**, 310, 1957.
4. BEAUFOY, R., 'Transistor switching circuit design using the charge control parameters', *Proc. Inst. Elect. Engrs.*, **106 B**, Suppl. No. 17, 1092, 1959.
5. MILLMAN, J., and C. C. HALKIAS, *Integrated Electronics*, McGraw-Hill, 1972.
6. MORRIS, N. M., *Advanced Industrial Electronics*, McGraw-Hill, 1974.

4. Integrated circuits and logic families

Progress in electronics has resulted in the miniaturization of equipment with the benefit of space saving and the by-products of more economic and reliable components. The art of miniaturization has led to the development of integrated circuits, which are broadly divided into three groups: (1) film circuits, (2) monolithic integrated circuits, and (3) hybrid circuits.

4.1 Film circuits

In the film-integrated circuit passive elements are manufactured by depositing films of conducting and non-conducting materials on an insulating or passive substrate. Materials used for the substrate include borosilicate glass and ceramic materials having a high alumina content.

Resistors are in the form of a film of conducting material, nickel–chromium alloys being typical, having a thickness of a few millionths of an inch. During manufacture it is convenient to deposit all the resistors in one operation, leading to a uniform depth of conductor material. A feature of components manufactured by film techniques is that they can be accurately adjusted in value during manufacture by cutting away part of the component. The resistance (R) between opposite faces of a bar of conducing material is given by

$$R = \rho l/wd \ \Omega$$

where ρ = resistivity of the bar in Ω m
       l = length of the bar in m
       w = width of the bar in m
       d = depth of conducting material in m

If $w = l$, i.e., the bar is square in plan view, then $R = \rho/d$. This expression is independent of the physical sizes of both w and l. In any given manufacturing process depth d is constant, and the ratio ρ/d is usually defined as the *sheet resistance* in ohms per square and is assigned the symbol p. Thus the resistance of a conducting bar of length l and width w is

$$R = pl/w \ \Omega \tag{4.1}$$

For a given sheet resistance the ratio of length to width can be calculated for any value of resistance. If $p = 500 \ \Omega/\text{square}$, a 5 k$\Omega$ resistor requires the ratio $l/w = 10$.

The power dissipated per unit area of the substrate is limited by heating effects. If the maximum permissible power dissipation per unit area is W_m watt, then the actual power dissipated, W, is

$$W = W_m \times \text{area} = W_m w l$$

or

$$wl = W/W_m \tag{4.2}$$

With given values of R, p, and W_m the geometry of the film resistor can be calculated. The maximum power dissipation depends to a great extent upon the substrate material, 3 W/cm^2 being acceptable on glass substrates, but this is increased to 15·5 W/cm^2 on glazed ceramic materials.

Example 4.1: Calculate the dimensions of a film resistor of value 5 kΩ given that $p = 500 \ \Omega/\text{square}$, $W_m = 2$ W/cm^2, and that the power dissipation of the resistor is to be 0·1 W.

Solution: From Eq. (4.2),

$$W/W_m = 0 \cdot 1/2 = 0 \cdot 05 = wl \tag{4.3}$$

From Eq. (4.2),

$$l = Rw/p$$

Substituting this value in Eq. (4.3) gives

$$Rw^2/p = 0 \cdot 05$$

or

$$w^2 = 0 \cdot 05 \ p/R$$

$$= 0 \cdot 05 \times 500/5000 = 0 \cdot 005$$

Therefore

$$w = 0 \cdot 0707 \ \text{cm}$$

$$l = 0 \cdot 05/w = 0 \cdot 707 \ \text{cm}$$

Capacitors for film-integrated circuits are often manufactured in the parallel plate form, comprising successive layers of conducting and insulating material. The range of values of capacitance obtainable is restricted by the substrate area available and the thickness of the insulating material that may be used, the latter depending on the breakdown strength of the insulating material. The maximum value of capacitance at present practicable is a few thousand picofarads. Above this value, capacitors are attached externally as discrete components.

Inductances of a few microhenrys can be manufactured by depositing conducting material in a spiral form, but these occupy a large area on the substrate and have a low Q-factor. Whenever possible the use of inductors is avoided by redesigning the circuit to make use of active components. If this is not possible, inductors may be added as discrete components external to the film circuit.

Transistors can be manufactured in small quantities using film technology in the form of MOSFETs.

Film circuits are subdivided into thin- and thick-film circuits. The division is one of relative magnitude, since both are 'thin' by normal standards. In *thin-film* circuits the conductor depth is in the range 10^{-6}–10^{-4} in, while *thick-film* conductors have depths of about 10^{-4}–10^{-2} in. The type of film depends to a large extent on the material used and the method of manufacture. The performance of both types is similar, although it is sometimes claimed that thick-film circuits are more rugged and cheaper than thin-film circuits.

The sheet resistance and range of resistance values available differs with the type of film used. Thin-film methods give sheet resistances between $10\ \Omega$/square and $1\ k\Omega$/square, with a range of resistance values between $10\ \Omega$ and $100\ k\Omega$. Thick-film sheet resistances lie between $100\ \Omega$/square and $50\ k\Omega$/square, with resistance values between $20\ \Omega$ and $1\ M\Omega$. Capacitors in thin-film circuits have values between 100 and 10 000 pF, while those in thick-film circuits lie between 20 and 5000 pF. It is often more convenient to add large capacitors as discrete components to the film circuit.

4.2 Hybrid circuits

A hybrid integrated circuit is one combining the high component packing density of monolithic circuits (see Sec. 4.3) with the accuracy of the components on a film circuit. Moreover, it is possible to produce a hybrid integrated circuit in the form of a film circuit with added discrete components such as transistors (see below).

Active elements are added as discrete components to the film circuit. The transistors used are in the form of a small piece or *chip* of semiconductor material. The chip is 'flipped' or turned over to enable connections to be made to it, as shown in Fig. 4.1, the connections being made by ultrasonic or thermocompression bonding. This is known as the *flip-chip* method of mounting active devices. Since active components are added to passive film circuits, the circuit designer can initially test out all his circuits using a discrete component design and worst-case design techniques. The design can then be transferred directly to a film circuit. Film circuits are best utilized where the

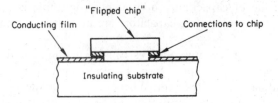

Fig. 4.1   'Flip-chip' method of mounting an active device on a passive substrate

ratio of active to passive elements is low. For small-batch production of special circuits, the film circuit is cheaper than the monolithic circuit, since these require high production rates to justify their economics.

4.3   Monolithic integrated circuits

Monolithic or semiconductor integrated circuits are manufactured in a silicon substrate, both passive and active elements being made in a small 'chip' of about 1 mm² or less. Resistors, capacitors, and transistors are relatively easy to manufacture, but at the present time no suitable replacement for inductors has been found. As in the case of the film circuit, it may be necessary to redesign the circuit if inductors are required.

In order to manufacture a range of components, several p-n junctions may have to be developed in the semiconductor chip. Two methods are commonly used: epitaxial deposition and diffusion.

In the process of *epitaxial deposition*, layers are formed on the surface of a silicon chip by raising the chip to a high temperature and passing a gas containing special compounds over it. The thin layer so formed has the same crystal structure as the silicon on which it is formed, having a higher resistivity than the chip. Resistors, capacitors, diodes, and transistors are formed in the epitaxial layer by the process of *diffusion*.

Junctions are formed by diffusion as follows. The silicon chip is heated in a steam atmosphere at a high temperature, allowing the surface to oxidize. 'Windows' are then cut in the skin of SiO_2 by a photoengraving process. The slice is again raised to a high temperature in a furnace, and gases containing dopants which result in a crystal structure of the opposite type to that of the substrate diffuse into the substrate. This process is illustrated in Fig. 4.2. Transistors are formed by a process of multiple diffusion.

A monolithic integrated *resistor* is shown in Fig. 4.3, together with its approximate equivalent circuit. The resistive element between A and B is the collector region of a parasitic p-n-p junction transistor. The resistor is isolated from the substrate by making the n-region positive with respect to the resistive p-region. A resistor tends to take up a bigger substrate area than a transistor, and for this reason pinch-effect resistors are often preferred in monolithic

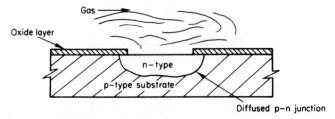

Fig. 4.2   Manufacturing a diffused p-n junction

circuits. The *parasitic transistor* between the two p-regions can cause feedback effects to other components in the integrated circuit. This is one of the problems associated with this type of circuit. Due to the difficulties in accurately controlling the diffusion process, the tolerance of the resistance values developed by this technique is very wide, typically ± 20 per cent.

A *diode* is formed using the collector junction of the transistor, shown in Fig. 4.4. The diode is isolated from the substrate by making the substrate negative with respect to the point C.

Transistors are formed by a process of three diffusions. The useful n-p-n transistor is connected to a parasitic p-n-p transistor, shown dotted in Fig. 4.5(a). The n-p-n transistor is isolated by connecting the substrate to the point in the circuit with the most negative potential.

There are two methods in general use for the production of monolithic integrated circuit *capacitors*. One is to utilize the capacitance of a reverse

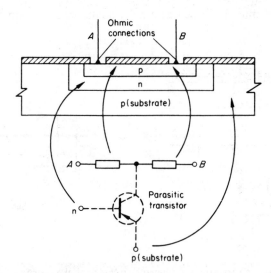

Fig. 4.3   A monolithic integrated circuit resistor which is isolated from the substrate; the structure forms a parasitic transistor

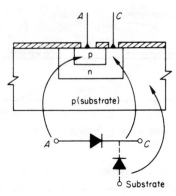

Fig. 4.4   One form of monolithic integrated circuit diode

biased diode, shown in Fig. 4.5(b). The resulting capacitance has a low value and is dependent on both the applied reverse voltage and the impurity doping of the diode regions. The second method is to utilize the oxide layer on the surface of the chip as a dielectric. The upper plate is made in the form of a metallic film deposited on the surface of the oxide layer, while the lower plate is a suitably doped semiconductor region in the chip. The value of capacitance normally obtainable is not much more than 100 pF since there are limits to both the surface area available on the chip and the minimum thickness of the oxide layer due to its dielectric strength. This type of capacitor is known as a MOS capacitor.

Inductors cannot normally be produced by conventional semiconductor techniques and must be added externally as discrete components.

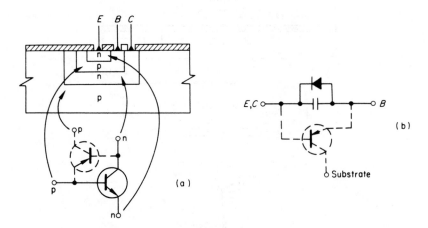

Fig. 4.5   (a) An n-p-n transistor is produced by diffusion in the substrate, but is associated with the parasitic transistor shown dotted. (b) A capacitor can be constructed by reconnecting the transistor in (a)

4.4 Manufacture of a bipolar integrated circuit

We will now consider how the circuit in Fig. 4.6(a) can be constructed in integrated circuit (IC) form; the network shown could be a part of a switching circuit. When completed, the IC appears as shown in Fig. 4.6(b), with the overall size of the transistor being typically 100 μm (0·004 in) square. The steps involved are summarized below.

4.4.1 The n^+ buried layer

The silicon chip or die manufactured in the initial process is used as a *substrate*, upon which the whole circuit is constructed. The resistivity of the substrate material is fairly high and would result in any transistor constructed in it being unsuitable as a switching device. In order to overcome this defect, a 'buried layer' of n^+ semiconductor material having a high conductivity is diffused into the substrate at a point on the chip which is to be directly below where the final transistor is to be placed. An n^+ material is one which has a higher value of conductivity than a conventional n-type material. The process of diffusion is

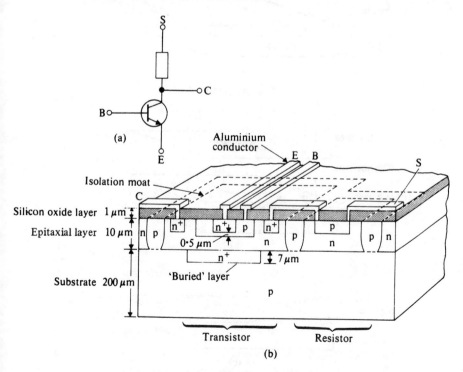

Fig. 4.6 The manufacture of a simple monolithic IC

described below under the two headings of *oxide growth and photomasking* and *diffusion*, and is generally similar to the diffusion process used in the construction of the remainder of the circuit. The reason that the buried layer is so named is because it is buried below the surface of the circuit.

4.4.2 Oxide growth and photomasking

After cleaning and inspection, the upper surface of the substrate is oxidized by passing steam over it; the oxide layer produced by this process is only about 1 m thick. The upper surface of the oxide is then coated with a light-sensitive material known as *photoresist*, as shown in Fig. 4.7(a). The photoresist is exposed to ultraviolet radiation through a photographic mask (see Fig. 4.7b) and exposed areas of the photoresist harden. The unexposed areas covered by the opaque areas of the mask are 'soft' and are dissolved by a solvent, leaving an aperture in the photoresist. The slice is then etched in acid to remove the exposed area of the oxide film, leaving a 'window' through to the upper surface of the substrate. The remaining photoresist is next removed by other solvents, after which the slice is rinsed and dried.

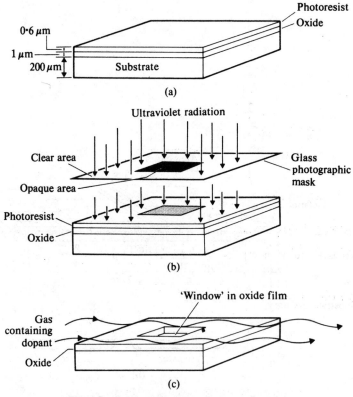

Fig. 4.7 Production of the n$^+$ buried layer

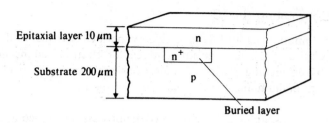

Fig. 4.8 A section through the wafer after the epitaxial layer has been formed

4.4.3 Diffusion

In the next stage of manufacture the slice is passed through a diffusion furnace, where it is heated to a temperature of about 1200 °C and gases containing appropriate dopants are passed over it (see Fig. 4.7c). The dopant in the gas causes the exposed area of the p-type substrate to be converted into n^+ material. The buried layer, diffused through the window in the oxide layer in this manner, finally penetrates to a depth of about 7 μm. After this, the oxide layer is etched away leaving the p-type substrate together with the 'buried' n^+ layer at its surface.

4.4.4 Epitaxial layer

Next, the slice is heated once more in a furnace and is subjected to a gas which causes an n-type *epitaxial layer* to 'grow' uniformly over the whole surface (see Fig. 4.8). It is in this 10-μm thick epitaxial layer that the whole integrated circuit is formed.

4.4.5 Circuit components

In order to isolate the components within the circuit from one another, it is next necessary to form isolation 'moats' around the areas in which the components are to be formed. By a process of masking, etching, and diffusion similar to that described above, p-type isolation moats are diffused into the epitaxial layer (see Fig. 4.6b). The moat provides a link between the surface of the IC and the substrate, and electrically isolates the area it surrounds.

Next, windows are cut in the oxide layer to allow the p-type base and resistor diffusions to be introduced. After this, the next diffusion process enables not only the emitter of the transistor but also the two n^+-regions in the collector to be introduced. The latter regions are required to allow a connection to be made to the collector region itself and to enable the collector and the resistor to be interconnected.

4.4.6   Completing the IC

A layer of aluminium about 1·5 μm thick is evaporated over the whole surface of the circuit, and the regions not required for electrical connections are removed by an etching process. Connections are then made between the remaining aluminium and the external 'pins' of the IC.

The above is a simplified description of the processes involved and, as the reader will appreciate, the sectional sketch in Fig. 4.6(b) is also a simplified picture. In all, about 80–100 individual processes are involved in the manufacture of a bipolar IC, some requiring a few hours to complete and others several weeks.

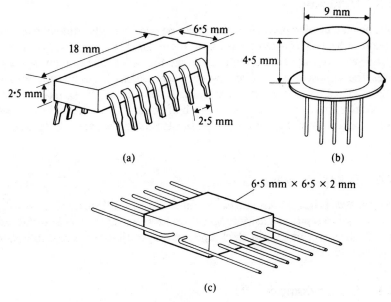

(a)   (b)

(c)

Fig. 4.9   IC packages

4.5   Integrated circuit packaging

The three most popular forms of IC packages (or *packs*) are shown in Fig. 4.9. The most popular form is the plastic encapsulated 14-pin *dual-in-line pack* (DIP) in Fig. 4.9(a). The 14-pin DIP has seven connecting pins per side, pairs of pins being in line with one another and the pins being 2·5 mm (0·1 in) apart to allow the IC to be fitted directly into standard printed circuit boards. Many forms of DIP are available, depending on the complexity of the chip; typically 8-, 14-, 16-, 18-, 20-, 22-, 24-, 28-, and 40-pin packs are manufactured. The latter

(40-pin) include microprocessor chips. The *canister* (or *can*) form (Fig. 4.9b) contains the IC in a hermetically sealed metal can. The *flatback* (Fig. 4.9c), frequently of ceramic construction, is hermetically sealed also.

4.6 MSI, LSI, and VLSI circuits

The terms *medium-scale integrated* (MSI) circuit, *large-scale integrated* (LSI) circuit, and *very-large scale integrated* (VLSI) circuit are commonly used when describing certain types of complex logic circuits. They refer to the number of complete logic gates in an IC pack and, though not precisely defined, may be interpreted as follows:

1. MSI circuits contain between about 10 and 100 gates.
2. LSI circuits contain between about 100 and 1000 gates.
3. VLSI circuits contain more than about 1000 gates.

4.7 Multiple emitter transistor

Monolithic production techniques have led to the manufacture of many unique devices. One of the most useful is the multiple emitter transistor (MET) illustrated in Fig. 4.10(a) which is widely used in TTL circuits. Its operation is described with reference to Fig. 4.10(b) and (c).

Inputs *A*, *B*, and *C* are connected to the collectors of other transistors which are either at zero potential (saturated) or at logic '1'. Figure 4.10(c) shows the simple equivalent circuit of the MET, and its similarity to the input circuit of the DTL gate in Fig. 3.26 should be noted.

With all inputs in the '1' state, all the emitter junctions of the MET are reverse biased. In this event the collector potential of the MET is 'high' since the collector is connected via R_1, r_b, and the forward biased collector diode. If any of the inputs are taken to '0', the base current is diverted to those emitters and the MET saturates. Since the emitter-collector potential of a saturated transistor is very small, the output voltage level falls to logical '0'. In the mode described, the MET performs the AND function.

A feature of this device is that the base current is similar in both the ON and OFF states (assuming that the output is connected to a transistor), since one or other of the MET junctions are forward biased at all times. Switching the transistor is then a matter of redistributing the base current between the junctions, which is accomplished in approximately one nanosecond.

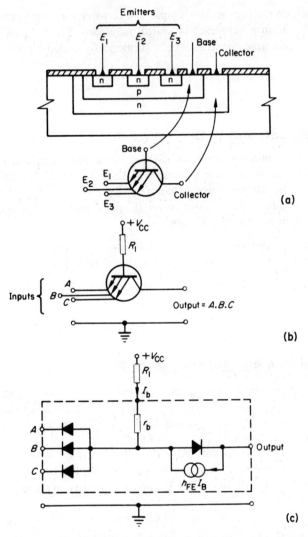

Fig. 4.10 (a) The construction and the circuit symbol of the multiple emitter transistor. A usual form of circuit configuration is shown in (b) together with the approximate equivalent circuit in (c)

4.8 Lateral transistors

The bipolar transistors described above are all of the *vertical* type, i.e., the structure (either n-p-n or p-n-p) is vertical to or is perpendicular to the oxide layer.

In some cases it is necessary to use a *lateral transistor* in which the structure

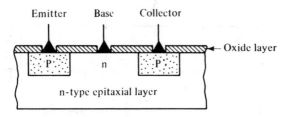

Fig. 4.11   A lateral p-n-p transistor

is parallel to the oxide layer. An example of a lateral p-n-p resistor is shown in Fig. 4.11.

4.9   Monolithic integrated logic circuits

In the early days of the development of monolithic circuits, an attempt was made to duplicate conventional circuits which used discrete components. Examples of this type included DTL (see Sec. 4.10). In this section of the book, a number of the more important logic families are described including:

DTL	diode-transistor logic
TTL	transistor-transistor logic
I²L	integrated injection logic
ECL	emitter-coupled logic
p-MOS and CMOS	MOS logic families

A summary of the principle characteristics of the major logic families is given in Sec. 4.15.

4.10   Diode-transistor logic (DTL)

A popular monolithic DTL NAND gate is shown in Fig. 4.12. When comparing this circuit with the discrete component version in Fig. 3.26, readers will note that diode D1 in the latter circuit is replaced by transistor TR1 in Fig. 4.12. The advantage of this arrangement is that the current flowing through the input diodes need only be equal to the base current of TR1 in Fig. 4.12; these diodes carry a much greater current in the discrete component version. This results in the monolithic version having a greater fan-out and a more rapid switching speed than is the case in the discrete component version in Fig. 3.26.

The noise immunity of Fig. 4.12 is improved if diode D2 is replaced by the Zener diode shown in inset (i) in the figure. Versions using the Zener diode have a noise immunity of about $(V_Z + 0.7)$ V, where V_Z is the breakdown voltage of the Zener diode. A disadvantage of this arrangement is that Zener diodes

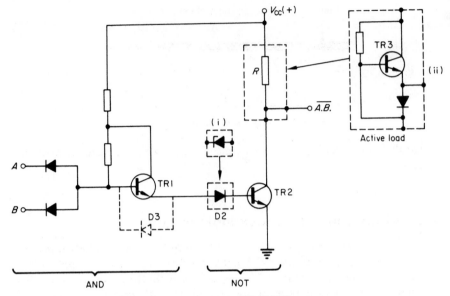

Fig. 4.12   A monolithic DTL NAND gate

have a relatively large value of self-capacitance, and this reduces the switching speed of the circuit. Diode D3 is sometimes used as a means of quickly discharging the charge stored in the parasitic capacitance of the Zener diode.

In this circuit (and also other types of NAND gate), unused inputs should either be connected to a logic '1' signal or should be connected to a used input line. This provides the gate with the best possible noise immunity.

Since the output resistance of Fig. 4.12 is approximately equal to R when the output voltage is 'high', and has a small value when the output voltage is 'low', it is possible to use these gates in distributed logic or WIRED-OR networks.

The switching performance of the circuit is improved if the collector load resistance R is replaced by an active load, such as that shown in inset (ii) in Fig. 4.12. The principal reason for the improvement in switching speed is that the current gain of the transistor used in the active load reduces the effective time constant of the collector load. DTL gates with an active load of this kind cannot be used in WIRED-OR networks for the following reason. If two NAND gates with active loads have their output terminals connected together, then when TR2 is turned ON in one gate and TR3 is ON in the second gate, a short-circuit is applied to the power supply through the WIRED-OR link. This type of active load increases the 'low' output voltage by about 0·6 V.

4.11   Transistor-transistor logic (TTL)

When TTL was introduced it represented a revolution in logic circuit design, and was only made possible by monolithic IC technology. TTL has become the 'work horse' of the logic world, and is manufactured in six main forms, namely *standard TTL, low-power TTL, high-speed TTL, Schottky TTL, low-power Schottky TTL,* and *tri-state TTL.* Essential features of these types are described below.

A basic TTL NAND gate is shown in Fig. 4.13, and uses a multiple emitter transistor (MET) TR1 in the input circuit. The operation of the MET was

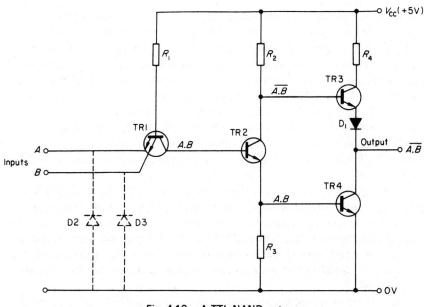

Fig. 4.13   A TTL NAND gate

described in Sec. 4.7, when it was shown that the logic function developed at its collector is the AND function of the signals applied to the emitter electrodes. The circuit shown has only two input lines; other NAND gates having METs with three or more inputs are also manufactured. The signal $A.B$ at the collector of TR1 is applied to the base of TR2, which functions as a phase-splitting amplifier. By emitter follower action, the logic function at the emitter of TR2 is $A.B$ and, by the inverting action of TR2, the signal at its collector is $\overline{A.B}$. Since these two signals are complementary they cause TR3 to be ON when TR4 is OFF, and vice versa. The fact that the circuit generates the NAND function overall is explained below.

A circuit generates the NAND function if its output is logic '1' when any input or combination of inputs is logic '0', and is '0' only when all inputs are 1's. Consider the case when either of the inputs in Fig. 4.13 is logic '0'; the output from the collector of TR1 is logic '0', resulting in a '1' signal being applied to the base of TR3 and a '0' signal being applied to the base of TR4.

These respectively turn TR3 ON and TR4 OFF, so that the output line is connected to V_{CC}, i.e., the output is logic '1'.

When $A = B = 1$, a logic '1' is applied to TR4 and a '0' to TR3. This action causes TR4 to be in the ON state, and the output line is now connected to the zero potential line, i.e., the output is logic '0'. From the above, readers will note that the output line is coupled either to V_{CC} or to the zero voltage line via a saturated transistor and R_4, i.e., the output resistance of the circuit is low for either logic state.

Due to its appearance, the rather unusual output circuit in Fig. 4.13 is known as a *totem-pole* output circuit. The diode D1 is a voltage level shifting diode, and is included to ensure that TR3 can be turned off under all operating conditions of the circuit. The reason for resistor R_4 is explained in the following. During the turn-on and turn-off periods of operation, transistors TR3 and TR4 do not switch at the same speed. In the absence of resistor R_4, and with TR3 and TR4 conducting simultaneously, a transient short-circuit would be applied to the power supply. The function of R_4 is to restrict the peak transient current drawn from the supply at this time; in standard TTL the peak value of transient current is limited to about 40 mA per gate.

Because the output resistance of the circuit in Fig. 4.13 is low in either logic state, it cannot be used in WIRED-OR networks. This problem is overcome in one of two ways. One method is by the use of *open-collector* TTL gates, in which the components R_4, TR3, and D1 (see Fig. 4.13) are omitted. By using a single external pull-up resistor, it is possible to use a number of open-collector TTL gates in WIRED-OR networks in the same way as other logic families may be used.

There are three versions of the basic circuit shown in Fig. 4.13, namely low-power TTL, standard TTL, and high-speed TTL, the essential difference between them being in the values of the components used in the circuits. These values are listed in Table 4.1.

The propagation time of the signal through the gate is primarily determined by the time taken for the inherent capacitances of the circuit components to be charged or discharged. To speed up this process it is necessary to reduce the circuit time constants, i.e., to reduce the values of the resistors. Hence the high-speed branch of the family has the lowest values of resistance and the largest power consumption per gate.

Table 4.1

Type	R_1 (kΩ)	R_2 (kΩ)	R_3 (kΩ)	R_4 (Ω)	Power per gate (mW)	Propagation time (ns)
Low-power TTL	40	20	12	500	1	30
Standard TTL	4	1.6	1	130	10	12
High-speed TTL	2.8	0.75	0.5	58	20	6

Sub-units used in data processing equipment have various speed requirements, and in arithmetic sections it may be desirable to use high-speed TTL. In other sections with less demanding requirements, it is possible to use standard TTL. Since the fan-out capability of a TTL gate depends on the current it has to 'sink', its fan-out varies with the type of driven gate. A list of typical fan-out values is given in Table 4.2.

Table 4.2

Driving gate	Fan-out into the following types of TTL		
	Low-power	Standard	High-speed
Low-power TTL	10	1	1
Standard TTL	40	10	8
High-speed TTL	50	12	10

A feature worthy of attention in connection with TTL is the very fast rise- and fall-times associated with the change in output signal. In the wake of these rapid changes in signal level come problems of signal reflections along the transmitting lines. A transmission line is described as being electrically 'long' if the time taken for the signal to propagate down the line is of the same order of magnitude as the rise-time of the signal being propagated. In the case of TTL, an electrically long line is one of length about 0·75–1·0 m. Under certain circumstances, the voltage reflections generated by this means may cause a transient voltage undershoot of -2 V or greater to appear on the line; this signal, when applied to the input of a driven gate, may cause damage to the gate. One solution used to overcome the worst effects of these transients is to connect diodes D2 and D3 (see Fig. 4.13) between the input lines and the common line. In normal operation each of the diodes is reverse biased (or, alternatively, has no bias applied to it), but when the input polarity is negative, the appropriate diode conducts heavily and damps out the voltage undershoot.

Small values of propagation time ($\simeq 3$ ms) are obtained using *Schottky diode clamped TTL* gates. The general principle of reducing the storage time of logic gates by means of a clamping diode was outlined in Sec. 3.9. In this branch of the TTL family, a Schottky diode is used as the clamping device. The Schottky diode is a rectifying metal-to-semiconductor junction device,[1] in which (in TTL) an aluminium conductor is the anode. The n-type collector region acts as the cathode. The geometry of the structure is shown in Fig. 4.14(a). The equivalent electrical circuit of the Schottky diode clamped transistor is shown in Fig. 4.14(b), while Fig. 4.14(c) gives a symbol used for this structure. A complete Schottky TTL NAND gate is illustrated in Fig. 4.14(d), the propagation time of this type of gate being about 3 ns; the dissipation per gate is about 20 mW.

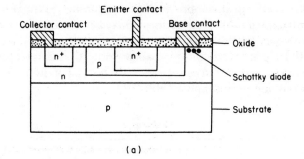

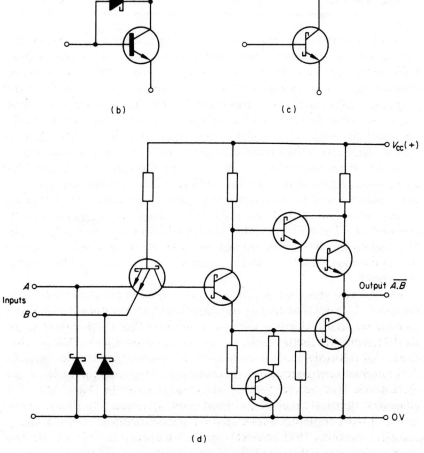

Fig. 4.14   (a) Construction of a Schottky diode clamped transistor; (b) and (c) are circuit symbols, (d) Schottky diode clamped TTL gate

As the ambient temperature rises, so the Schottky clamp becomes less effective and the transistors are driven further into saturation. The noise immunity of Schottky TTL is lower than that of other branches of the TTL family. These drawbacks are frequently outweighed by the lower propagation time of Schottky TTL.

Standard TTL gates have been replaced in many circuits by low-power Schottky TTL gates, which are low-power versions of Schottky TTL. This branch of the TTL family has the advantage of low power consumption combined with the low propagation time of Schottky TTL.

In microcomputer systems and other bus-organized systems, the outputs from many gates (frequently many hundreds of gates) share a common connection known as a *bus*. Normally only one of the many gates connected to the bus has access to the bus, the output circuit of the other gates meanwhile being held in an open-circuit state or high-impedance state (see also Sec. 2.14). The branch of the TTL family having this ability is known as *three-state TTL* or *tri-state TTL*; gates of this kind have an additional control line (the output enable line) in addition to the normal input and output lines. The signal applied to the control line allows the logic signal generated by the gate either to be connected to the output terminal of the chip or to be disconnected from it (the gate is then in its high-impedance output state).

A simplified version of a two-input three-state NAND gate is shown in Fig. 4.15. When the control line, C, has a logic '1' on it, diodes D1 and D2 are reverse biased and the gate functions normally. That is, the signal at output F is the NAND function of inputs A and B.

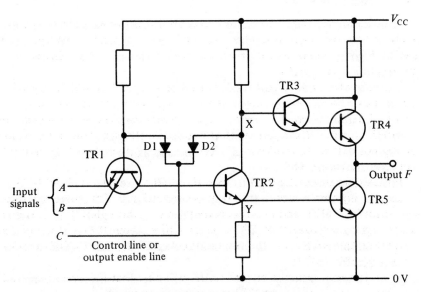

Fig. 4.15   Simplified three-state TTL gate

When control line C has a logic '0' applied to it, diodes D1 and D2 are forward biased. When diode D1 conducts, it prevents base current from flowing into TR1; in turn, this causes the base current of TR2 to be zero (which prevents current flowing through TR2). The net result is that point Y is at zero potential and TR5 is cut off; i.e., output F is isolated from the zero volts line. Also, diode D2 conducts at the same time, so that point X is practically at zero potential. This has the effect of reducing to zero the base current in the Darlington-connected pair of transistors TR3 and TR4. The net result is that point F is isolated from the supply rail, V_{CC}. That is to say, when $C = 0$, the output terminal of the gate is in its high-impedance state. Thus the NAND gate in Fig. 4.15 has an active-high output enable control line (the output is enabled when $C = 1$ and is disabled when $C = 0$).

The design of TTL gates continually evolves, and sub-branches of the family are developed to meet the needs of new problems and challenges. As an example, Texas Instruments have developed *advanced Schottky* (AS type) and *advanced low-power Schottky* (ALS type) versions of TTL. The 'advanced' technology allows smaller and shallower geometries to be produced, which enable an improvement in the speed–power performance of the gate to be obtained. The AS branch offers a switching speed which is about twice that of Schottky TTL at approximately the same power, while the ALS branch offers both lower power and faster speed than low-power Schottky TTL.

4.12 Integrated injection logic (I^2L) or merged transistor logic (MTL)

Integrated injection logic is a version of bipolar transistor logic which not only rivals the low-power consumption of CMOS logic (typically 5 nW per gate) and its high packing density (typically 100 gates/mm^2) but also the low propagation delay of TTL.

The basis of a single I^2L gate is shown in Fig. 4.16(a), its equivalent electrical circuit being shown in Fig. 4.16(b). The lateral p-n-p transistor TR1 acts as a constant current source, the emitter (a p-region) being known as the *injector* electrode. Current I is injected into the p-well of the gate, the latter region acting not only as the collector of TR1 but also as the base of the multiple collector transistor TR2.

If the external signal applied to base B or TR2 is less than about 0·7 V, it causes the injected current to flow out of connection B. This effectively turns transistor TR2 OFF and prevents current flowing through it. If the external signal applied to base B of TR2 is greater than about 0·75 V, the injected current saturates TR2 and the voltage at collectors C_1 and C_2 falls to a low value (typically 0·02 V).

From the above discussion, the reader will note that the overall function generated by the gate is the NOT function of the input applied to base B. Other

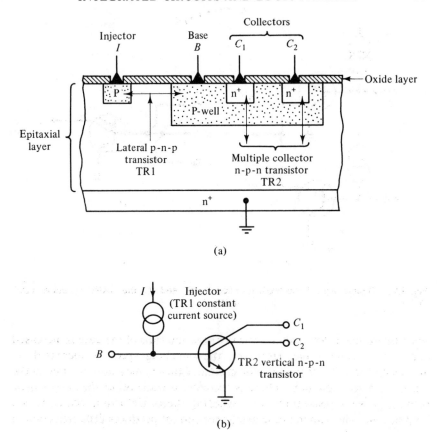

Fig. 4.16   Basic I²L gate

functions are generated by connecting the outputs of a number of gates together in the manner of the WIRED-OR connection described in Sec. 2.12. For example, the function generated by the combination in Fig. 4.17(a) is the NOR function of signals A and B, i.e., $F = \overline{A + B}$. Moreover, since the outputs of gates can be connected together without damaging the output circuit of the driving I²L gates, the NAND function of three variables A, B, and C is generated by the circuit in Fig. 4.17(b). The effect of wiring inputs A, B, and C together is to generate their AND function at the input terminal of the gate, i.e., $F' = A . B . C$; the driven I²L gate (the one shown) generates the NOT function of F', so that, for Fig. 4.17(b), $F = \overline{A . B . C}$.

Each collector output of an I²L gate can only drive one I²L load. Where a higher fan-out is required, a buffer stage must be incorporated between the I²L system and the equipment it is driving.

I²L gates can operate at very low supply voltage levels (down to about 0·85 V), when the current drawn is also very low (typically 1 nA per gate). However,

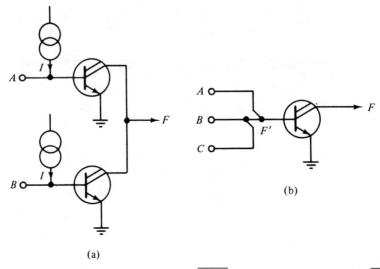

Fig. 4.17 Generating (a) the NOR function $\overline{A+B}$ and (b) the NAND function $\overline{A.B.C}$ using I²L

when operating at low voltage, the propagation time of the gate is increased above its normal value. However, the switching speed is increased by increasing the value of the injector current, I (which may have a value in the range 1 nA to a few mA). There is therefore a trade-off *at the design stage* between power consumption and switching speed. Unfortunately, there is a limit beyond which an increase in injector current produces little reduction in switching speed.

A feature of I²L technology is that other devices such as light-emitting diodes can be fabricated on the same chip; this enables complete calculators and other circuits to be fabricated on the same chip. Additionally, linear devices such as operational amplifiers can also be fabricated on the same chip as an I²L device.

I²L technology is particularly suited to the construction of high-density complex-function chips, but is less suited to devices needing only a few gates. Various versions of I²L technology have been used, and it is expected that its impact on computer-like applications will increase.

4.13 Emitter-coupled logic (ECL)

The basis of ECL is the *emitter-coupled amplifier* or *long-tailed pair* circuit, which is shown in the central section of Fig. 4.18. In this circuit, the value of the current flowing in resistor R_E is constant, so that a change in the value of current (say an increase) flowing through the left-hand side of the circuit, i.e.,

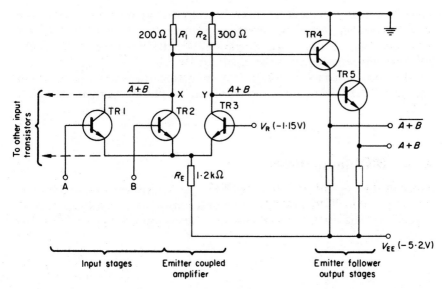

Fig. 4.18   An ECL OR/NOR gate

through TR1 or TR2, results in an opposite change (a decrease) in the current flowing through TR3.

The principal advantage of this logic family over other types is that all the transistors in the circuit work in a linear or non-saturating mode. Consequently, the time delay associated with the charge storage phenomenon in saturated logic gates is eliminated. ECL is nearly always used with matched line interconnections to make full use of its high-speed capability. The circuit shown simultaneously generates both the OR and the NOR functions of the input signals. Drawbacks associated with this logic family include a high-power dissipation (about 60 mW per gate) and a high sensitivity to temperature change.

The operation of the circuit is now described. The base of TR3 is connected to a voltage reference source, V_R, of value about -1.15 V, which lies about midway between the two logic levels. Typically, logic '0' corresponds to a voltage of about -1.55 V and logic '1' to about -0.75 V, i.e., positive logic notation is used. When either input A or input B is at the logic '1' level, the current through the appropriate transistor increases and that in TR3 decreases. As a result, the potential at point X decreases and that at Y increases. The output lines are driven by emitter-follower amplifiers which fulfil two functions, namely to provide the circuit with a low output impedance and high fan-out capability and to restore the output voltages to the correct levels for the driven stages.

Since TR1 and TR2 have their collectors connected together (the **WIRED-OR** connection), the logic function generated at point X is $\bar{A} \cdot \bar{B} = \overline{A + B}$. Since an increase in the voltage at X causes a corresponding reduction in the voltage at Y, then the logic function generated at point Y is $A + B$. By emitter-follower action the logic signals at the emitters of TR4 and TR5 are the NOR and the OR functions respectively of the input signals.

Other names used to describe this type of circuit are *emitter-emitter coupled logic* (E²CL), *emitter-coupled transistor logic* (ECTL), and *current-mode logic* (CML).

4.14   MOS logic gates

Basic fersions of p-MOS and CMOS NOT gates were described in Sec. 3.16. Typical p-MOS NOR and NAND gates are illustrated in Fig. 4.19(a) and (b) respectively. The circuits operate with a negative supply potential and use the

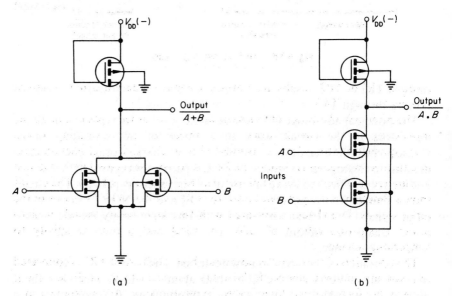

Fig. 4.19   A p-MOS NOR gate and (b) a p-MOS NAND gate

negative logic notation. Their propagation time of about 100 ns is modest when compared with both TTL and ECL, and is limited by the input capacitances of the circuits.

The circuit in Fig. 4.20(a) is that of a two-input CMOS NOR gate and that in Fig. 4.20(b) is of a two-input CMOS NAND gate. These devices use a positive supply voltage and operate in the positive logic notation. Due to the use of n-channel elements in the structure, the propagation time is reduced by a factor of about one-half[1] when compared with p-MOS logic. Moreover, when the n-MOS devices conduct, the p-MOS devices in the circuit are cut off, and

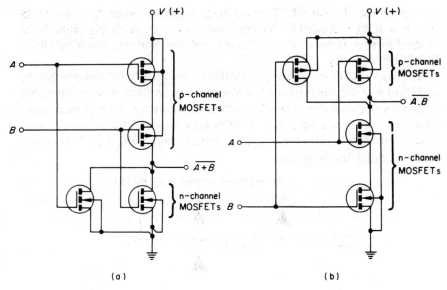

Fig. 4.20   (a) CMOS NOR gate and (b) CMOS NAND gate

vice versa; since the resistance of a non-conducting MOS transistor is of the order of 5000 MΩ, the current drain per gate in either logic state is very small. The resistance of the conducting transistor is about 750 Ω; hence the output resistance for either output logic state is relatively low.

In operation, a 'high' value of input voltage causes the p-MOS device to be cut off, and the n-MOS device conducts. Only when the output logic level is changing state do both the p- and n-MOS devices conduct simultaneously for a very short period of time; however, the peak magnitude of the current pulse drawn from the supply does not usually exceed about a few hundred microamperes per gate.

A section through a CMOS structure is illustrated in Fig. 4.21. The p-MOS devices are diffused into high-resistivity n-type material and the n-MOS devices are formed in a 'tub' of p-type semiconductor. Additionally, heavily doped p^+ and n^+ diffusions are introduced between the FETs; these act to

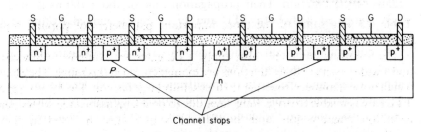

Fig. 4.21   CMOS geometry

prevent undesirable MOSFET action in the regions between the two n-MOS devices and the two p-MOS elements, and are known as *channel stops*. If the channel stops were not introduced, unwanted inversion channels would form between the devices.

Because the gate insulation is very thin, it may easily be ruptured by the application of a comparatively low voltage such as those it may experience when being handled during manufacture and installation. To prevent damage from this cause, each input line of MOS logic families incorporates a *gate–oxide protection circuit*, a typical circuit being shown in Fig. 4.22. In the event

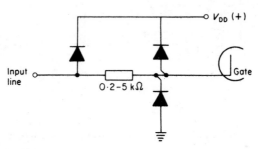

Fig. 4.22 One form of CMOS gate–oxide protection circuit

of a transient voltage being applied to the input terminal, one or more of the diodes conduct and dissipate much of the energy in the transient pulse.

Three-state or *tri-state* operation can be obtained from CMOS gates simply by incorporating additional gates as shown in Fig. 4.23. When the enable line, EN, has a logic '1' applied to it, transistors TR1 and TR4 are enabled, so allowing transistors TR2 and TR3 to operate as a conventional NOT gate; i.e., $X = \bar{A}$ when EN = 1. When EN = 0, transistors TR1 and TR4 are disabled, so that the supply rail and the zero voltage line are disconnected from TR3 and TR2 respectively. This isolates output X from input A, leaving the output in its high-impedance state.

4.15 Summary of the features of the principal logic families

Table 4.3 lists some of the more important parameters of popular logic families, the figures quoted being typical of the available ranges.

The following comments also apply. TTL gates are available at low cost, and a wide variety of logic functions are manufactured in this range. They have a high noise immunity, together with a usefully large fan-out. The basic form of TTL gate is unable to drive 'long' lines due to problems associated with signal reflection phenomenon, and 'line driver' stages must be used in these applications.

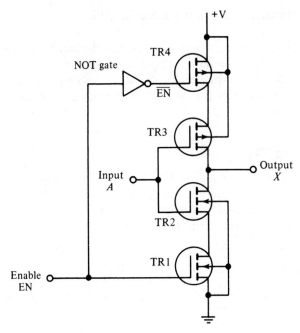

Fig. 4.23 CMOS tri-state invertor

Table 4.3
Features of logic families

Feature	DTL	TTL	ECL	p-MOS	CMOS
			Logic family		
Basic function	NAND	NAND	OR/NOR	NOR	NOR or NAND
Logic notation	+	+	+	−	+
Supply voltage, V_S, volts	+5	+5	−5·2	−20	3 to 15
Logic levels '1'	3·0	3·3	−0.74	−10	$\simeq V_S$
'0'	0·2	0·2	−1.6	−2	$\simeq 0$
Noise immunity, mV	750	1000	200	1000	0·45 V_S
Fan-out	8	10	25	5	Large
Propagation delay, ns	25	13	<3	100	40
Interconnection type	Current sinking	Current sinking	Current mode	Voltage	Voltage

The highest switching speeds are provided by the ECL family, while the lowest power consumption and most compact circuits are obtained using CMOS logic or I^2L. The CMOS family can also work with a wide range of supply voltages and has a large value of noise immunity.

4.16 Interfacing between logic families

Interfacing is the process of interconnecting one logic family either to another logic family or to some other device or system. A number of general principles are outlined below, but with some devices it is necessary to take special precautions. The reader is advised to study manufacturers' literature for more detailed information.

4.16.1 TTL to TTL

In general, the output from any TTL gate can be directly connected to any TTL input. However, be careful to study the fan-out rules for the type of driving gate; e.g., a standard TTL output will drive 10 standard TTL inputs, but a low-power TTL output will only drive one high-power TTL input.

4.16.2 TTL to DTL (and also DTL to TTL)

These are usually directly compatible and can freely be interconnected.

4.16.3 TTL to CMOS

When both systems operate on a $+5$ V supply, any TTL gate with a *pull-up resistor* (typically 2·2 kΩ) connected between its output terminal and the $+5$ V supply line will drive any number of CMOS gates.

4.16.4 CMOS to TTL

CMOS gates are incapable of providing much current and special precautions may be necessary to prevent loss of switching speed. In general, any CMOS output can drive *one* low-power Schottky TTL input. If a CMOS buffer such as a 4049, a 4050, or a 4502 is used, the output from the buffer can drive two inputs of the following gates: normal TTL, low-power TTL, or low-power Schottky TTL.

4.16.5 CMOS to DTL

CMOS and DTL are fairly compatible with one another.

4.16.6 CMOS to CMOS

These gates can be interconnected in any numbers, but a fan-out of less than 50 is usually recommended.

4.16.7 TTL to ECL (and CMOS to ECL)

Interfacing is very difficult, and commercially available logic translators are recommended.

4.16.8 TTL or CMOS to LEDs and lamps

Since a TTL gate sinks a large amount of current into its output terminal in the *output low* state, this condition should be used to activate a lamp. A LED can be driven via a current-limiting resistor, R (say about 330 Ω) — see Fig. 4.24(a) — while a low-current incandescent lamp can be driven via a transistor — see Fig. 4.24(b).

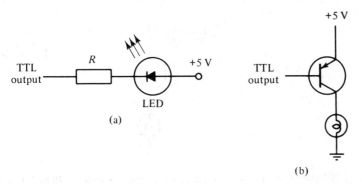

Fig. 4.24   TTL lamp interface: a logic '0' illuminates the lamp in each case

A CMOS gate can drive a high brightness LED directly and can illuminate it either by applying a logic '0' to the cathode of the LED (Fig. 4.25a) or by applying a logic '1' to the anode of the LED (see Fig. 4.25b) (a CMOS gate can act either as a current source or a current sink). Figure 4.25(c) shows how a CMOS gate can be used to drive a low-current incandescent lamp (a typical value of R is 470 Ω).

4.17 Programmable logic arrays

A *programmable logic array* (PLA)[2,3] is an AND-OR/NOR combination of gates which is interconnected by fusible links to provide a given logic function (see Fig. 4.26). Each PLA has a number of input variables $I_0, I_1, I_2, \ldots, I_n$ (where n is typically up to 18) and a number of output lines $O_0, O_1, O_2, \ldots, O_m$ (where m is typically up to 16). Each input line is connected via a buffer/inverter to a pair of internal bus lines, each bus line being connected via a fusible link to all the AND gates in the PLA. Initially all the fuses are intact, but after the device has been programmed, all unwanted fuses are 'blown'; the

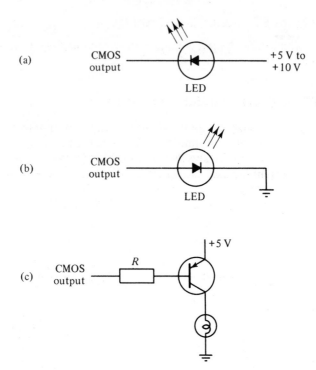

Fig. 4.25   CMOS lamp interface: (a) and (c) a logic '0' illuminates the lamp and (b) a logic
'1' illuminates the lamp

programming process involves applying a higher-than-normal voltage (typically 11 to 12 V) to appropriate terminals of the PLA. When a fuse is blown, the net effect is to apply a logic '1' to that input of the AND gate.

To simplify the circuit diagram, each AND gate is shown as having only one input line (see inset (i)). (This input represents *all of the lines* $I_0, \bar{I}_0, I_1, \bar{I}_1, \ldots, I_n$ and $\bar{I}_n$ in the figure.) Where a fuse is left intact by the programming process, an × is placed at the intersection of the data line and the input line to the AND gate. Thus output P in inset (i) is $P = I_0 . \bar{I}_1$.

The output from each AND gate is connected via another fusible link to a number of EXCLUSIVE-OR gates which provide the outputs from the PLA chip. One input to each EXCLUSIVE-OR gate is connected via a fusible link to a logic '0' (earth) connection. If the fuse is left intact, the EXCLUSIVE-OR gate acts as an OR gate; if the fuse is blown by the programming process, the EXCLUSIVE-OR gate acts as a NOR gate (i.e., as an OR-INVERT gate). Each programmable OR-INVERT gate is represented by the diagram shown in inset (ii) of Fig. 4.26. Each OR-INVERT gate has as many input lines as there are AND gates, all its input lines being represented in inset (ii) by a single line; where a fuse is left intact by the programming process, an × is placed at the

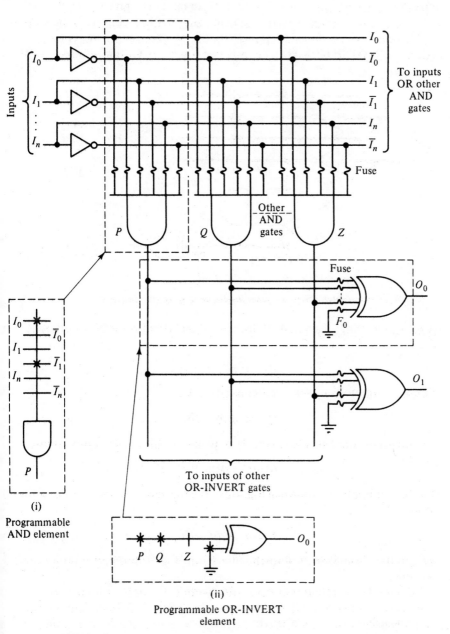

Fig. 4.26   The basis of a programmable logic AND OR-INVERT gate array

intersection between the AND gate output and the EXCLUSIVE-OR gate input line. If fuse F_0 is left intact, output O_0 in inset (ii) is given by $O_0 = P + Q$.

To illustrate a simple design problem using a PLA, consider a network which generates the function $O_0 = I_1 . \bar{I}_0 + \bar{I}_1 . I_0$, i.e., output O_0 is logic '1' when I_1 is NOT EQUIVALENT to I_2 (see Fig. 4.27). Output P is seen to be

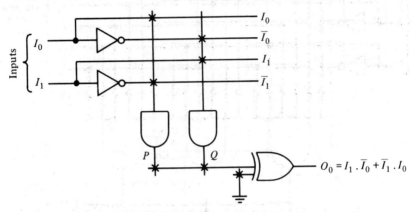

Fig. 4.27 Programmable logic array implementation of the function $I_1 . \bar{I}_2 + \bar{I}_1 . I_2$

$Q = I . \bar{I}_0$ and P is $\bar{I}_1 . I_0$; output O_0 from the PLA is the OR function of P and Q, i.e.,

$$O_0 = I_1 . \bar{I}_0 + \bar{I}_1 . I_0$$

Consider a more complex function of the form

$$O_0 = \overline{A . B . (C + D)}$$

The equation is implemented in the PLA in a sum-of-products form as follows:

$$O_0 = \overline{A . B} + (\overline{C + D}) = A . B + \bar{C} . \bar{D}$$

One form of solution is shown in Fig. 4.28. Had the desired function been of the form

$$O_0 = \overline{A . B} . (C + D)$$

one solution would be to blow the fuse F_X in Fig. 4.28 (other solutions are possible).

Various PLA internal geometries are possible; the configuration described above is a *programmable AND/programmable OR-INVERT* configuration. A *programmable array logic* (PAL) — which is a tradename of Monolithic Memories Inc. — uses a *programmable AND/fixed OR-INVERT* configuration. Both PLA and PAL chips may contain *J-K* or *D*-type output latches and may have programmable three-state output buffers.

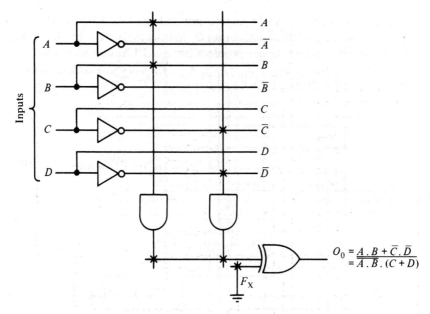

Fig. 4.28 PLA implementation of the function $A.B + \bar{C}.\bar{D}$

A simplified version of one form of programmable array with a three-state output and an output latch on one line is shown in Fig. 4.29; the reader should note that the fuse at the junction of each point where the internal bus wires cross is initially intact. There are three input lines, I_0, I_1, and I_2, which are fed to six internal bus lines, I_0, $\bar{I}_0$, I_1, $\bar{I}_1$, I_2, and $\bar{I}_2$, via buffer/inverters. The AND-OR function generated by G1 is transmitted to output O_0 when gate G4 is enabled by the signal applied to its control input (which is also programmable). Similarly, output O_1 is obtained via the three-state gate G5.

Output O_2 is obtained from a D-type latch when gate G6 is enabled by means of a logic '0' applied to its output enable pin. The latter occurs either when fuse F_2 is blown and F_1 is left intact (in this case, gate G6 is continuously enabled) or when F_1 is blown and F_2 is left intact AND a logic '0' is applied to the $\overline{OE}$ output enable pin of the chip.

The reader will note that each output and its complement is fed back to the internal bus system so that connections between various stages can be made by the fusible links.

In order to reduce the effort involved in converting complex logic equations into their AND-OR versions, special high-level computer languages are available. Programs written in these languages assemble the logic equations into the correct fuse-blowing pattern for the programmed array; the programmable array is then inserted into a standard PROM programmer and the appropriate fuses are blown.

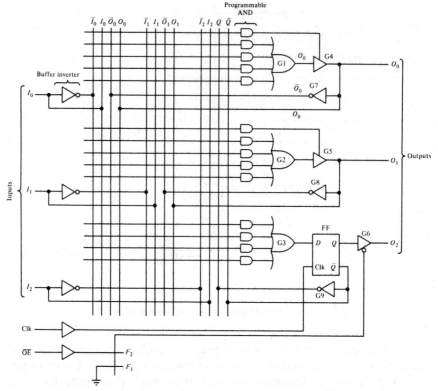

Fig. 4.29   Programmable logic array with an output latch (all fuses initially intact)

4.18   Uncommitted logic arrays

An *uncommitted logic array* (ULA) is a large-scale integrated circuit chip containing thousands of uncommitted active and passive components and gates, and is complete except for the final interconnection between the elements. The customer specifies the form of circuit he requires, this specification being used to design the photomasking process which establishes the final interconnections on the chip.

Many technologies are used to produce ULAs, including I^2L, Schottky-clamped I^2L, ECL, and CMOS. The lowest propagation delays are associated with ECL and the lowest power consumption with CMOS.

4.19   Decoder chips

A decoder is a device which alters data in one code format to another code format. In many microcomputer circuits, a decoder is used to convert a code combination given by the signals on the address bus of the microcomputer (see Chapter 8) into a logic signal (frequently a logic '0') on one of several output lines of the decoder (the remaining output lines having logic 1's on them).

A logic block diagram of a *one-out-of-four decoder* or a *two line-to-four line decoder* chip is shown in Fig. 4.30(a). The power supply line and the zero volts line have been omitted for clarity. The chip has two address lines, A_1 and A_2,

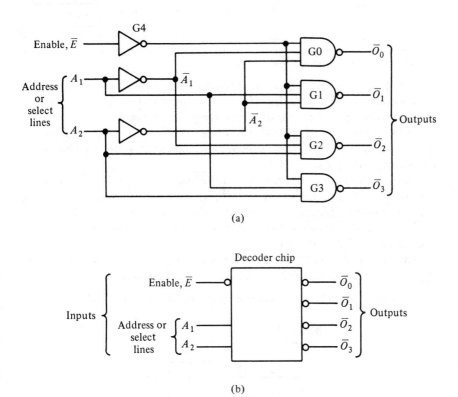

(a)

(b)

Fig. 4.30   (a) A simplified logic block diagram of a one-out-of-four decoder (or two line-to-four line decoder) and (b) graphic symbol of the decoder

which 'address' internal gates, a chip enable line ($\bar{E}$), and four active low-output lines, $\bar{O}_0$, $\bar{O}_1$, $\bar{O}_2$, and $\bar{O}_3$. The output gates G0 to G3, inclusive, are enabled when the signal $\bar{E}$ is logic '0'; when the $\bar{E}$ line has a logic '1' on it, the output from G4 is logic '0', which forces all the output lines to have a logic '1' on them irrespective of the signals on the address lines A_1 and A_2 (see also the first row of Table 4.4).

When the chip is correctly enabled, i.e., when $\bar{E}=0$, gates G0 to G3 are addressed or selected by the signals on lines A_1 and A_2 respectively. The operation of the gate is described by Table 4.4. If A_1 has a decimal 'weight' of

Table 4.4
Function table for a two line-to-four line decoder

Inputs			Outputs				
$\bar{E}$	A_1	A_2	O_0	O_1	O_2	O_3	Comment
1	×	×	1	1	1	1	Chip disabled
0	0	0	0	1	1	1	Selected output
0	0	1	1	0	1	1	given by the
0	1	0	1	1	0	1	'weight' of
0	1	1	1	1	1	0	A_1 and A_2

×='don't care', i.e., it could be a '0' or a '1'.

1_{10} and A_2 has a weight of 2_{10}, the output having a logic '0' on it is given by the total 'weight' of the input signal. Thus if $A_1 = 1$ AND $A_2 = 1$, there is a logic '0' on output O_3 (the other output lines having 1's on them).

Although the $\bar{E}$ signal is listed independently of the other input signals, the signal activating the $\bar{E}$ line could also be an address bus line in a microcomputer system.

The decoder described above is based on one-half of a 74LS139 dual two line-to-four line decoder. Many microcomputers require relatively complex decoding systems (see also Sec. 8.6), and three line-to-eight line decoders (or one-out-of-eight decoders) are frequently used. One of these devices, based on the 74LS138 chip, is described below.

The three line-to-eight line decoder chip in Fig. 4.31 has three chip enable signals G1, G2A, and G2B, and the chip is enabled when

$$G1 = 1 \text{ AND } G2A = 0 \text{ AND } G2B = 0$$

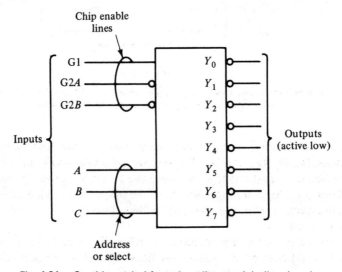

Fig. 4.31 Graphic symbol for a three line-to-eight line decoder

The chip is disabled when the above condition is not satisfied; this results in all outputs having a logic '1' on them. If input A has a weight of 1_{10}, B has a weight of 2_{10}, and C has a weight of 4_{10}, the output having a logic '0' on it is given by the total weight of the input signals A, B, and C. The operation of the decoder is described by Table 4.5; the reader will note that the logic conditions associated

Table 4.5
Function table for a three line-to-eight line decoder

Inputs					Outputs							
Enable		Select										
G1	G2	C	B	A	Y_0	Y_1	Y_2	Y_3	Y_4	Y_5	Y_6	Y_7
×	1	×	×	×	1	1	1	1	1	1	1	1
0	×	×	×	×	1	1	1	1	1	1	1	1
1	0	0	0	0	0	1	1	1	1	1	1	1
1	0	0	0	1	1	0	1	1	1	1	1	1
1	0	0	1	0	1	1	0	1	1	1	1	1
1	0	0	1	1	1	1	1	0	1	1	1	1
1	0	1	0	0	1	1	1	1	0	1	1	1
1	0	1	0	1	1	1	1	1	1	0	1	1
1	0	1	1	0	1	1	1	1	1	1	0	1
1	0	1	1	1	1	1	1	1	1	1	1	0

×='don't care'.

with inputs G2A and G2B are combined in the form of a single input G2, where G2 = G2A OR G2B. Thus G2 = 0 is one condition for the chip to be enabled.

As with the chip in Fig. 4.30, the microcomputer address bus lines are connected to lines A, B, and C, and other address or control bus lines may be connected to inputs G1, G2A, and G2B. An application of this type of decoder is described in Sec. 8.6.

References

1. MORRIS, N. M., *Semiconductor Devices*, Macmillan, 1976.
2. CLARE, C., *Designing Logic Systems Using State Machines*, McGraw-Hill, 1973.
3. PROUDFOOT, J. T., 'Programmable logic arrays', *Electronics and Power*, **1980**, 883–887, November/December 1980.

5. Flip-flops and data storage

In counting and *sequential networks* it is necessary to provide some form of memory element to record the state of the problem at any given time. The most commonly used device is known as the *flip-flop* or *bistable* element, which has two stable operating states. These correspond to the '0' and '1' logic levels, the output flipping from one stable state to the other upon demand. A flip-flop may therefore be defined as a device which stores binary information in the form of a '0' or a '1', and can be maintained indefinitely in either of the states. It can also be switched from one state to the other.

5.1 Types of memory element

Memory elements can broadly be divided into *non-volatile* and *volatile* types. Non-volatile memories retain their information almost indefinitely, even in the event of a power supply failure. Magnetic tapes and discs are typical of this type. Volatile memories retain information only so long as the power supply to them is maintained. The majority of electronic memories are of the latter type, and are the subject of this chapter.

Two subgroups of volatile memories are *static memories* and *dynamic memories*. The information stored in a static memory is retained by the use of feedback between cross-connected gates and, subject to power supply continuity, the data stored are retained indefinitely. In dynamic memories, the data are stored in the form of an electrical charge on a capacitor; due to the inherent nature of capacitors, this charge decays with time and periodically requires to be 'refreshed'.

5.2 Static memory elements

The three most popular types of *bistable memory elements* or *flip-flops* are known as the *S-R* (Set-Reset), *J-K*, and *D* (Delay or Data latch) elements, and are described in the following sections. A further type, the T (Trigger or Toggle) element is also widely used, and is constructed either from J-K or from D elements.

The truth table describing the operation of the above memory elements depends not only on the signals applied at a given instant of time but also on the history of the preceding events. That is, the truth table is 'dynamic' in nature and is subject to change.

5.3   The Set-Reset (S-R) flip-flop

The S-R flip-flop has two input lines, known as the S-line (Set line) and the R-line (Reset line), and two output lines, namely the Q-output (the normal output) and the $\bar{Q}$-output (or complementary output) lines. A typical block diagram is shown in Fig. 5.1, and its truth table is given in Table 5.1. In this

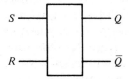

Fig. 5.1   A set-reset (S-R) flip-flop or bistable element

Table 5.1
Truth table of the S-R flip-flop

Inputs		Output		Comment
S	R	Q_n	Q_{n+1}	
0	0	0 1	0 1	$Q_{n+1}=Q_n$ (Storage stage)
0	1	0 1	0 0	$Q_{n+1}=0$ (Reset)
1	0	0 1	1 1	$Q_{n+1}=1$ (Set)
1	1	0 1	? ?	Not defined

table, the column headed Q_n is the state of output Q *prior* to the application of the conditions listed in the input columns. The column headed Q_{n+1} lists the state of output Q *after* the application of the listed input conditions.

The 'storage' state of the S-R flip-flop occurs when the signal applied to both the S- and R-lines is logic '0'. In this state the output is unchanged, and $Q_{n+1} = Q_n$ (whatever the previous state of Q_n), illustrated in the first row of the truth table. Output Q is 'reset' to zero by applying a logic '1' to the R-line ($S = 0$ at this time), shown in the second row of the truth table. The application of a logic '1' signal to the S-line (when $R = 0$) causes output Q to be 'set' to the logic '1' state.

When both the S- and R-lines are energized by logic '1' signals, the state of the output is not strictly defined since a simultaneous attempt is made both to set Q to '1' and to reset it to '0'. What usually happens is that outputs Q and $\overline{Q}$ are no longer complementary, and *both* output lines assume the same logic level; depending on the type of gates used in the flip-flop, the output signals in this state may either both be '0' or both be '1'. This operating state is usually avoided, although there is no reason why it should not be used.

Two versions of S-R flip-flops are shown in Fig. 5.2. In the NOR version, Fig. 5.2(a), the S- and R-signals are applied directly to the principal gates, these gates being cross-connected to ensure that they form a self-latching system. This cross-connection provides positive feedback between the gates. In the NAND version, Fig. 5.2(b), the inputs are each applied to an inverter before being transmitted to the principle gates of the flip-flop; the reason is that logic '0' signals are required to activate NAND gates. Once again, the principal gates are cross-connected to form a self-latching pair. Some versions of the NAND S-R flip-flop omit the input inverters, when the inputs are usually defined as $\overline{S}$ and $\overline{R}$.

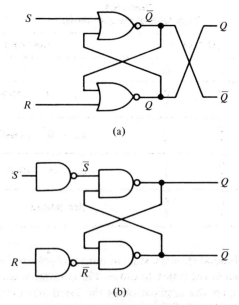

(a)

(b)

Fig. 5.2   Versions of the S-R flip-flop using (a) NOR gates and (b) NAND gates

5.4   Contact bounce elimination circuits

Electrical contacts are frequently used to provide input signals to logic systems. The contacts are frequently a source of electrical noise, which is due to 'contact bounce' arising from the mechanical properties of the contacts. If the 'noisy' signal is applied to a high-speed counting system, the system 'sees' each noise impulse as a complete OFF-ON-OFF pulse; such a counting system would record the total number of noise 'pulses' (of which there may be several thousand in all) rather than record a single pulse. Two popular methods of eliminating contact bounce effects are shown in Fig. 5.3.

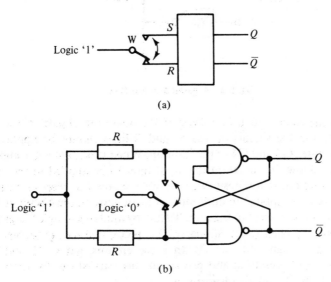

(a)

(b)

Fig. 5.3   Contact bounce elimination circuits

In Fig. 5.3(a), the first logic '1' signal applied to the S-input causes Q to become '1'. If the contacts of switch W 'bounce', the resulting train of pulses applied to the S-line have no further effect on the state of output Q. In Fig. 5.3(b), a logic '0' is used to control the switching operation of a NAND flip-flop.

5.5   A clocked (gated) S-R flip-flop

In some circuits, the application of the S- and R-signals to the flip-flop is controlled by a *clock signal*. This signal is usually in the form of rectangular pulses and is used to control the sequencing of events in the system. A typical clocked S-R flip-flop is shown in Fig. 5.4.

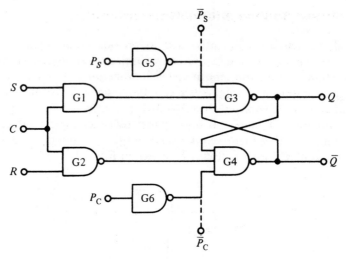

Fig. 5.4   A gated *S-R* flip-flop

When the clock signal, C, is logic '0' the operation of gates G1 and G2 is inhibited, and the signals on the *S*- and *R*-lines cannot be applied to the principal gates G3 and G4 of the flip-flop. When $C = 1$, gates G1 and G2 are opened to allow the signal on the input lines to be applied to the memory.

In certain circuits, it is desirable to be able to *preset* or *preclear* output Q by means of signals applied to additional control lines. In the circuit in Fig. 5.4, output Q can be present to the logic '1' state by applying a logic '1' signal to the preset line, P_S, when $C = 0$. Similarly, Q is precleared (i.e., Q becomes '0') by applying a '1' signal·to line P_C. In some circuits, gates G5 and G6 are eliminated, and presetting and preclearing are carried out by applying a '0' signal to lines $\bar{P}_S$ and $\bar{P}_C$ respectively.

5.6   Master-slave *S-R* flip-flop

In many high-speed counting circuits, race conditions (see Chapter 7) are encountered which may result either in the output from the flip-flop being oscillatory or in it assuming an unpredictable state. To overcome this problem, a family of elements known as master-slave flip-flops were developed. The basic element is the *S-R* master-slave flip-flop, described below.

The principle of operation can best be understood by reference to Fig. 5.5. The sequencing of signals through the flip-flop is controlled by the clock signal, C, and when it has the logical value '0', switches G1 and G2 are open and G3 and G4 are closed. In this state, the data stored in the master flip-flop, MFF, are transmitted directly to the slave flip-flop, SFF, and thence to the output terminals. In practice, switches G1 to G4, inclusive, are replaced by

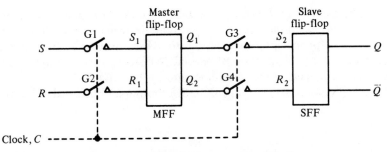

Fig. 5.5   The basis of the master-slave flip-flop

electronic gates. When the clock signal changes to the logic '1' level, G1 and G2 close while G3 and G4 open. In this operating state, new data are fed into MFF, while the former state of MFF is stored in SFF and continues to be presented at the output terminals. A feature of the circuit described above is that data are transferred through the flip-flop in a series of steps which is related to the clock pulse waveform (see Fig. 5.6) as follows:

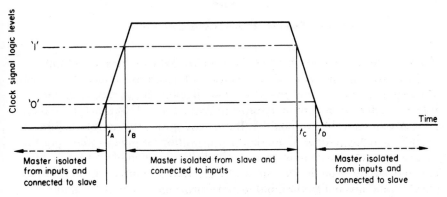

Fig. 5.6   Operating sequence of the master-slave flip-flop in terms of the clock pulse

1. *Clock signal* $= 0$ $(t < t_A)$. In this state G1 and G2 are open and G3 and G4 are closed. Data stored in the master are transferred to the slave and are presented at the output.
2. *Clock signal* $= 1$ $(t_B < t < t_C)$. Here G1 and G2 are closed and G3 and G4 are open. New data are fed into the master, the data stored in the slave being unchanged.
3. *Clock signal* $= 0$ $(t > t_D)$. G1 and G2 are open and G3 and G4 are closed. The new data stored in the master are transferred to the slave and are presented at the output.

Hence, *in the master-slave flip-flop, new data are applied to the master stage when the clock signal is '1' and are transmitted to the slave stage (i.e., to the output) when the clock signal is '0'.* To prevent electronic hazard conditions occurring, the sequencing of switches G1 to G4 is arranged so that all four switches can never be simultaneously closed. In practice, this is brought about by the inherent delays in the electronic gates in the circuit.

A practical version of the master-slave S-R flip-flop is illustrated in Fig. 5.7,

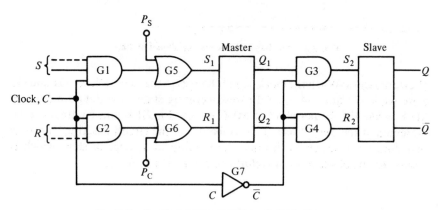

Fig. 5.7   One form of master-slave S-R flip-flop

in which gates G1 to G4 correspond to switches G1 to G4 respectively in Fig. 5.5. Synchronous operation of these gates is obtained by applying the clock signal to G1 and G2, and $\bar{C}$ to G3 and G4. In addition, gates G5 and G6 are incorporated to permit output Q either to be preset to '1' by signal P_S or to be precleared (reset to '0') by signal P_C. In some cases, signal $\bar{P}_S$ may be applied to G1 and $\bar{P}_C$ to G2 in order to inhibit their operation during the presetting and preclearing cycle. The circuit shown can also accommodate several S-input lines and several R-input lines (shown by the dotted connections to gates G1 and G2), and this enables the flip-flop to perform logic functions in addition to its operation as a memory element.

5.7   The K-J master-slave flip-flop

Many early versions of flip-flop have been superceded by the master-slave J-K flip-flop, which is a modified version of the master-slave S-R flip-flop. A simplified block diagram of the J-K master-slave element is illustrated in Fig. 5.8. Gates G1, G2, and G7 in Fig. 5.8 correspond to gates with these numbers in Fig. 5.7; the essential difference between the two circuits is that, in Fig. 5.8, output Q is fed back to one input of G2 and output $\bar{Q}$ is fed back to one input of G1. The signal input to G1 is now designated the J-input and the input to G2 is the K-input; the circuit can accommodate several inputs J and K in the

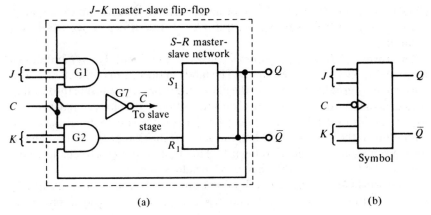

(a)   (b)

Fig. 5.8   A master-slave J-K flip-flop

Table 5.2
Truth table of the J-K master-slave flip-flop

Inputs		Output	Comment
J	K	Q_{n+1}	
0	0	Q_n	Storage state
0	1	0	'Reset'
1	0	1	'Set'
1	1	Q_n	'Trigger' or 'toggle'

manner shown by the dotted links to G1 and G2 in Fig. 5.8. The truth table for the J-K flip-flop is given in Table 5.2.

In the truth table, Q_n is the state of output Q prior to the application of the nth clock pulse and Q_{n+1} is its state after the clock pulse has been applied.

When $J = K = 0$, both G1 and G2 are inhibited and the output is unchanged. When $J = 0$, $K = 1$ (row 2 of the truth table), a logic '1' is transmitted to the output $\bar{Q}$ of the master stage when the clock signal is at the logic '1' level, and is transferred to the output $\bar{Q}$ of the slave stage (i.e., Q is forced to be '0') when the clock signal falls to the '0' level. By a similar reasoning, it can be seen that, when $J = 1$, $K = 0$, output Q becomes '1' after a clock pulse has been applied. Thus, the first three rows of the truth table of the J-K master-slave flip-flop correspond to those of the S-R flip-flop (with the J-input being equivalent to the S-input and the K-input being equivalent to the R-input). The final row of Table 5.2 yields an interesting operating condition in which the output state of the flip-flop changes after the application of *each* clock pulse. This is known as *trigger operation* or *toggle operation*, and forms the basis of many counting circuits. This mode of operation arises from the fact that, when $J = K = 1$, the clock pulse causes the state of $\bar{Q}$ to be gated through the flip-flop to output Q, i.e., $Q_{n+1} = \bar{Q}_n$. When operated with $J = K = 1$, the device is described as a *T flip-flop*.

One form of *J-K* flip-flop symbol is shown in Fig. 5.8(b). The symbol shown has two *J*-inputs and two *K*-inputs. The mode of operation of the clock is also illustrated by graphic symbols in the figure; the triangle just inside the flip-flop indicates that the flip-flop is 'active' on a transition of the clock signal from one logic level to another. Where the clock line has an inversion 'bubble' associated with it (as in the case of Fig. 5.8b), the active transition of the clock signal is from a change from logic '1' to logic '0'. That is, if output Q is to change state, then it does so on a '1'→'0' change of the clock signal.

One form of master-slave *J-K* flip-flop using only NAND gates is illustrated in Fig. 5.9. In this circuit, preset and preclear inputs are provided, presetting

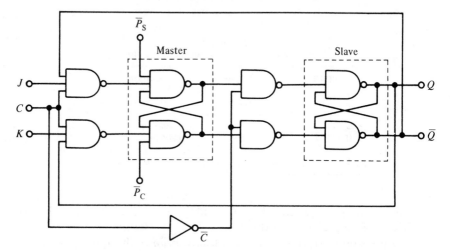

Fig. 5.9   One form of master-slave *J-K* flip-flop using only NAND gates

being carried out by applying a logic '0' signal to input $\bar{P}_S$ and preclearing by applying a logic '0' to $\bar{P}_C$.

5.8   Functions performed by *J-K* flip-flops

The *J-K* master-slave flip-flop can be directly used to replace the *S-R* master-slave element provided that the condition $J = K = 1$ is not allowed to occur. When used as a *S-R* replacement, the *J*-inputs are used as *S*-inputs and the *K*-inputs as *R*-inputs.

It may also be used as a trigger (T) flip-flop in either of the modes shown in Fig. 5.10. In Fig. 5.10(a), both the *J*- and the *K*-lines are connected to logic '1'

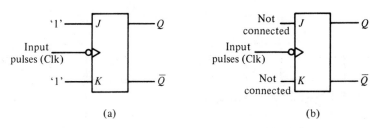

Fig. 5.10 The J-K flip-flop used as a trigger flip-flop

signals, the clock line being energized by incoming pulses (i.e., the clock line acts as the T-input line). In this mode of operation, the state of output Q changes state when the clock signal changes from '1' to '0'. A train of input pulses causes output Q to change in the sequence ..., 0, 1, 0, 1, 0, ... The same effect can be obtained in some logic families by leaving both the J- and K-input lines disconnected, as shown in Fig. 5.10(b); this connection should not be used in electrically noisy environments, since an induced noise signal on one of the input lines may cause the flip-flop to malfunction.

5.9 The D flip-flop

The D flip-flop has only a single control line, the D-line, and satisfies the logical conditions set out in Table 5.3. The output from the flip-flop is equal to the state of the input signal one clock pulse earlier.

Table 5.3
Truth table of the master-slave D flip-flop

Input D	Output Q_{n+1}
0	0
1	1

The basis of one form of D flip-flop is shown in Fig. 5.11(a). It consists of a J-K flip-flop (or, alternatively, a master-slave S-R flip-flop), whose input lines are energized by complementary input signals. The truth table of the D-flip-flop is therefore equivalent to the second and third rows of the J-K- flip-flop truth table (Table 5.2), with the J-input representing the D-input. It is also equivalent to the second and third rows of the truth table of the S-R flip-flop (Table 5.1), with the S-input replacing the D-input.

The D flip-flop is frequently used as a *data latch* element or *straticizer*, in

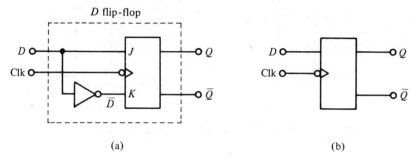

Fig. 5.11　(a) The basis of a *D* master-slave flip-flop and (b) its circuit symbol

which the state of one stage of a binary counter can be stored at the completion of a counting sequence. It is also used as a 'one-bit' delay element in serial arithmetic processors; it can be used, for example, to store the 'carry' or 'borrow' bit in an adder or subtractor respectively.

5.10　Edge-triggered flip-flops

In an edge-triggered flip-flop, the output changes state in sympathy with the *leading edge* of the clock pulse (i.e., the '0'→'1' edge); this differs from the master-slave type, whose output changes in sympathy with the completion of the clock pulse. Truth tables of edge-triggered devices generally conform to those of equivalent master-slave types.

In these elements, the data signals (*J*, *K*, or *D*) must be applied to the input(s) of the flip-flop for a minimum period of time known as the *set-up time* (typically 10 ns) prior to the clock pulse being applied. After the clock pulse has passed a threshold value (typically 1·5 V in TTL devices), the input information must be maintained for a period of time known as the *hold time* (typically a few nanoseconds). After the latter period of time, the input signals are 'locked-out' and have no further control over the state of the flip-flop output during the remainder of the clock waveform.

Edge triggering is brought about by modifying the logic circuitry of the flip-flop.

Since the output signal changes in an edge-triggered flip-flop in sympathy with the leading edge of the clock pulse, the inversion 'bubble' on the clock pulse line is omitted (see Fig. 5.12). In this case, any change in output *Q* occurs on a '0'→'1' change of the clock signal.

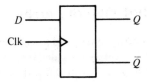

Fig. 5.12 Edge-triggered *D* flip-flop symbol

5.11 MOS dynamic memories

In this family of memories, data are stored in the form of an electrical charge on the gate insulation of a MOSFET. A popular form of three-transistor circuit is shown in Fig. 5.13, in which the charge is stored in the gate-to-source capacitance, *C*, of TR2. When a signal is applied to the 'write select line', TR1 is turned ON, and the 'write data line' is connected to the gate of TR2. Applying a

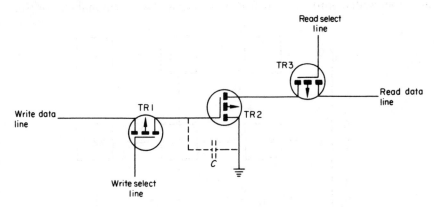

Fig. 5.13 One form of MOS dynamic memory element

logic '1' to the latter line causes capacitor *C* to become charged, and applying a logic '0' to the line causes *C* to be discharged. In this way data are 'written' into the storage location.

The data stored are sampled or 'read' by energizing the 'read select line', which turns TR3 on. The data are read by monitoring the current flowing in the 'read data line'.

The charge stored by capacitor *C* will ultimately decay, and it is usually necessary to *refresh* the stored charge every few milliseconds. This process is carried out automatically by means of additional logic circuitry.

5.12   Integrated circuit memory arrays

A wide variety of IC memory arrays exist, and are broadly divided into the two categories outlined in Sec. 5.1, namely volatile stores and non-volatile stores. Included in the former are *S-R*, *J-K*, *T*, and *D* flip-flops, together with dynamic memory elements of the type discussed in Sec. 5.11. Non-volatile semiconductor memories include *read-only memories* (ROM), *programmable read-only memories* (PROM), and *erasable programmable read-only memories* (EPROM). Non-volatile semiconductor memories are used in a wide variety of applications, including storing microprograms for computers and storing character patterns for optoelectronic display devices.

Semiconductor memory arrays are frequently used in the form of *random access memories* (RAM), in which an individual bit or stored word can be obtained at random by means of *addressing* a location or group of locations in the store. The memory cells in a RAM are generally arranged in a matrix pattern in the form shown in Fig. 5.14. A single cell such as M3,2 may be addressed by energizing row wire *X*3 and column wire *Y*2. This is known as *X-Y selection* or *coincident selection*. Having selected one cell in this way, data are either written into it or read from it by means of an additional line (or pair

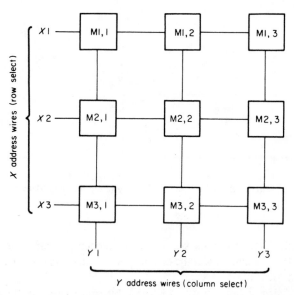

Fig. 5.14   Matrix arrangement of cells in a semiconductor RAM

of lines) which run through every cell in the matrix. Non-selected cells are inhibited, and are unaffected by the signals on the data line. Alternatively, if all the 'row select' wires and the *Y*2 wire are addressed simultaneously, it causes memories M1,2, M2,2, and M3,2 to be addressed at the same time. This is known as *word selection* or *linear selection*. Data can simultaneously either be read from or written into the selected group of cells.

In some cases, it is preferable to address a memory by means of its stored contents, rather than by its address within a storage bank. For example, it is sometimes convenient in an educational establishment to store data about a student in the form of the course he attends, the day or days he attends, his age, and the name of his employer. This information can be stored in a *content addressable memory* (CAM) in which the stored data are addressed simply by inspecting part of the contents of the memory. Thus, it would quickly be possible to locate, for example, students who are employed by employer X, and who are attending course Y on day Z.

5.13 ROMs, PROMs, and EPROMs

The name read-only memory (ROM) is applied to memories whose stored data cannot be altered. Many of these fall into the category of *mask programmed ROMs*, which contain data in the form of 1's and 0's at addresses specified by the user; the data are written into the memory during the IC manufacturing process by means of photographic masks, and these specify which diodes or transistors in the array are in the ON state and those which are in the OFF state.

A small part of one form of *electrically programmable ROM* (PROM) is shown in Fig. 5.15; in this case each memory element consists of a diode in series with a fusible link. The fuses can be 'blown' individually by addressing a location and applying a current impulse to it. When the memory location is to be left ON, the fusible link is left intact, and where it is to be OFF the fuse is blown. The programming is carried out by means of electronic apparatus, and can be completed either by the manufacturer or by the user. The PROM in Fig. 5.15 is word-organized, and when a logic '1' is applied to the appropriate row (address) wire (logic '0' meanwhile being applied to other address wires), the binary word corresponding to the state of the fuses appears at the column (bit) wires.

Erasable programmable read-only memories (EPROM) contain MOS devices into which it is possible to introduce a 'permanent' charge package in the gate oxide regions. In this type of device the stored charge does, in fact, slowly leak away, but it may take more than about 10^{11} read accesses for the charge to have reduced to an unusable value. The data stored are usually erased by exposing the chip to ultraviolet radiation. After erasure, new data can be electrically written into the memory, the 'writing' period usually taking a few milliseconds.

When a ROM has been programmed, it can be regarded as a logic array which contains a number of combinational sequences, different combinations being obtained by addressing combinations of input (address) lines. In this way the ROM can be used to replace a number of combinational logic arrays. When used in this mode, it is equivalent to a *programmable logic array* (PLA).

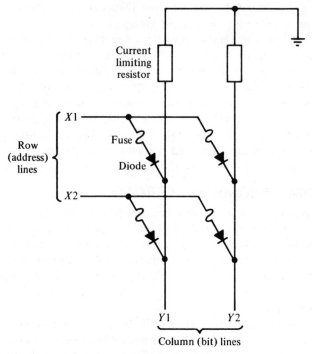

Row (address) lines

Current limiting resistor

$X1$

Fuse

Diode

$X2$

$Y1$ $Y2$

Column (bit) lines

Fig. 5.15   One form of PROM

5.14   Typical ROM organization

The internal organization of many ROM chips can be simplified to that shown in Fig. 5.16. The memory shown stores 4096 eight-bit words (4K byte memory), the 4096 locations being addressed by signals on the 12 address lines A_0 to A_{11}. (*Note*: $2^{12} = 4096$.) The address line signals are applied to buffer amplifiers before being decoded to form an address in the storage matrix.

When an address has been selected, the eight bits stored at that address are transmitted to eight three-stage output buffers; these buffers are enabled by signals applied to the chip select input lines of the ROM. In the case shown, line $\overline{CS1}$ must have a logic '0' applied to it* AND CS2 must simultaneously have a logic '1' applied to it before the buffers are enabled. When the output buffers are enabled, the data stored in the selected location are transmitted to the eight output lines O_0 to O_7, inclusive. If the chip select lines are not correctly activated, i.e., $\overline{CS1}$ has a logic '1' on it or CS2 has a logic '0' on it, the three-state output buffers remain in a high-impedance output state and isolate the selected location from the data lines of the system.

In a number of mask programmable ROMs the chip select inputs are programmable. That is, at the time of ordering the chips the consumer specifies

---

*   This signal could, for example, be obtained from an 'active low' output from a decoder of the type described in Sec. 4.19.

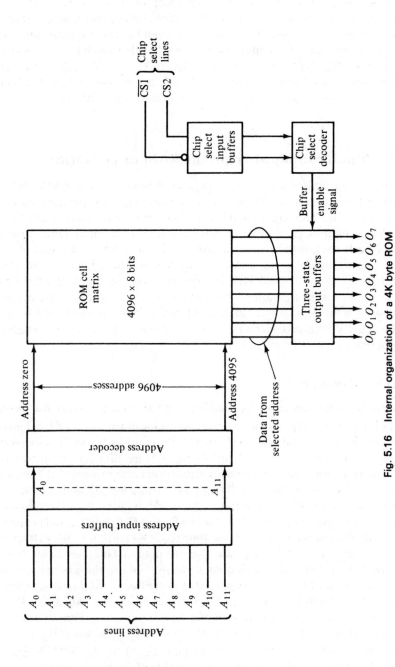

Fig. 5.16 Internal organization of a 4K byte ROM

the logic signals to be applied to the chip select inputs which will enable the three-state output buffers. He could, for example, specify that both of the chip select signals must be logic '0' to enable the output buffers. A typical chip with programmable chip select conditions is the 4K byte Rockwell R2332 (which is identical to the NEC μPD2332 and Synertek SY2332 chips). Another manufacturer may order the same ROM chip, but he may specify that both chip select signals must be logic '1' to enable the output buffers.

5.15   Bipolar integrated circuit RAM organization

The simplified structure of a word-organized bipolar static RAM chip is shown in Fig. 5.17. The RAM has a set of common input/output data lines D_0 and D_1 (only two lines are used in order to simplify the internal architecture, and there would be eight input/output lines in an eight-bit system). A basic memory cell contains the two transistors TR1 and TR2, only one of the transistors in the cell carrying current at any instant of time. Let us assume that the cell stores a logic '1' when TR2 is carrying current and a logic '0' when TR1 carries current. When data are stored in the cell, i.e., when data are neither being written into nor being read from the cell, the word wires W_0 and W_1 are held at logic '0'; this provides a path for the current in the transistor which is conducting to return to the supply.

5.15.1   Writing data

When data are written into a location in the RAM, a logic '0' is applied to the $\overline{\text{WRITE}}$ line of the chip (a logic '1' being applied meanwhile to the $\overline{\text{READ}}$ line). This 'enables' the tri-state gates G1 and G2. We consider below the process of writing a logic '0' into cell C_{00} of word W_0. (Note: since this is a word-organized store, data will simultaneously be written into other cells in word W_0.) The data (logic '0') to be written into the cell is applied to data line D_0, and the internal logic of the chip causes the appropriate word address wire, W_0, to be raised to logic '1'. This raises the potential of emitters E_1 and E_1' in cell C_{00} and prevents current flowing in them. At the same time it allows current to flow either in emitter E_2 or in emitter E_2' (depending on the potential on these lines). Now, since $D_0 = 0$, current will flow through transistor TR1 to this line via emitter E_2; moreover, since $\bar{D}_0 = 1$, no current flows in emitter E_2'. At this stage, a logic '0' has been written into cell C_{00}. When the logic level on word line W_0 is returned to logic '0', the current in emitter E_2 transfers to E_1. Simultaneously, the logic signal on data line D_1 is written into cell C_{01} of word W_0.

The write cycle is complete when the logic signal on the $\overline{\text{WRITE}}$ line is changed to logic '1', which disables the outputs of gates G1 and G2.

Having simultaneously written data into all the cells of word W_0, other data

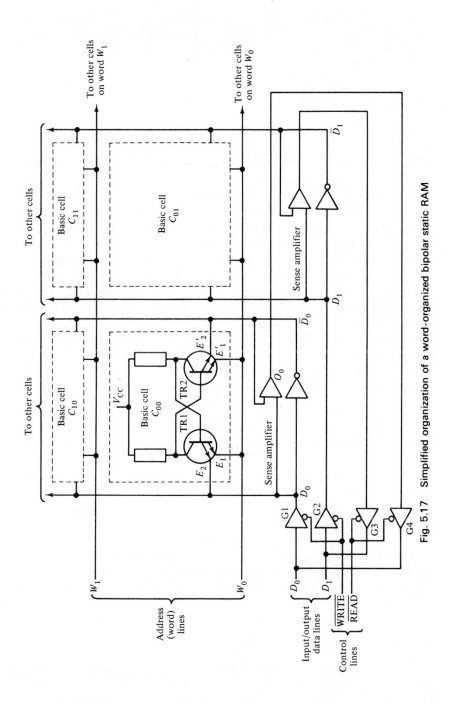

Fig. 5.17 Simplified organization of a word-organized bipolar static RAM

can then be written into any other word in the chip. For example, data are written into word W_1 of the RAM merely by repeating the above sequence with the exception that word wire W_1 has its potential changed in the sequence logic '0', logic '1', logic '0'.

5.15.2   Reading data

We now consider the process of reading data from cell C_{00} of word W_0. (*Note*: data are simultaneously read from all other cells in the same word.) When data are read from the memory, a logic '0' is applied to the $\overline{\text{READ}}$ line of the chip (a logic '1' being applied meanwhile to the $\overline{\text{WRITE}}$ line), and this signal enables gates G3 and G4. At the same time the logic level on the selected word line, W_0 in this case, is changed from logic '0' to logic '1'. In the case of cell C_{00}, this forces the current in the conducting transistor (which is TR1 if a logic '0' has been written into cell C_{00}) to flow in the appropriate bit line. The sense amplifier associated with each bit in the word detects which emitter is supplying the current, and generates the appropriate logic signal at its output. In our case emitter E_2 provides the current, so that the output O_0 from the sense amplifier is logic '0'. This logic signal is transmitted to data line D_0 via the tri-state buffer G4.

Simultaneously the logic data stored in cell C_{01} appears at the output of sense amplifier O_1 and is transmitted to data line D_1 via the tri-state gate G3.

The read cycle is complete when the logic level on the $\overline{\text{READ}}$ line returns to logic '1', thereby disabling the output of gates G3 and G4.

5.16   MOS RAM operation

MOS RAM devices can either be static or dynamic memories, and are briefly described below.

5.16.1   Static MOS RAM

A static MOS RAM cell comprises two cross-connected invertors to form a flip-flop in much the same way as in the basic bipolar RAM cell in Fig. 5.17. The organization of a complete MOS RAM is generally similar to that of Fig. 5.17.

5.16.2   Dynamic MOS RAM

In this case the data are stored in the form of a charge in the gate-to-substrate capacitance of a field-effect transistor in the MOS RAM cell (see also Sec. 5.11). Since the charge stored by a capacitor leaks away with time, the charge must be 'refreshed' every 2 ms or so. This is achieved by means of circuitry inside the RAM chip which reads the data in each cell and rewrites them back into the same cell.

5.16.3   Low-voltage standby operation

Many MOS RAM chips operate with a battery back-up, which allows them to retain data in the event of a power supply failure. Since the current drain of a MOS RAM in its standby mode is very small, the battery may either be a primary battery (non-rechargeable), such as a mercury battery or a silver oxide battery, or it may be a secondary battery (rechargeable), such as a nickel–cadmium or lead–calcium battery. The use of primary cells is usually limited to applications where standby data retention is infrequent or where a physically small battery is required.

A typical rechargeable battery circuit is shown in Fig. 5.18. Under normal operation, the value of the supply voltage is greater than E_2, and the MOS

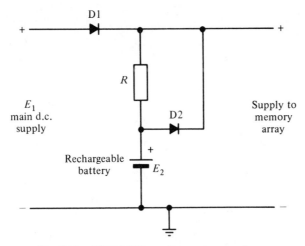

Fig. 5.18   MOS RAM standby power supply

RAM draws its current via diode D1 (D2 meanwhile being reverse biased). During this period of time, the battery is charged via resistor R. When the supply voltage falls to a low value (or to zero), the RAM power supply is maintained from battery E_2 via diode D2.

5.17   Storage capacity of IC memories

The storage capacity of a memory (either RAM or ROM) is related to the number of wires or lines used to address locations within the memory. If the memory has n address lines, it contains 2^n addressable locations; a memory with 10 address lines contains 2^{10} or 1024 addressable locations. *The number 1024 is referred to as 1K of memory.* If each location stores an eight-bit (one-byte) word, then a memory with 10 address lines stores 1K byte (1K × 8 bits) of data.

Eight-bit microprocessors have 16 address lines and can therefore address up to $2^{16} = 65\,536$ memory locations, i.e., 64K bytes of data.

6. Asynchronous counting systems

Counting systems can broadly be divided into two categories, namely *asynchronous* and *synchronous* systems. Asynchronous counting systems function in a step-by-step manner, and a simple analogy of the process is given here. Suppose that we wish to add 893_{10} to 655_{10}; the simplest method is to add to the number stored in the counter (655_{10}) the number 1_{10} eight hundred and ninety three times. This sum illustrates the basic mechanics of asynchronous counting. The name asynchronous is derived from the fact that the states of the flip-flops do not change synchronously, since the '1' added at the least significant end of the sum causes a change to 'run through' or to 'ripple through' the stored value. As a result, these counters are sometimes known as *ripple-through* counters.

In synchronous counters, the states of all the flip-flops change synchronously under the control of a clock pulse. Counters of this type are described in Chapter 7.

6.1 A pure binary counter

Table 6.1 illustrates the pure binary sequence for a four-bit counter, in which D is the least significant bit. From this table it is possible to deduce a simple rule for counters which operate in the 'forward' mode, i.e., for increasing value of count. From the table, it is observed that *each bit, except the least significant bit, changes state when the next less significant bit changes from '1' to '0'. The least significant bit changes state following the application of each input pulse.* These conditions are satisfied by the T flip-flop described in Chapter 5.

A basic form of asynchronous pure binary counter is illustrated in Fig. 6.1(a). This circuit uses four J-K flip-flops, each connected to operate as a T flip-flop. The preclear (P_C) input lines or reset lines are connected to a common wire; a logic '1' applied to this line causes all outputs to be reset to zero.

131

Table 6.1
Pure binary code

Decimal value		A	B	C	D	
0		0	0	0	0	
1		0	0	0	1	
2		0	0	1	0	
3		0	0	1	1	
4		0	1	0	0	
5	Forward count	0	1	0	1	Reverse count
6		0	1	1	0	
7		0	1	1	1	
8		1	0	0	0	
9		1	0	0	1	
10		1	0	1	0	
11		1	0	1	1	
12		1	1	0	0	
13		1	1	0	1	
14		1	1	1	0	
15		1	1	1	1	

The input pulses arrive in a random sequence, and the pulse width may vary without affecting the accuracy of the count in any way. Flip-flop D (FFD) changes state at every $1 \rightarrow 0$ edge, i.e., the trailing edge, of the input pulse. FFC changes state every time the output of FFD changes from '1' to '0'. Ideally both flip-flop outputs change simultaneously, but, for reasons given below, this does not occur. As the forward count proceeds, the outputs of the flip-flops change in accordance with Table 6.1, to the count of 15_{10}, when the outputs of all the flip-flops are in the '1' state. The next input pulse resets FFD to zero, and this change ripples through the counter making all the outputs zero.

In practice each flip-flop introduces a propagation delay, and there is a time delay between the change in the input signal occurring and the corresponding output change taking place. This is assumed to have a value τ in each of the flip-flops here. Figure 6.1(b) illustrates the state of affairs during the transition from the count of 3_{10} to 4_{10}. The output of FFD changes state τ seconds after the $1 \rightarrow 0$ edge of its input pulse. Thus τ seconds after the end of the fourth pulse the output of FFD falls to zero, giving a transient count of $0010_2 = 2_{10}$. After a further period of τ seconds, the output of FFC becomes zero, giving a second transient count of 0000. This change triggers FFB into the '1' state after a further delay of τ, giving a final count of $0100_2 = 4_{10}$. In the T flip-flop the $0 \rightarrow 1$ transition does not alter the output state, and the output of FFA remains stable at '0'. The change from 3_{10} to 4_{10} is thus achieved in 3τ seconds, with two erroneous states having occurred during the transition. Normally τ is small, being a fraction of a microsecond or less in electronic devices and a few milliseconds in pneumatic devices. In many applications it may be ignored. It is in high-speed systems that the propagation delay is significant.

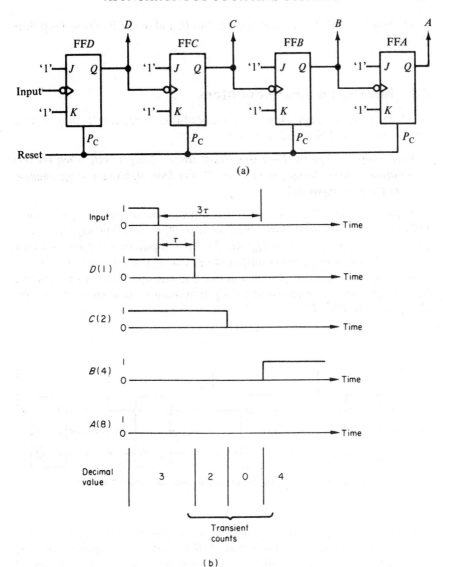

Fig. 6.1   (a) A ripple-through pure binary counter. (b) The effect of the individual time delays in the transition from 3_{10} to 4_{10}

In the case of the sixteenth pulse, each flip-flop must change its output state, and the final state (0000) is achieved after 4τ seconds.

The counter can be preset to some initial value by generating a preset signal at the final stage of the count. This signal is then applied to appropriate inputs of the flip-flops. If the initial condition is to be $ABCD = 0011$, a '1' signal must be applied to the P_S-lines of flip-flops C and D, and to the P_C-lines of flip-flops A and B.

6.2 Reversible binary counters

A rule for reverse binary counting can be deduced by reading Table 6.1 in the reverse order, and is stated as follows:

> *Each stage, except the least significant stage, changes state when the less significant stage changes from '0' to '1'. The least significant stage changes state for each input pulse.*

Thus, if the state of the counter at the commencement of the reverse count is 0001 (1_{10}), then the next pulse must set it to 0000, and following successive pulses to 1111 (15_{10}), 1110 (14_{10}), etc. Using T flip-flops, reverse counting is achieved by connecting the $\bar{Q}$-output of the less significant stage to the C-line of the following flip-flop, as shown in Fig. 6.2. The operation can be followed by recalling that the output from a T flip-flop changes state whenever its input changes from '1' to '0'.

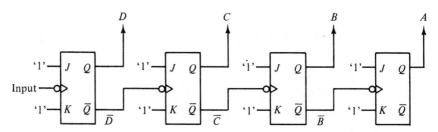

Fig. 6.2 A 'reverse' counter or 'down' counter using T flip-flops

Reverse counting can also be achieved in the forward counter, shown in Fig. 6.1(a), by monitoring the outputs from $\bar{A}$, $\bar{B}$, $\bar{C}$, and $\bar{D}$. An inspection of Table 6.1 shows this to be correct, since, if each term in the group is complemented, the result is the complement of 15 of the number.

6.3 Bidirectional counters

Bidirectional counters can be developed by combining the simple forward and reverse counters, by AND gating the output signals with a control signal, which has the value '1' or '0'. This control signal then allows either the forward count or the reverse count to proceed.

An alternative rule for *forward counting* is deduced by inspecting Table 6.1. It is observed that:

1. *Each stage, except the least significant stage, changes state following the condition when all the less significant stages are in the '1' state.*
2. *When counting in reverse, each stage, except the least significant stage, changes state following the condition when all the less significant stages are in the '0' state.*
3. *When counting in both forward and reverse the least significant stage changes state following each input pulse.*

A network which satisfies these conditions is shown in Fig. 6.3.

A '1' applied to the control input activates AND 1 and inhibits AND 2. Since the output of AND 2 is zero, all the lower AND gates are inhibited. A series of pulses applied at input P result in a forward, or 'up', count taking place, since a signal is only applied to the flip-flop when the input pulse is present AND all the less significant stages are in the '1' state. When the input pulse falls to zero, the appropriate outputs change state. When the control signal is '0', the upper AND gates are inhibited, and AND 2 is activated. A signal is applied to each stage only when the input pulse is present AND the outputs of the less significant stages are in the '0' state. This results in a reverse, or 'down', count.

6.4   Non-pure binary counters

All the outputs of the flip-flops, in the counters described earlier, are zero simultaneously only on a count of zero, or after a count of 2^N, where N is the number of stages in the counter, i.e., with four stages the count is zero at the count of zero, and again after the sixteenth pulse. If the counter is to be reset to zero after some other value, e.g., 5, 6, 10, etc., additional logic circuits are required. Many circuits are possible, a popular counter circuit being discussed here.

6.4.1   An 8421 BCD counter

A circuit which generates the 8421 BCD code is shown in Fig. 6.4. The counter uses J-K flip-flops connected to function as T elements; in order to simplify the diagram, the J- and K- input lines are omitted, and these would be connected to a logic '1' signal (or left open-circuited in TTL gates in a noise-free environment). The sequence of operations is given in Table 6.2.

Initially, when all the outputs are zero, the signal $\overline{A}$ which is fed back to G1 enables this gate and connects the four flip-flops together in the form of a basic pure binary counter. At the same time, G2 is disabled (since $A = 0$) and has no effect on the operation of the counter in its early stages of operation. During the time interval when the first seven pulses are applied to the counter, it

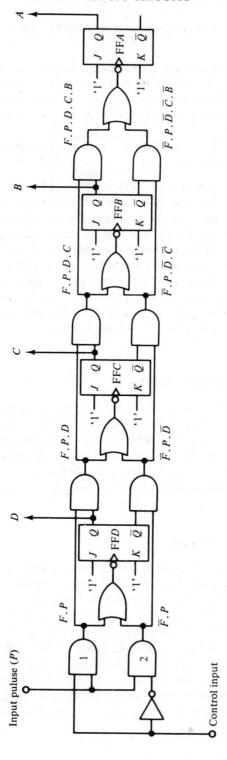

Fig. 6.3 A bidirectional pure binary counter

'1' – forward count (F)
'0' – reverse count ($\bar{F}$)

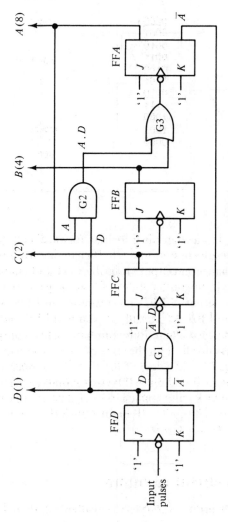

Fig. 6.4 An asynchronous 8421 BCD counter

LOGIC CIRCUITS

Table 6.2
Sequence of events in an 8421 BCD counter

Pulse number	State of outputs	State of gates	
	ABCD	G1	G2
Initial conditions	0000		
1	0001		
2	0010		
3	0011	open	closed
4	0100		
5	0101		
6	0110		
7	0111		
8	1000		
9	1001	closed	open
10	0000	open	closed

functions normally, i.e., as described for the 'forward' counter in Fig. 6.1(a).

Pulse number 8 results in outputs *ABCD* changing from the combination 0111 to 1000; the change in output *A* disables G1 and enables G2. The net result of the change in operating states of these gates is that any transition which occurs at the output of FFD is transmitted to FFA, and is prevented from being applied to FFB. As a result, the states of FFC and FFB remain at logic '0' until G1 is opened again. Pulse number 9 causes output D to change from '0' to '1'; this has no effect on the state of FFA, whose output remains at '1'. The trailing edge ('1'→'0' edge) of input pulse number 10 results in the output of FFD falling to '0' and, since this corresponds to the trailing edge (i.e., a '1'→'0' edge) of the clock pulse applied to FFA, it causes the output of FFA to change from '1' to '0'. Thus, after 10 input pulses the counter recycles to its initial condition of $A = B = C = D = 0$.

6.5 Integrated circuit counters

A wide range of asynchronous counters is available both in TTL and CMOS form. They include count-up only, count-down only, up-down counters, pure binary, non pure binary, BCD, ring counters, variable modulus counters, counters which are presettable, counters which are resettable, counters whose output changes on the leading edge of the clock pulse, counters whose output changes on the falling edge of the clock pulse, etc.

Clearly, it is impossible to give a survey of available devices here, and the reader is referred to manufacturers' literature[1] for full details of available types. However, a range of applications are described in specialized books.[2,3]

Problems

6.1   Show how four bistable devices may be used in a binary counter. Sketch waveform diagrams for each stage to illustrate the operation of the counter.

6.2   Design a ripple-through counter which works in the following code, and state the 'weight' of each digit.

$$0000$$
$$0001$$
$$0011$$
$$0100$$
$$0101$$
$$0111$$
$$1100$$
$$1101$$
$$1111$$
$$\overline{}$$
$$0000$$
etc.

6.3   Design a counter which works in the following code, and state the 'weight' of each digit.

$$0000$$
$$0001$$
$$0010$$
$$0011$$
$$0111$$
$$1000$$
$$1001$$
$$1010$$
$$1011$$
$$1111$$
$$\overline{}$$
$$0000$$
etc.

References

1. TEXAS INSTRUMENTS STAFF, *The TTL Data Book*, Texas Instruments.
2. LANCASTER, D., *TTL Cookbook*, Howard W. Sams & Co. Inc.
3. LANCASTER, D., *CMOS Cookbook*, Howard W. Sams & Co. Inc.

7. Synchronous counters, code convertors, and parallel adders

In asynchronous systems the state of the system is independent of the clock or input pulse since it takes a finite time for all the changes to 'ripple through' the system. The time taken to count a pulse in an asynchronous system is dependent on the total number of stages involved. In *synchronous* systems the clock or input pulse initiates all the changes simultaneously, and the total time taken to count one pulse is generally much less than that of an equivalent asynchronous counter.

Synchronous systems are usually more complex than asynchronous systems, since it is necessary to prepare the input logic gates to count the pulse, in advance of the pulse being received. This complexity is offset by the increase in operating speed.

Synchronous systems are also prone to stability problems which do not normally exist in asynchronous systems. These problems are discussed more fully in Secs 7.1 and 7.2.

7.1 Stability and cycling

Unstable operating conditions can arise in logical networks as a result of changes within the network. Consider the network in Fig. 7.1. If $x = 0$ the AND gate is inhibited giving an output $y = 0$, which is a stable operating state. When

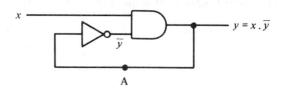

Fig. 7.1 Instability in a simple network

140

$y=0$ and x is changed to '1' both inputs to the AND gate are activated ($\bar{y}=1$), resulting in y rising to the logical '1' level. This signal is fed back via the NOT gate to its own input, giving a '0' at the lower AND input. This inhibits the AND gate and y falls to the logical '0' level. When the '0' is fed back, y rises again to the '1' level. This process is repeated indefinitely so long as $x=1$.

In this case the output of the network is oscillatory, the periodic time of the oscillations being dependent on the time taken for the logic signal to propagate through the network. By inserting a time delay at point A in Fig. 7.1, the frequency of the oscillations can be controlled.

The above argument is based on intuitive reasoning which is satisfactory for simple systems, but a more analytical approach is required in complex systems. A detailed discussion is beyond the scope of this book, but sufficient information is given here to outline the principles involved. Further information can be obtained from Refs 1 and 2.

One method of displaying the variations in output is the *Y-map* or flow table. The *Y*-map for the function $y=x \cdot \bar{y}$, generated in Fig. 7.1, is shown in Fig. 7.2. Horizontal movements in the map correspond to changes in the input

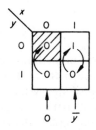

Fig. 7.2   The *Y*-map of the circuit in Fig. 7.1

variable x, and vertical movement to changes in the output y. Cross-hatched areas represent stable operating states. The entries outside the *Y*-map are known as the *energization* states, and those within the map are known as the *operation* states. The energization states define the operation states that the system must assume. The resulting operation states become the energization states for the following step. Stable operation is achieved when the operation states lead to their own energization states, i.e., when the energization and operation states are identical. Only one such state occurs in Fig. 7.2, that when $x=0$, $y=0$, which is shown cross-hatched.

The operation states are deduced from the logical equations of the system and the given input state. Thus, for $y=x \cdot \bar{y}$:

    (a) When $x=0$ then $y=0 \cdot \bar{y}=0$
    (b) When $x=1$ then $y=1 \cdot \bar{y}=\bar{y}$

The y-values of the function are '0' for $x=0$, and are plotted in the upper and lower left-hand cells. When $x=1$ the operation state is always $\bar{y}$, giving the values in the right-hand cells which are opposite to the y-value outside the cell.

The operation of the network may be analysed as follows. Initially if $y=1$ and $x=0$, the operation state is '0'. This becomes the new energization state. Corresponding to this energization state, the operation state is '0' and the system moves to the cell x, $y=0$, 0. This is a stable operating state since the energization and operation states are equal in value and the output locks in this state. If x is now changed to '1' the operating state becomes '1', and the state of the system moves to the cell defined by the energization states $x,y=1,1$. This results in a new operation state of $y=0$. The net result is that the output oscillates between the '0' and '1' levels, as shown by the arrows in the two right-hand cells, the periodic time of oscillation depending on the network delays. When x is changed to '0' again, the network always returns to its stable operating state $x,y=0,0$.

A succession of two or more unstable states, one leading to another, is known as a *cycle*. In nearly all cases in logical networks a cycle results in malfunctioning of the system if it is allowed to occur.

7.2 Race conditions

Most logic systems have several input lines, and if the change in output commanded is not a unit-distance change, then the actual mechanics of the change may be undefined. Suppose the system has two outputs, y_1 and y_2, which are to change from the state 0,0 to 1,1. Due to the physical nature of logic devices, one will operate more rapidly than the other, and the output will change in unit-distance fashion as follows:

$$0,0; \ 0,1; \ 1,1 \qquad \text{or} \qquad 0,0; \ 1,0; \ 1,1$$

Consider the NOR S-R flip-flop circuit in Fig. 7.3(a). The outputs from the NOR gates are

$$y_1 = \bar{x}_1 \cdot \bar{y}_2$$
$$y_2 = \bar{x}_2 \cdot \bar{y}_1$$

Clearly, when

$$
\begin{aligned}
x_1 &= 0, & y_1 &= \bar{y}_2 \\
x_1 &= 1, & y_1 &= 0 \\
x_2 &= 0, & y_2 &= \bar{y}_1 \\
x_2 &= 1, & y_2 &= 0
\end{aligned}
$$

These conditions are tabulated at the foot of the Y-map in Fig. 7.3(b) together with the appropriate operation states on the map.

It is assumed that the network is initially in the stable state $y_1,y_2=0,1$, with

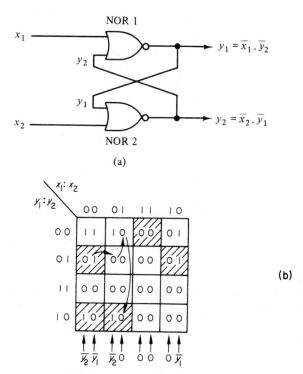

Fig. 7.3 (a) A NOR memory element and (b) the Y-map illustrating the changes that take place when input x_2 changes from '0' to '1'

$x_1,x_2 = 0,0$. If the input states are now changed to $x_1,x_2 = 0,1$, the output changes in the following manner, shown by arrows on the diagram:

$$y_1,y_2 = 0,1; \quad 0,0; \quad 1,0; \quad 1,0 \text{ (stable)}$$

The first change $0,1 \rightarrow 0,0$ corresponds to a change of the state of y_2 since one input to NOR is '1'. The changed value of y_2 alters the input conditions to NOR 1 ($x_1,y_2 = 0,0$), leading to the new output conditions $y_1,y_2 = 1,0$. It should be noted that all the changes are unit-distance. A change of input conditions back to $x_1,x_2 = 0,0$ results in a horizontal movement on the Y-map to the stable state $y_1,y_2 = 1,0$, i.e., no change in output.

Had the input conditions changed from $x_1,x_2 = 0,1$ to $x_1,x_2 = 1,1$ the final stable output condition would be $y_1, y_2 = 0,0$, i.e., both outputs are zero. If both inputs are reduced to zero simultaneously, the outputs are commanded to change from 0,0 to 1,1 as shown in Fig. 7.4. As stated above, one of the gates would operate more rapidly than the other and either of the two intermediate values 0,1 or 1,0 would first occur before the 1,1 state, as illustrated in Fig. 7.4. Since both lead to stable operating states, the condition $y_1,y_2 = 1,1$ is never achieved.

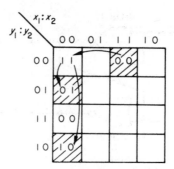

Fig. 7.4   A critical race condition

If more than one operation state changes at a time, a *race condition* is said to exist. If the race terminates in two or more unequal states, it is said to be a *critical race*. A critical race condition exists in Fig. 7.4 since the race terminates in two unequal stable conditions. In the NAND *S-R* flip-flop of Fig. 5.2(b) similar critical race conditions hold.

In some networks two or more patterns exist which lead to the same stable state. Such a race is described as *non-critical*. An example is given in Fig. 7.5. It

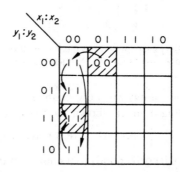

Fig. 7.5   A non-critical race condition

is assumed initially that the network is in the stable state $y_1,y_2 = 0,0$, when the inputs x_1,x_2 are changed from 0,1 to 0,0. The new operation state is 1,1, and the output changes from 0,0 to 1,1 by either of the patterns 0,0; 0,1; 1,1 or 0,0; 1,0; 1,1. In either case the same stable state is finally reached.

Combinations of cycles sometimes occur if information is fed back, an example being given in Fig. 7.6. The Y-map for the network in Fig. 7.6(a) is given in Fig. 7.6(b). Assume that the network is in the stable state $y_1,y_2 = 0,1$ with input signals $x_1,x_2 = 1,0$. When the inputs are changed to 1,1, the y_1 output remains at '0' and the y_2 output oscillates, giving the cycle $y_1,y_2 = 0,0$; 0,1; 0,0; 0,1, etc. If both inputs are simultaneously reduced to zero, when

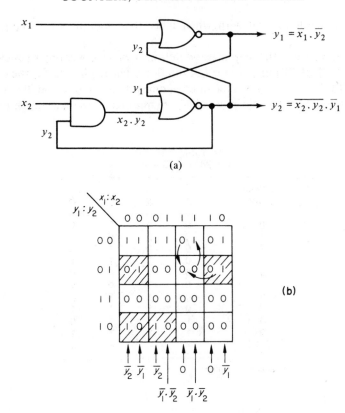

Fig. 7.6 The Y-map in (b) illustrates how unstable operation results when the feedback loop in (a) is added to a NOR S-R flip-flop

$y_1, y_2 = 0,1$, a critical race condition occurs and the final state of the output could be 0,1 or 1,0.

Where feedback is applied around flip-flops, care should be taken to ensure that cycles and critical races do not occur. Non-critical races can be allowed to exist if they do not affect the performance of the system. One method of overcoming these problems, where flip-flops are employed, is to use master-slave or edge-triggered flip-flops (Chapter 5) in which the inputs and outputs of the flip-flop are never connected directly together.

7.3 The design of parallel counters

Several methods of designing parallel counters have been evolved including analytical[3] and map[4,5] methods. The main advantage of map methods are that they are simple to use and understand. Their principle disadvantage is that they are difficult to deal with when more than four to six variables are involved.

An example using the map method follows. Consider a counter which is to count in 2421 BCD and is to use J-K flip-flops. The truth table for the code is given in Table 7.1, where A is the most significant digit and $\times$ signifies a 'can't happen' condition. The decimal values are marked on the Karnaugh map in Fig. 7.7.

Table 7.1
The 2421 BCD code

Decimal count	A	B	C	D
0	0	0	0	0
1	0	0	0	1
2	0	0	1	0
3	0	0	1	1
4	0	1	0	0
5	0	1	0	1
6	0	1	1	0
7	0	1	1	1
8	1	1	1	0
9	1	1	1	1
10–15	×	×	×	×

$\times$ = 'can't happen' condition.

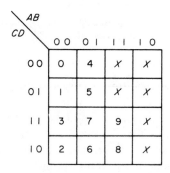

Fig. 7.7 The Karnaugh map for the 2421 BCD code in Table 7.1

In parallel counters the outputs of all the flip-flops change simultaneously. To do this the input logic must be prepared in advance of the incoming pulse to be counted. Immediately after the nth pulse has passed, the input logic must be prepared for the $(n+1)$th pulse, and must be held in that state until the pulse is received. After this the logic must be prepared for the $(n+2)$th pulse. It is therefore necessary in any given state to study the following state to be assumed by the counter.

Consider flip-flop C. At the zero count its output is '0', and it must be retained at this level for the count of unity, after which it must change to the '1' level. This level is maintained for the counts of 2_{10} and 3_{10}, after which it must change back to '0' and remain at this level for the count of 5_{10}. The logical level must rise to '1' on the sixth pulse, and remain at this level to the count of 9_{10}. On the tenth pulse its output becomes zero and the cycle begins again. In order to reproduce this cycle accurately the input conditions to the flip-flop for a given change in output must be known. These changes for the J-K flip-flop are listed in Table 7.2. The code change information from Table 7.1 is transferred to a code change map for each flip-flop, and thence to the input logic maps using Table 7.2.

Table 7.2
Input conditions to the J-K flip-flop

	Input logic levels	
Output change	J	K
$0 \rightarrow 1$ (change from '0' to '1')	1	×
$1 \rightarrow 0$ (change from '1' to '0')	×	1
$0 \rightarrow 0$ (maintain '0')	0	×
$1 \rightarrow 1$ (maintain '1')	×	0

× = 'don't care', i.e., could be '0' or '1'.

This procedure is illustrated in Fig. 7.8 for flip-flop A. From Table 7.1 it is observed that the flip-flop output is zero from the count of zero to 6_{10}. In the code change map in Fig. 7.8 the cells equivalent to 0_{10} to 6_{10}, in Fig. 7.7, are marked $0 \rightarrow 0$. After the seventh pulse the output of flip-flop A must change to

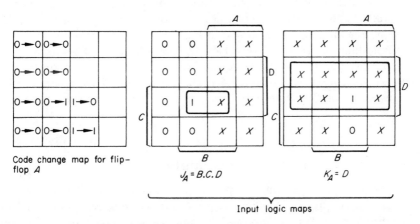

Code change map for flip-flop A

$J_A = B.C.D$

$K_A = D$

Input logic maps

Fig. 7.8   The input logic maps for any counter can be deduced by writing down the code change information on the Karnaugh map and then grouping terms on the logic maps, illustrated here for flip-flop A

the '1' level. This is recorded in the cell in the *code change map* equivalent to 7_{10} as a $0 \rightarrow 1$ change. This state is maintained after the eighth pulse, and is shown as a $1 \rightarrow 1$ change in the 8_{10} cell of the code change map. The final change after the ninth pulse is shown as a $1 \rightarrow 0$ change in the 9_{10} cell of the code change map.

By referring to Table 7.2, the input logic maps can now be completed. The J_A and K_A maps in Fig. 7.8 refer to the J- and K-input lines respectively of the 'A' flip-flop. In cells in the J_A and K_A maps corresponding to those marked $0 \rightarrow 0$ in the code change map, 0's and $\times$'s are marked respectively. This follows from the third row of Table 7.2. In the J_A and K_A cells corresponding to the cell marked $0 \rightarrow 1$ in the code change map, '1' and '$\times$' are marked respectively. The $1 \rightarrow 1$ and $1 \rightarrow 0$ cells are then dealt with giving the final input logic maps. When all the changes have been covered the input logic is minimized, giving

$$J_A = B.C.D \qquad \text{and} \qquad K_A = D$$

Maps for flip-flops B, C, and D are given in Fig. 7.9. The input equations are given below, and the corresponding logic block diagram, using master-slave flip-flops, is given in Fig. 7.10:

$$\begin{aligned} J_B &= C.D & K_B &= A.D \\ J_C &= D & K_C &= A.D + \overline{B}.D = D.(A + \overline{B}) \\ J_D &= 1 & K_D &= 1 \end{aligned}$$

Alternative modes of input connection are shown in Fig. 7.10, since the logic AND function can be performed internally in some J-K flip-flops. For flip-flop C the AND function on the K-inputs is performed externally, while in flip-flops A and B the internal AND function is used.

Designs may be carried out using S-R and T flip-flops using this technique. It is essential to use master-slave versions in parallel counters, otherwise instability and critical race conditions can occur when feedback is applied around the flip-flop, as illustrated in Fig. 7.6.

Input logic levels are listed in Table 7.3 for S-R, and T flip-flops for given output changes. The logic required at the inputs to the flip-flops, for the 2421 BCD counters, is given in Table 7.4. In the case of T flip-flops, no input logic is required for flip-flop D since the output changes state at each incoming pulse.

7.4   Bidirectional parallel counters

Designs for counting up and counting down can be produced by the technique outlined in the previous section, the 'up' and 'down' logic being OR-gated into the flip-flops to give the appropriate count. As with asynchronous systems, both 'count-up' and 'count-down' lines are necessary to ensure that only the correct logic is activated (see Table 7.5).

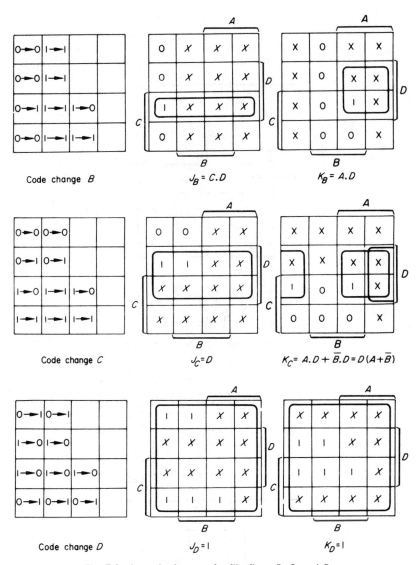

Fig. 7.9   Input logic maps for flip-flops B, C, and D

Counters which count up in one code and down in another can be constructed using the above technique.

7.5   Shift registers

A shift register comprises a number of cascaded flip-flops which contain a prearranged pattern of 1's and 0's. The application of a pulse, known as the

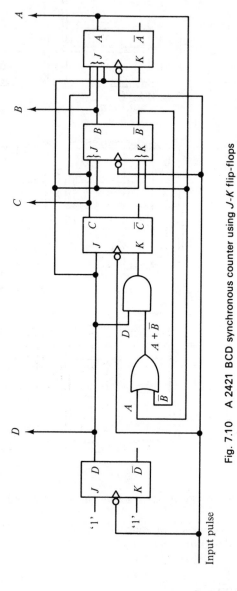

Fig. 7.10 A 2421 BCD synchronous counter using J-K flip-flops

Table 7.3

Input conditions to S-R and T flip-flops for given output changes

Output change	Input logic levels		
	S	R	T
$0\to1$	1	0	0
$1\to0$	0	1	0
$0\to0$	0	×	1
$1\to1$	×	0	1

× = 'don't care'.

Table 7.4

Input logic to S-R and T flip-flops for parallel 2421 BCD counters

Flip-flop	Input logic		
	S	R	T
A	$\bar{A}.B.C.D$	D	
B	$\bar{B}.C.D$	$A.D$	$B+\bar{C}+\bar{D}$
C	$\bar{C}.D$	$A.D+\bar{B}.C.D$	$\bar{D}+\bar{A}.B.C$
D	$\bar{D}$	D	Input pulse

shift pulse, moves the pattern by one step along the register.

Imagine four flip-flops A, B, C, D in a shift register, D being the least significant, all set to the '1' state when a series of shift pulses are applied. The result is shown in Table 7.6. After four shift pulses the complete pattern is moved along, and out of the register, the 1's being replaced by 0's. In general, if there are N flip-flops, it requires N shift pulses to shift all the data out of the register.

Master-slave J-K elements and D flip-flops are frequently used in these applications. The basis of operation of two stages of a shift register is illustrated in Fig. 7.11. The initial values stored at outputs C and D are '1', a '0' signal is applied to the J-input of FFD, and a '1' signal is applied to its K-input. *In all normal types of shift register, complementary logical signals must be applied to the J- and K-inputs.* The reason for this can be understood from the description below. The conditions mentioned above correspond to the initial conditions listed in Table 7.6 for the flip-flops C and D. The operation of the circuit during the first two clock pulse cycles is now described. At time t_1 (see Fig. 7.11b), when the shift signal (clock signal) is '0', the master stages of both flip-flops are isolated from their respective input signals. At t_2, the shift signal changes to logic '1' which results in the master stages (a) being isolated from the slave stages and (b) being connected to their respective input lines. This causes the Q-output of the *master stage* of FFD to store a '0', and the $\bar{Q}$-output of this

Table 7.5

Input logic for several counters using J-K flip-flops

Input line	Code							
	8421BCD		5211		642(-3)		8421 Pure binary	
	Up	Down	Up	Down	Up	Down	Up	Down
J_A	$B.C.D$	$\bar{B}.\bar{C}.\bar{D}$	$B.C$	$\bar{D}$	$C+B.\bar{D}$	$\bar{D}$	$B.C.D$	$\bar{B}.\bar{C}.\bar{D}$
K_A	D	$\bar{D}$	$B.C$	$\bar{D}$	$B.D+C.D$	$\bar{C}+\bar{B}.D$	$B.C.D$	$\bar{B}.\bar{C}.\bar{D}$
J_B	$C.D$	$A.\bar{D}$	C	$\bar{D}$	$A+\bar{C}$	$C+\bar{D}$	$C.D$	$\bar{C}.\bar{D}$
K_B	$C.D$	$\bar{C}.\bar{D}$	C	C	$A+\bar{C}$	$A+D$	$C.D$	$\bar{C}.\bar{D}$
J_C	$\bar{A}.D$	$A.\bar{D}+\bar{B}.\bar{D}$	D	$B+\bar{D}$	B	$A+\bar{B}$	D	$\bar{D}$
K_C	D	$C.\bar{D}$	1	1	$\bar{A}+B$	$\bar{B}+\bar{D}$	D	$\bar{D}$
J_D	1	1	1	1	1	1	1	1
K_D	1	1	$B.C$	$\bar{B}.\bar{C}$	1	1	1	1

Table 7.6
Movement of data in a shift register

	Direction of movement of data ←				
Shift pulse number	State of flip-flops				Input data
	A	B	C	D	
Initial state	1	1	1	1	0
1	1	1	1	0	0
2	1	1	0	0	0
3	1	0	0	0	0
4	0	0	0	0	

stage to store a '1'. Since the master and slave stages are isolated from one another, the Q-output of FFD continues to store a '1'. At this time, the master stage of FFC is connected to the slave stage of FFD, and therefore stores logic '1'; there is, therefore, no change in the condition of FFC. Hence *the data applied to the input lines (which must be complementary) of master-slave flip-flops are shifted into the master stages when the shift signal changes from '0' to '1'.*

The above conditions are maintained between t_2 and t_3, at which time the shift signal falls to logic '0'. This causes the master stages (1) to be isolated from the input lines and (2) to be connected to the slave stages. Consequently, *when the shift pulse signal changes from '1' to '0', the data in each master stage are transferred to the slave stage.* As a result of the above operation, the '0' stored in the Q-output of the master stage of FFD is transferred to its slave stage, and output D changes from '1' to '0'. At the same time, the state of the master stage of FFC is shifted into its slave stage, but since both store 1's, there is no apparent change in the output at FFC at time t_3.

During the second shift pulse, input data are shifted into both master stages at t_4 (0's in both cases) and are transferred to their slave stages at t_5. Hence, at time t_5, output D remains unaltered at logic '0', and output C changes from '1' to '0'. Readers will note that the above action causes data to be shifted serially into the register from the left-hand end and shifted serially out at the right-hand end.

Shift registers of any length can be constructed simply by cascading J-K flip-flops in the manner shown in Fig. 7.11(a). Shift registers are used in a wide variety of applications, ranging from temporary data storage to complete data transmission systems; in the latter type of system, the register is split between a master control station and several smaller outstations, possibly distributed over many miles in a large installation.

One industrial application of shift registers is the automatic rejection of faulty components in an automated production line. The 1's stored in the

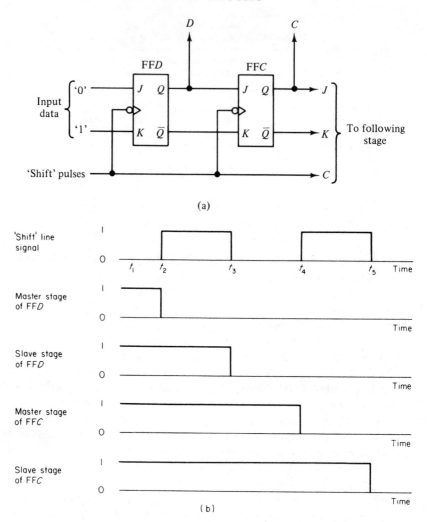

Fig. 7.11 (a) Two stages of a shift register. (b) Illustrative waveform diagrams when shifting the data shown into the register, output D and C originally being logic '1'

register represent the position of components on the production line that are satisfactory. If a test sequence indicates a fault on a component, a '0' is set into the appropriate flip-flop. This moves along the register as the component moves along the production line. The '0' in the register is used to inhibit further operations on the component, saving production time. At a suitable point the faulty component is rejected automatically by a circuit which recognizes the '0' in the register.

7.6 Ring counters

Ring counters are shift registers with the input to the register derived from the output flip-flop, as shown in Fig. 7.12. Assume initially that all the stages, except the first, are set to zero. The '1' in the first stage is then shifted one step along the register by each shift pulse. The pattern held in the counter is shown in Table 7.7.

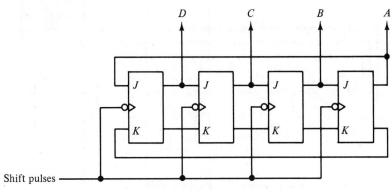

Fig. 7.12   A ring counter

Table 7.7
Pattern generated by a simple ring counter

Shift pulse	State of flip-flops				
	A	B	C	D	
Initial condition	0	0	0	1 ←	
1	0	0	1	0	
2	0	1	0	0	
3	1	0	0	0	
4	0	0	0	1	Repeat

Readers will note that, with the code sequence in Table 7.7, only four code groups are stored by the four bistables. The *maximum length* of the code patterns generated by this type of counter is N, where N is the number of flip-flops in the ring counter. Ring counters are uneconomic in terms of the electronic hardware required to produce a code sequence of a given length when compared with a pure binary counter since, in the latter case, four flip-flops produce a code sequence of $2^4 = 16$ combinations. An advantage, however, of the ring counter is that the process of decoding the stored data into decimal (and into many other codes) is very simple. The ring counter in Fig. 7.12 produces a variety of code sequences including three sequences of length four combinations (that in Table 7.7 being one of these), one sequence of length two code combinations, and two sequences of length one code combinations (the all-0's and the all-1's combinations).

At the instant of switch-on, it is very probable that the ring counter will enter an incorrect code sequence. Additional logic circuitry is required to ensure that the correct code sequence is generated. The circuit in Fig. 7.13 is one such

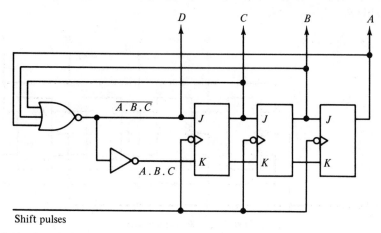

Fig. 7.13   One method of ensuring that the ring counter enters the code sequence in Table 7.7

circuit which ensures that, whatever sequence the counter enters initially, the four-bit ring counter returns to the sequence in Table 7.7. It does so by feeding back to the J-input of FFC the NOR function of outputs A, B, and C, which ensures that a '1' is presented to this input only when $A = B = C = 0$.

7.7   Feedback shift registers

By feeding back more or less complicated functions of the state of the register to its input, shift registers can be made to generate a sequence of binary combinations. The sequence need not necessarily follow the normal pure binary counting sequence.

By feeding back the complement of the output it is possible, with a register with N stages, to generate pattern lengths of $2N$. The general arrangement is shown in Fig. 7.14. These are known as *twisted-ring counters* or *feedback shift registers* (FSRs). FSRs generate one walking or creeping code of length $2N$, in addition to other codes. Consider a FSR with complementary feedback similar to that shown in Fig. 7.14, having three stages A, B, and C. If the initial conditions are A_1, B_1, C_1 then the cycle in Table 7.8 is generated.

Thus if $A_1 = 0$, $B_1 = 0$, $C_1 = 1$ the pattern generated is a walking code of length $2N = 6$, shown in Table 7.9. Since there are $2^3 = 8$ possible

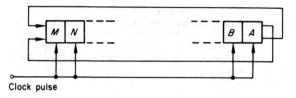

Fig. 7.14 A feedback shift register using the complement of its own output as its input

Table 7.8
Main code of the three-stage FSR

Shift pulse number	State of flip-flops		
	A	B	C
Initial condition	A_1	B_1	C_1 ←
1	B_1	C_1	$\bar{A}_1$
2	C_1	$\bar{A}_1$	$\bar{B}_1$
3	$\bar{A}_1$	$\bar{B}_1$	$\bar{C}_1$
4	$\bar{B}_1$	$\bar{C}_1$	A_1
5	$\bar{C}_1$	A_1	B_1
6	A_1	B_1	C_1 Repeat

Table 7.9
Walking code generated by a three-stage FSR

State of flip-flops			BCD equivalent
A	B	C	
0	0	1	1
0	1	1	3
1	1	1	7
1	1	0	6
1	0	0	4
0	0	0	0
0	0	1	1

combinations, another code of cycle length $2^N - 2N = 2$ exists. This is the code

$$A, B, C = 0,1,0 \rightarrow 1,0,1 \rightarrow 0,1,0 \rightarrow$$

Strictly speaking, the codes have no beginning and no end, and the code generated is dependent on the (arbitrary) state of the flip-flops at the commencement of the count. The code length of $2N$ is called the *main code* while the shorter code is called the *auxiliary code*. In general there may be an auxiliary code in addition to one or more main codes. The codes generated for a few values of N are given in Table 7.10.

Table 7.10
Number and length of the main auxiliary codes generated by FSRs

N	Number of main codes	Length of main codes	Length of auxiliary code
2	1	4	–
3	1	6	2
4	2	8	–
5	3	10	2
6	5	12	4

In general there are 2^N possible combinations, and the length of each main code is 2^N. The number of main codes is the integral part of $2^N/2N$, and the remaining number is the length of the auxiliary code, e.g., if $N = 5$, $2^N = 32$, and $2N = 10$. There are therefore three main codes of length 10, and an auxiliary code of length two.

The main drawbacks to this form of counter are the short length of the main codes and the fact that the counter may commence operation in any one of the codes. To ensure that the counter operates in only one code, the flip-flops have to be set initially to a predetermined pattern.

7.8   Linear FSRs

The length of the main code generated can be increased in some cases by feeding back an EXCLUSIVE-OR function of the states of the register, as shown in Fig. 7.15.

If the initial state is $A, B, C = 0,0,1$, the cycle in Table 7.11 ensues, bearing in mind that flip-flop C is set to the '1' state following the condition when $A \not\equiv B$. This results in a code cycle of length 7, or $2^N - 1$. The missing state is 000 which, if generated, would terminate the cycle since C would not be set to '1' at the next shift pulse. In general, with modulo-2 feedback the cycle length is $2^N - 1$,

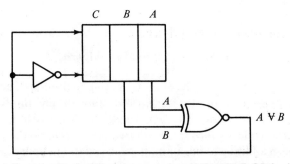

Fig. 7.15   A linear feedback shift register using an EXCLUSIVE-OR feedback function

Table 7.11
Code cycle produced by Fig. 7.15

A	B	C
0	0	1
0	1	0
1	0	1
0	1	1
1	1	1
1	1	0
1	0	0
0	0	1

and the condition in which all the outputs are zero should not be allowed to occur.

With the use of additional logic, the 'all 0's' state can be permitted to occur by ensuring that a '1' is injected into the register on the next shift pulse.

An alternative arrangement to that shown in Fig. 7.15 is obtained by feeding the lower input directly from the modulo-2 gate and the upper input from the NOT gate. This results in a cycle length of $2^N - 1$, the 'all 0's' state being included in the cycle. The state $A, B, C = 1,1,1$, in this case, should not be allowed to occur.

The length and number of the cycles generated is dependent on the points from which the feedback is generated. For example, a five-stage FSR, with feedback taken from the third and fifth or second and fifth stages, has a main cycle length of 31 and a minor cycle length of one (the cycle 00000). If the feedback is taken from the fourth and fifth stages, it has a main cycle length of 21, and three minor cycles of lengths 7, 3, and 1 respectively. A general treatment of linear FSRs has been given by Elspas.[6]

A list of maximum sequence lengths for various lengths of shift registers and for different modulo-2 feedback connections is given in Table 7.12.

The name linear FSR is given to shift registers with modulo-2 feedback, since they are amenable to mathematical theory in much the same way as linear networks. If the state of an N-stage FSR at some point in the count is

$$\phi_n = N,M,L,\ldots,C,B,A$$

where N is the least significant term and the modulo-2 feedback term is F, then the state of the counter after one shift pulse is

$$\phi_{n+1} = F,N,M, \ldots, D,C,B$$

The function fed back can be any modulo-2 term and is expressed mathematically as

$$F = nN \forall mM \forall \cdots \forall bB \forall aA$$

where $n, m, \ldots, b, a$ are coefficients which have a value of either '0' or '1'. If a

Table 7.12
Feedback connections and sequence lengths

Number of stages	Sequence length	Feedback connections
2	3	1, 2
3	7	2, 3
4	15	3, 4
5	31	3, 5
6	63	5, 6
7	127	6, 7
8	255	4, 5 or 6, 8
9	511	5, 9
10	1 023	7, 10
11	2 047	9, 11
12	4 095	6, 8 or 11, 12
13	8 191	9, 10 or 12, 13
14	16 383	4, 8 or 13, 14
15	32 767	14, 15

four-stage linear FSR is used and feedback is obtained from the third and fourth stages, then $F = 0011$. ϕ_{n+1} can be related to ϕ_n by a transition matrix which contains the information given above, viz.:

$$
\begin{bmatrix} F \\ N \\ M \\ \vdots \\ C \\ B \end{bmatrix} = \begin{bmatrix} n & m & l & \cdots & c & b & a \\ 1 & 0 & 0 & & 0 & 0 & 0 \\ 0 & 1 & 0 & & 0 & 0 & 0 \\ \vdots & & & & & & \vdots \\ 0 & 0 & & & 1 & 0 & 0 \\ 0 & 0 & & & 0 & 1 & 0 \end{bmatrix} \begin{bmatrix} N \\ M \\ L \\ \vdots \\ B \\ A \end{bmatrix}
$$

or
$$[\phi_{n+1}] = [T][\phi_n]$$

where $[T]$ is the transition matrix.

As a simple example, consider the three-stage linear FSR in Fig. 7.15 where $F = 011$. If the state of the register is $C, B, A = 1,1,0$ after 'n' pulses, then the two following states in the sequence are as calculated below:

$$
\begin{bmatrix} F \\ C \\ B \end{bmatrix}_{n+1} = \begin{bmatrix} 0 & 1 & 1 \\ 1 & 0 & 0 \\ 0 & 1 & 0 \end{bmatrix} \begin{bmatrix} 1 \\ 1 \\ 0 \end{bmatrix} = \begin{bmatrix} 1 \\ 1 \\ 1 \end{bmatrix} = \begin{bmatrix} C \\ B \\ A \end{bmatrix}_{n+1}
$$

$$
\begin{bmatrix} F \\ C \\ B \end{bmatrix}_{n+2} = \begin{bmatrix} 0 & 1 & 1 \\ 1 & 0 & 0 \\ 0 & 1 & 0 \end{bmatrix} \begin{bmatrix} 1 \\ 1 \\ 1 \end{bmatrix} = \begin{bmatrix} 0 \\ 1 \\ 1 \end{bmatrix} = \begin{bmatrix} C \\ B \\ A \end{bmatrix}_{n+2}
$$

This gives the states

A	B	C	Pulse number
0	1	1	n
1	1	1	$n+1$
1	1	0	$n+2$

This procedure allows any cycle to be fully calculated.

Linear FSRs can be used to generate binary sequences, known as *pseudo-random binary sequences* or PRBS. For example, the output sequence (in time order) from stage *C* of the FSR in Fig. 7.15 is 1, 0, 1, 1, 1, 0, 0. Using longer registers long PRBSs are generated. PRBSs are important tools which have found a wide range of applications. They are used to encode and decode digital messages for the purpose of error-free transmission, and also to test control systems and to generate random number sequences.

7.9 Non-linear FSRs

Feedback shift registers which are not amenable to the above treatment are described as being non-linear. The main difference between linear and non-linear FSRs is that, in non-linear FSRs, the feedback terms are not necessarily EXCLUSIVE-OR functions and multiple feedback loops may be used.

7.10 Parallel code conversion using PLAs and ROMs

While computers and other logical networks operate with one or another form of binary code, man prefers to work in the decimal code. It is therefore necessary to be able to convert between binary codes and decimal. Conversion between binary codes is also necessary. For instance, a unit-distance code may be employed by a *transducer* to measure the position of an object. If the information is to be processed by logic gates, it may be advisable to convert the information into some other code, say pure binary.

Consider the case in which an 'input' code *ABCD*, i.e., a code which is derived from a logic system, given in Table 7.13 (in which *A* is the most significant bit, or MSB), is to be converted by a code converter in the 'output' code *A'B'C'D'* in Table 7.14 (*A'* being the MSB), to be used by some other part of the system.

With the aid of a suitable programmable logic array or ROM, any form of code can be converted into any other code. The designer of the PLA first deduces the logic equation relating the input code to the output code in an

Table 7.13
Input code

Decimal number	A (8)	B (4)	C (2)	D (1)
0	0	0	0	0
1	0	0	0	1
2	0	0	1	0
3	0	0	1	1
4	0	1	0	0
5	0	1	0	1
6	0	1	1	0
7	0	1	1	1
8	1	0	0	0
9	1	0	0	1
10–15	×	×	×	×

×='can't happen' condition.

Table 7.14
Output code

Decimal number	States of output lines			
	A'	B'	C'	D'
0	0	0	0	0
1	0	0	0	1
2	0	0	1	1
3	0	1	1	1
4	1	1	1	1
5	1	1	1	0
6	1	1	0	0
7	1	0	0	0
8–15	×	×	×	×

×='can't happen' condition.

AND-OR form, after which the PLA is programmed to perform the required conversion. It is left as an exercise for the reader to verify the following relationships between the input signals $ABCD$ and the output signals $A'B'C'D'$:

$$A' = B$$
$$B' = B.\bar{C} + B.\bar{D} + \bar{B}.C.D$$
$$C' = B.\bar{C} + \bar{B}.C$$
$$D' = \bar{B}.C + \bar{B}.D + B.\overline{C}.\overline{D}$$

A simplified block diagram of a PLA providing one solution to the above logical equations is shown in Fig. 7.16. Each output line has a three-state buffer

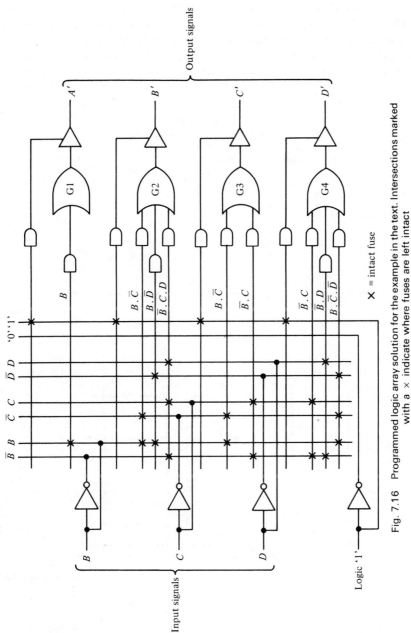

Fig. 7.16   Programmed logic array solution for the example in the text. Intersections marked with a × indicate where fuses are left intact

which is permanently enabled. Gate G1 provides output A', gate G2 gives the AND-OR version of B', gate G3 furnishes C', and gate G4 generates D'.

Alternatively, a read-only memory (ROM) can be used as a code convertor. When each location is 'addressed' by an input code, the contents of that location are 'read out' on the output lines of the ROM. Consider the problem in Table 7.15 (see also Fig. 7.17) in which the pure binary code ABC is to be converted into the unit-distance code WXY. When the input combination

Table 7.15
ROM code convertor truth table

| Input code | | | ROM location | Output code | | |
A	B	C	number	W	X	Y
0	0	0	0	1	1	0
0	0	1	1	0	1	0
0	1	0	2	0	0	0
0	1	1	3	0	0	1
1	0	0	4	0	1	1
1	0	1	5	1	1	1
1	1	0	6	1	0	1
1	1	1	7	1	0	0

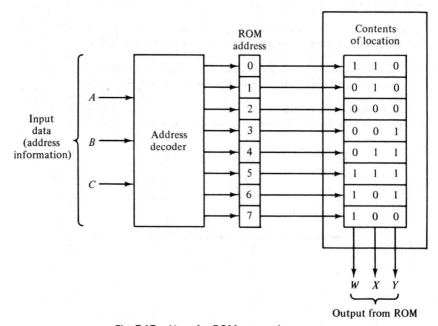

Fig. 7.17   Use of a ROM as a code convertor

$ABC = 000$ is applied to the ROM decoder, the contents of location 000 appear on the output lines WXY of the ROM. If the input combination $ABC = 101$, the contents of location 5 of the ROM, i.e., $WXY = 111$, appear at the output of the ROM.

7.11 A parallel adder/subtracter

In a parallel adder, each binary digit in the same relative position in the two words to be added together is applied simultaneously to a full adder. If each word contains eight bits, then the parallel adder contains eight independent full adders. Binary subtraction is carried out by means of 2's complement addition of the subtrahend, and is described later in this section.

The basis of a three-bit parallel adder/subtracter is shown in Fig. 7.18. When the control line has a logic '0' on it, gates G0, G1 and G2 act as non-inverting buffers which allow signals B_0, B_1, and B_2 respectively to be simultaneously applied to the adders. The binary words $A_0 A_1 A_2$ and $B_0 B_1 B_2$ are stored in registers in the digital system. Thus with a logic '0' on the control line, the sum of A_0 and B_0 appears at output S_0 (which is stored in the result register), the sum of A_1 and B_1 (together with the carry from the previous stage) appears at S_1, etc. If a carry is generated at output C_{02}, it is stored in a *carry flag* or carry flip-flop.

Consequently, when a logic '0' is applied to the control line, the data in register A is added to the data in register B, the result appearing in the result register S and any carry generated by the final stage is recorded in the carry flag. The carry flag therefore stores the carry generated by the sum of two *unsigned binary numbers*. For example, since the block diagram in Fig. 7.18 can handle the sum of two unsigned numbers in the range 000_2 to 111_2, the sum of 111_2 and 101_2 gives the following result:

> Contents of register $A =$ 111
> Contents of register $B =$ 101
> Contents of register $S =$ 100
> Content of carry flag = 1↵

That is, since the carry flag has been set to logic '1', the result is larger than the storage capacity of the result register.

All microprocessors have a carry flag in a register known as the *status register* of the microprocessor; the data stored in this register can be interrogated at any time to allow the programmer to check if a carry has occurred after the addition of two numbers.

However, if *signed binary numbers* are used, the most significant bit of each number is reserved for use as a sign bit. Hence a three-bit register can store a binary number in the range 011_2 (or $+3_{10}$) to 100 (or -4_{10}). If a value outside this range is generated, i.e., a number greater than $+3_{10}$ or -4_{10}, we say that

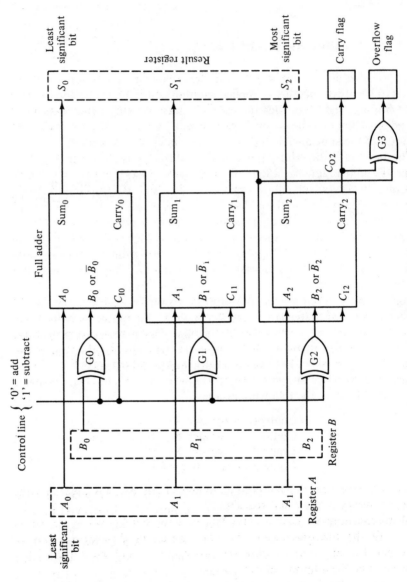

Fig. 7.18   A three-bit parallel adder/subtracter with carry and overflow flags

an *overflow* has occurred. One method of checking if an overflow has occurred is to compare the carry generated by the sum of the penultimate bits of the two words with the carry generated by the most significant bits of the two words. If the two carries are NOT EQUIVALENT to one another, then an overflow has occurred. In Fig. 7.18, a result which is 'in range', i.e., between $+3_{10}$ and -4_{10}, results in a logic '0' at the output of G3 and an 'overrange' result produces a logic '1' which 'sets' the *overflow flag*. This is verified by the following examples:

Contents of register $A = $ 001 $(+1)$
Contents of register $B = $ 001 $(+1)$

Contents of register $S = $ 010 $(+2)$ (true result)
       $\text{Carry}_2 = 0 \longleftrightarrow \text{carry}_1 = 0$

The result of this addition is 'true' or is in range since carry_1 and carry_2 are EQUIVALENT to one another and the overflow flag is not set. Consider the following example:

Contents of register $A = $ 010 $(+2)$
Contents of register $B = $ 011 $(+3)$

Contents of register $S = $ 101 (-3) (false result)
       $\text{Carry}_2 = 0 \longleftrightarrow \text{carry}_1 = 1$

The result is a positive value that is too large, i.e., greater than $+3_{10}$; in this case carry_1 is NOT EQUIVALENT to carry_2 and the overflow flag is set. Consider, now, the addition of two large negative numbers:

Contents of register $A = $ 110 (-2)
Contents of register $B = $ 101 (-3)

Contents of register $S = $ 011 $(+3)$ (false result)
       $\text{Carry}_2 = 1 \longleftrightarrow \text{carry}_1 = 0$

The result of the above addition, i.e., $(-2)+(-3)$, is a negative value which is out of range, so that carry_1 and carry_2 are once more NOT EQUIVALENT to one another and the overflow flag is set.

Many microprocessors (but not all of them) have an overflow flag in their status register, and the condition of this flag can be interrogated at any time to verify if an overflow has occurred when two signed binary numbers have been added together.

Binary subtraction is carried out by 2's complement addition. When the control line in Fig. 7.18 has a logic '1' on it, gates G0, G1, and G2 act as inverters; the outputs from these gates therefore represent the 1's complement of the contents of register B. Since the logic '1' on the control line is also applied to the carry-in pin of the least significant full adder, C_{10}, the net effect is to add the 2's complement of the register B to the contents of register A. That is, the contents of register S is the sum $A + (-B) = A - B$. Once again, the overflow flag indicates if the result is in range.

7.12 A binary multiplication circuit

Many microcomputer systems need to multiply numbers together as part of their operating program. One method of doing this is by means of a program or *software* written by a computer programmer (see also Chapter 10). One limitation of software multiplication is that the multiplication program not only takes up space in the memory of the system (usually not a serious limitation) but also requires the microcomputer to dedicate a certain amount of time to performing the calculation (which may be a more serious limitation if the computer has many other functions to perform).

One method of eliminating the need for software multiplication in a computer is to use an integrated circuit which is dedicated to the multiplication of two binary words. Since the electronic parts associated with such a multiplier can be physically touched, it is described as part of the *hardware* of the computer system. Where a hardware multiplier is used, the circuit can perform the multiplication while the computer is carrying out some other function in association with the process it is controlling. When the circuit has completed the multiplication, it advises the computer that the result is ready (often by means of an 'interrupt' signal — see Chapter 10), at which point the computer accepts the result from the multiplier circuit. Another advantage of this arrangement is that hardware multiplication is faster than software multiplication, and time is saved. From the above, the reader will appreciate that there is a trade-off in computer systems between certain aspects of hardware and software.

The basis of one form of three bit-by-three bit integrated circuit multiplier is shown in Fig. 7.19. The circuit comprises two three-bit parallel adders together with AND gates to form a three-bit parallel multiplier. The carry generated by each stage ripples through to the next stage, and is shown by an arrow inside the adders; the internal connection for the carry is not shown for simplicity. The multiplication process is illustrated below, in which A_0 and B_0 are the least significant bits of words A and B respectively and P_0 is the least significant bit of the product. It is important to note than an n-bit by n-bit multiplication requires a register of length $2n$ (described as a *double-length register*) to handle the product. The product register, P, must therefore have six locations (P_0 to P_5) to store the result of the calculation:

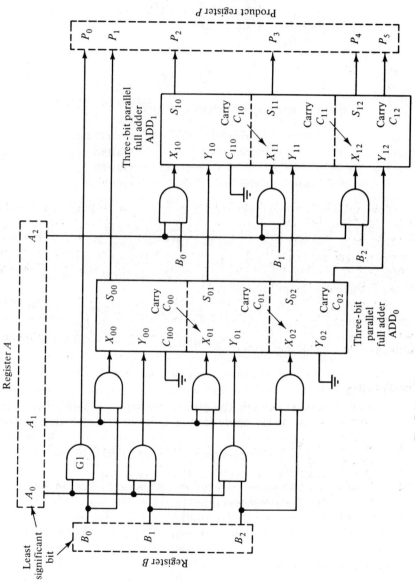

Fig. 7.19   The basis of one form of hardware multiplier

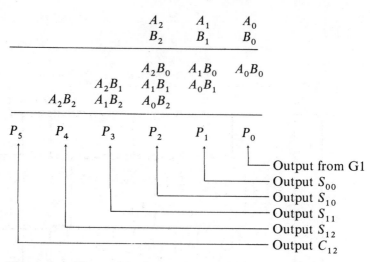

The reader will note that the product term P_0 is the AND function of the two least significant bits $(A_0 B_0)$, so that AND gate G1 generates the required product term. Product term P_1 is the binary sum of $A_1 B_0$ and $A_0 B_1$; these signals are applied respectively to inputs X_{00} and Y_{00} of the least significant adder section of adder unit ADD_0. The output S_{00} from this part of the full adder is therefore the product term P_1.

The reader will find it an interesting exercise to verify that the remaining connections in Fig. 7.19 generate the product terms P_2 to P_4, inclusive. The product term P_5 is the carry-out, C_{12}, of the most significant full-adder element of the adder unit ADD_1.

Problems

7.1   What is meant by the term *synchronous* as applied to counters? Discuss the need for synchronizing pulses or clock pulses in a synchronous counting system.

7.2   Write down a BCD code with a weighting of 3321 and design a synchronous counter employing *J-K* flip-flops which generates this code.

7.3   Design a counter which generates a four-bit Gray code.

7.4   Design a counter using (a) *J-K* flip-flops, (b) *T* flip-flops, and (c) *S-R* flip-flops, which counts in the following sequence:

$$
\begin{array}{c}
0000 \\
0001 \\
0010 \\
0100 \\
1000 \\
1001 \\
0110 \\
\underline{1111} \\
0000 \\
\text{etc.}
\end{array}
$$

7.5 What is meant by the expression *shifting register*? Illustrate, with waveform diagrams, the operation of a shifting register.

7.6 Write down all the possible code patterns for a five-stage feedback shift register.

7.7 A linear feedback shift register has four stages, designated A, B, C, and D. The feedback signal to stage D is generated from stages A and C. Compute the code sequence generated.

7.8 A position encoder generates the following unit-distance decimal code, known as the Petherick code. Design a convertor, using only NOR gates, to convert the output into the pure binary code.

$$0101$$
$$0001$$
$$0011$$
$$0010$$
$$0110$$
$$1110$$
$$1010$$
$$1011$$
$$1001$$
$$\underline{1101}$$

$$0101$$
etc.

References

1. MARCUS, M. P., 'Cascaded binary counters with feedback', *Trans. Inst. elect. Electron. Engrs.*, **EC-12**, 4, 361, 1963.
2. CALDWELL, S. H., *Switching Circuits and Logical Design*, John Wiley, 1958.
3. PHISTER, M., *Logical Design of Digital Computers*, John Wiley, 1958.
4. BIWAS, N. N., 'The logic and input equations of flip-flops', *Electron. Engng.*, **38**, 2, 107, 1966.
5. DEAN, K. J., 'The design of parallel counters using the map method', *J. Inst. Elect. Radio Engrs.*, **32**, 159–162, 1966.
6. ELSPAS, B., 'The theory of autonomous linear sequential networks', *Trans. Inst. Radio Engrs.*, **CT-6**, 45, 1959.

8. Microprocessors and microcomputers

8.1 Introduction to microcomputers

A basic computer system comprises a number of separate sections which communicate with one another by means of a system of electrical connections known as *buses*. The basic blocks of a computer (see Fig. 8.1) are the *central processing unit* (CPU), the *memory* (which comprises a range of ROMs and RAMs), and *input/output ports* (I/O ports) which enable the CPU to communicate with *peripherals* such as switches, keyboards, printers, video display units (VDU), etc.

The CPU or microprocessor chip (which is usually in a 40-pin DIP form in the case of an eight-bit processor) houses the arithmetic and logic unit and also the control unit. The *arithmetic and logic unit* (ALU) performs arithmetic and logic operations on operands (binary values) in the system. The range of arithmetic functions is usually limited, typical instructions include binary (hex) addition, decimal addition, and binary (hex) subtraction; shift instructions and rotate instructions (which can be regarded as a special version of shift

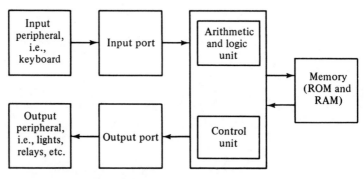

Fig. 8.1   A basic microcomputer system

172

instructions) are also available, and are used in many calculations. The logic functions available to the programmer include the AND, OR, and EXCLUSIVE-OR functions. The range of arithmetic and logic functions available differs between makes of microprocessor, and those listed above must be regarded as typical.

The *control unit* decodes the computer instructions, after which it initiates the required instruction by sending out signals to parts of the computer along the bus system.

The *memory* of the computer (which is a combination of ROM and RAM) stores not only the program but also some of the data. When data need to be read from a location in memory, the control unit sends signals along the address bus to activate the appropriate address, after which the CPU reads data from the address. In the case of RAM, data may either be written (or *loaded*) into any location or may be *read* from any location. The process of reading from and writing into a location in RAM was described in Sec. 5.15.

An input peripheral such as a keyboard generates a logical signal which is transmitted via an *input port* (which is an IC) to the CPU. When the CPU has processed the data, it can transmit new data to an output peripheral such as a VDU via an *output port*. Many systems have ICs which are dedicated solely to operating either as an input port or as an output port; however, many systems have *programmable input/output ports* which, under program control, can operate either as an input port or as an output port or as both (simultaneously) — see also Sec. 10.6.

The reader will appreciate from the above that a *microprocessor* is part of a complete microcomputer system, and the microprocessor needs additional support chips such as memory, I/O ports, etc., before it can function usefully.

Where a microprocessor is used in a general purpose system which can easily be reprogrammed by the user, the system is generally known as a *microcomputer*. Where a microprocessor is used to control a single system such as a numerically controlled machine tool, the electronic system is described as a *dedicated microprocessor-based system*.

8.2   The microcomputer three-bus system

The basis of a microcomputer system is shown in Fig. 8.2. The diagram illustrates the architecture of a simplified microcomputer (see Sec. 8.3 for a description of the CPU) and the three-bus system which controls the computer.

The system needs a *data bus* which contains as many lines in it as there are bits in the word length of the CPU, allowing parallel transmission of data. Most microprocessors have an eight-bit word length, and there are eight lines in the data bus (a range of 16-bit and 32-bit chips are also available).

The *address bus* enables the CPU to address individual locations within the

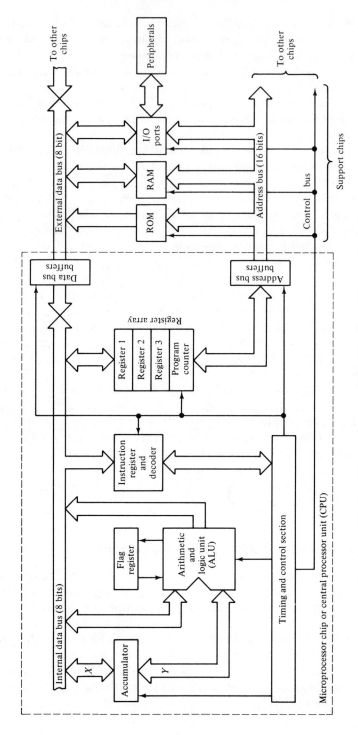

Fig. 8.2   Simplified microprocessor architecture and three-bus system

computer system. The address bus of an eight-bit CPU usually has 16 wires in it, allowing up to $2^{16} = 65\,536_{10}$ locations (or 64K locations) to be addressed. Certain of the address bus lines are used to address, say, individual locations within a memory chip, and other the address lines are used to activate the chip enable pins or chip select pins of memory chips, etc.

The *control bus* contains a number of lines (the number varies between CPU chips, but about 10 to 15 is typical) which not only control the operation of the computer but also synchronize the operation of the chips. An example of the use of two control bus lines, namely the $\overline{\text{READ}}$ and $\overline{\text{WRITE}}$ lines, was described in Sec. 5.15 of the chapter on memories.

8.3 Architecture of a microprocessor chip

The general structure of a microprocessor chip is shown in Fig. 8.2. The *accumulator* is a register which is used for many operations; e.g., when data are loaded into the CPU from an external device such as a memory, a copy of the contents of the specified location is deposited (usually) in the accumulator. Also, when a mathematical or a logical operation is carried out on an operand, a copy of the result is left in the accumulator. Data can be transferred between the accumulator and the internal data bus of the CPU via link X in Fig. 8.2 or between the accumulator and the ALU via link Y. These links have arrows on them pointing in opposite directions, indicating that they are bidirectional links. The accumulator is as 'wide' as the data bus, i.e., it can handle eight bits if the data bus is eight bits 'wide'.

The function of the ALU has been described earlier, and data can be transferred between it and the accumulator or between it and the internal data bus.

The *control unit* comprises the instruction register (which handles eight bits in an eight-bit CPU), the instruction decoder, and the control section. The instruction currently being executed by the CPU is transferred to the instruction register and decoder section, where it is interpreted. Appropriate control signals are generated by the timing and control section of the control unit, and are transmitted either internally to parts of the ALU or externally to the support chips.

An important element of the CPU is the *register array* which contains a number of registers which can be used by the programmer. Figure 8.2 shows three general purpose registers numbered 1, 2, and 3, which may either be 8-bit or 16-bit registers (the length of the registers depends on the design of the CPU) and a *program counter* (PC). The program counter contains the address of the instruction byte currently being executed; since the address bus is 16 bits wide, the PC is a 16-bit register. If the instruction at memory address $19EF_{16}$ is currently being executed, the instruction register contains 0001100111101111_2.

Both the data bus and the address bus have internal buffer amplifiers which enables the CPU to provide a small amount of current to the external circuit. However, in order to provide adequate current to drive support devices, additional external buffers are needed in many systems.

8.4 Microcomputer instruction cycle

An instruction cycle basically has two phases, namely:

1. The *instruction fetch cycle*.
2. The *instruction execution cycle*.

During the fetch cycle, an instruction is fetched from the memory of the computer and, after it has been interpreted by the control unit, the CPU is given the address of the operand to be used. During the execution cycle, the CPU obtains the operand and performs the operation called for by the instruction, e.g., to ADD the operand to the contents of the accumulator.

Depending on the complexity of the operation to be carried out, the instruction may be one-, two-, three-, or four-bytes long (taking up respectively one, two, three, and four consecutive memory locations).

When the control unit has decoded the first byte of the instruction, it decides whether it is a one-, two-, three-, or four-byte instruction. If it is a one-byte instruction, it executes the instruction and automatically increments the contents of the program counter by unity so that the PC 'points' at the next instruction to be fetched. If, however, after decoding the first byte, the control unit discovers it is a two-byte instruction, the PC is incremented and the CPU fetches the second byte before executing the instruction and incrementing the PC once more. Thus the PC is incremented n times during an n-byte instruction. This ensures that, on the completion of each instruction, the PC holds the address of the next instruction to be fetched. Thus for a three-byte instruction commencing at the hex address $ABC2$, the instruction cycle has three phases as follows:

Fetch cycle
Fetch cycle
Execute cycle

On completion of the instruction, the PC stores the address

$$ABC2 + 3 = ABC5_{16} \text{ or } 101010111100 0101_2$$

8.5 Memory map of a microcomputer

The range of addresses used by the CPU and the type of memory or type of device using a range of addresses is shown on the *memory map* of the computer.

The range of addresses allocated to a specific device such as a memory depends on the connections made between the address bus lines and the address lines and chip select lines of the device (see Sec. 8.6). A CPU having 16 address lines can address up to 64K memory locations ($65\,536_{10}$ locations); i.e., it can address any location having an address in the range 0000_{16} to $FFFF_{16}$. A memory map of a typical small microcomputer is shown in Fig. 8.3. As a matter of convenience, the memory map is said to have a *page* structure, with one page of memory storing $\frac{1}{4}$K bytes (or 256_{10} bytes) of data.

The storage capacity of RAM chips depends on their internal architecture; in this book the 'standard' size of RAM chip is taken to be 1K byte. Thus a 1K byte RAM chip occupying memory locations 0000_{16} to $03FF_{16}$ includes pages zero to three of memory. The 1K byte RAM chip occupying locations 0400_{16} to $07FF_{16}$ includes pages four to seven of memory. (*Note*: the decimal notation is used when referring to the page number.)

Pages zero to three are vital to the operation of the microcomputer described in this book, since the CPU needs to use certain RAM locations for temporary storage of data (some of these are shown as 'system RAM' from address $00DF$ to $00FF$ on page zero of the memory map). The remainder of the locations in pages zero to three, i.e., addresses 0000_{16} to $00DE_{16}$, are available to the user and are described as on-board user RAM in Fig. 8.3.

The user can extend the on-board RAM to 4K bytes by connecting three optional 1K byte RAM chips to suitable bus lines, to give addresses ranging from 0400_{16} to $OFFF_{16}$; these are described as 'optional user RAM' in Fig. 8.3. The system in Fig. 8.3 provides for a possible 36K byte 'off-board expansion' of addresses external to the computer, with addresses ranging from 1000_{16} to $9FFF_{16}$.

The computer system also provides for a certain amount of on-computer or 'on-board' input/output facilities. This includes a keyboard for inputting data manually, a number of light-emitting diode displays, a small on-board printer, and serial input/output terminals for retrieval of data from magnetic tapes. Other CPUs also have input/output facilities, allowing connections to be made to teletypes and video display units.

Many computers use a high-level language such as BASIC (Beginners All-purpose Symbolic Instruction Code). In the microcomputer described here, 8K of addresses are allocated to ROM chips storing a *compiler program* which converts the high-level BASIC program into the *machine code instructions* in binary that the computer can understand.

A programming language which is one step above a machine code language is known as an *assembly language*. Each assembly language instruction comprises a combination of alphabetical characters and numerical and other characters; a typical example is LDA $03. A program known as an *assembler*, which is stored in a ROM, is connected into the microcomputer and takes up address locations ranging from $D000_{16}$ to $DFFF_{16}$.

Finally, *a monitor program* is stored in ROM and takes up address locations

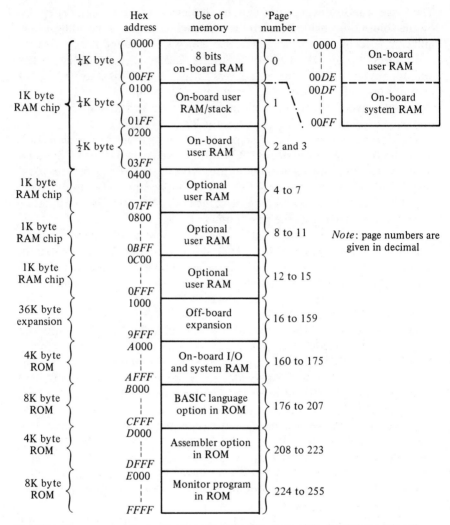

Fig. 8.3 Memory map of a small microcomputer (Courtesy of Rockwell International)

$E000_{16}$ to $FFFF_{16}$. The function of the monitor program is to assist the user in running and developing programs. The minimal features of any monitor program are:

1. To provide control of the keyboard and display.
2. To store the program in successive bytes of memory.
3. To allow the user to examine the contents of memory locations and registers.
4. To allow the user to start his program from a specified location.

5. To allow the user to insert 'breakpoints' in the program for the purpose of testing the program.

Not all addresses on the memory map need to be occupied, and in a basic system it is only necessary to provide some RAM (in our case, the first 1K byte is all that is necessary) and some ROM (in our case, the monitor program is necessary). It is also necessary to use the address dedicated to on-board system I/O and the system RAM (addresses $A000_{16}$ to $AFFF_{16}$, inclusive). The remaining addresses can be left unused in a simple system.

8.6 Address decoding

Every microprocessor has many devices connected to it, and each device must respond when a request is sent to it from the CPU. To ensure that the correct device responds to the request (and that other devices do not respond), each chip has one or more chip select control lines (these lines may be known as chip enable, or as device select, or as device enable lines). At the appropriate time, the CPU sends signals along the address bus and control bus to activate the chip select lines. This process is known as addressing the chip.

One form of arrangement associated with address decoding is shown in Fig. 8.4. Many devices have a number of internal registers and storage elements, and the signals on the least significant address bus lines are used to address the internal sections of the device being accessed. The most significant address bus lines are decoded (frequently by a decoder of the type described in Sec.

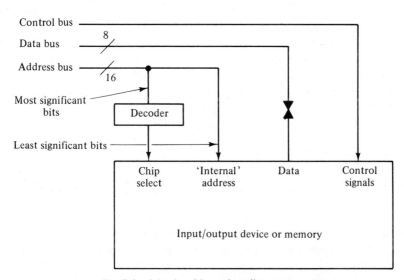

Fig. 8.4   A basic address decoding system

4.19), an output from the decoder being connected to the chip select pin(s) of the device being addressed. In many cases, signals from the control bus are also needed to activate sections of the chip being accessed.

A practical example of address decoding in part of a small microcomputer is shown in Fig. 8.5. The diagram illustrates how five ROM chips, each storing 4K bytes, are addressed in a typical microcomputer (the addresses shown correspond to part of the memory map in Fig. 8.3). The 12 least significant address bus lines (lines A_0 to A_{11}) are needed to address the 4K bytes of data stored in each ROM. (*Note*: $2^{12} = 4096$ or 4K.) These lines are connected to a bank of address buffers inside each ROM chip (see also Sec. 5.14 for a description of a typical 4K byte ROM).

In order to select one of the chips in Fig. 8.5, it is necessary to correctly activate the chip select pins on one of the chips. Each chip has two of these, $\overline{CS1}$ being an 'active low' pin and CS2 being an 'active high' pin. In each case, CS2 is connected to the supply voltage (logic '1') so that it is correctly activated continuously. The $\overline{CS1}$ pin on each chip is connected to one of the outputs from the one-of-eight decoder (or three line-to-eight line decoder) in the figure (see Sec. 4.19 for a description of the decoder). When output $\overline{CSB}$ from the decoder is driven low, the upper ROM (which stores one-half of the BASIC interpreter program) is selected or is enabled; at this point in time, the remaining ROM chips are disabled since they have a logic '1' applied to their $\overline{CS1}$ line.

When one of the other outputs from the decoder is driven low, say $\overline{CSD}$, then another ROM is enabled (in this case it is the ROM containing the ASSEMBLER program) and all other ROMs are disabled. It is left as an exercise for the reader to verify the addresses given in Fig. 8.5 for the five chips relating to the memory map in Fig. 8.3.

When a ROM has been enabled, the address on address lines A_0 to A_{11} specify which location in the ROM is given access to the data bus; the binary word in that location is then transmitted to the CPU.

In the case considered, the remaining three outputs ($\overline{CS8}$, $\overline{CS9}$, and $\overline{CSA}$) from the decoder are used for 'off-board' address expansion, which could either refer to memory addresses or I/O addresses.

8.7 Register structure of a practical microprocessor

Each CPU has a number of general purpose registers together with a number of special purpose registers (see also Sec. 8.3). The number of registers and also the storage capacity of the registers depends to a great extent on the philosophy of the CPU design. In this section of the book we look at two types of register structure of eight-bit CPUs.

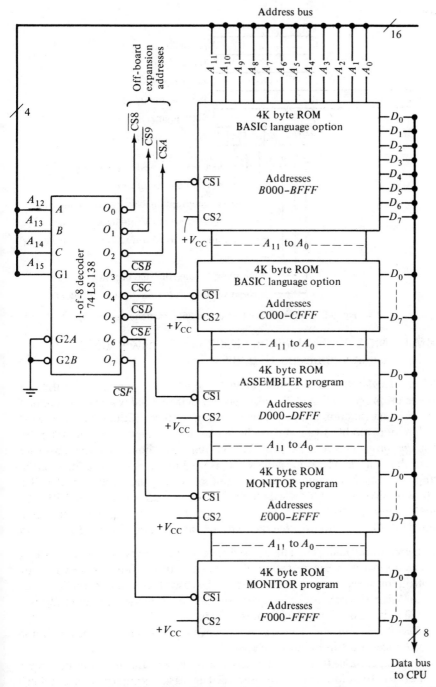

Fig. 8.5   An example of address decoding in a typical microcomputer (Couresty of Rockwell International)

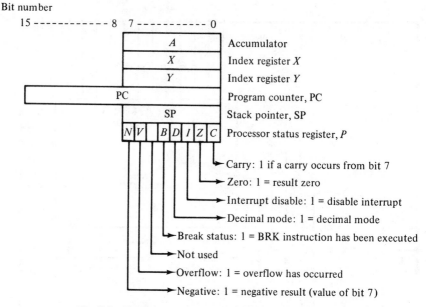

Bit number

15 ----------- 8   7 ----------- 0

Fig. 8.6   Register structure of the 6502 microcomputer

8.7.1   MOS Technology Inc. 6502 and Rockwell 6502 register structure (Fig. 8.6)

The *accumulator*, A, is an eight-bit register which is used in many operations of the microprocessor. The CPU also has two eight-bit *index registers*, X and Y, the primary function of these registers being to store a value which is used to 'index' or to modify a value in another location in the memory of the computer. The *program counter*, PC, is a 16-bit register whose function has been described earlier. The *stack pointer*, SP, is used to 'point' to the address at the 'top' of a 'stack' in memory; the function of this register is described in Sec. 10.18. Unlike many CPUs, which have a 16-bit stack pointer, the SP in the 6502 is an eight-bit register. The *processor status register*, P, stores six status bits N, V, B, D, Z, and C, together with an interrupt control bit I as follows:

1. *Carry status flag*, C.   This is used to 'save' the 'carry' or 'borrow' which occurs in arithmetic operations. In the case of an addition, it is the carry-out from bit seven of the accumulator. In the case of subtraction, the flag is set to '1' if no borrow is needed and is set to '0' if a borrow is required (this is a different usage from that of most CPUs).
2. *Zero status flag*, Z.   This is set to '1' when an arithmetic or logic operation produces a result of zero.
3. *Interrupt disable flag*, I.   When this flag is set to '1', the maskable interrupts (see Sec. 10.21 for details) are disabled. The maskable interrupts are enabled when $I = 0$.

4. *Decimal mode status flag, D.* When this flag is set $(D=1)$, the CPU performs a BCD (decimal) addition when an add-with-carry instruction is executed and a BCD (decimal) subtraction when a subtract-with-carry instruction is executed.

5. *Break status flag, B.* When a BRK instruction is executed (which is a software 'interrupt'), the *B*-flag is set $(B=1)$.

6. *Overflow flag, V.* This flag is set $(V=1)$ if an overflow occurs during signed arithmetic operations (see also Sec. 7.11). This flag is set by the EXCLUSIVE-OR function of the carry-out of bit six and the carry-out of bit seven of the accumulator.

7. *Negative flag, N.* The *N*-flag is set $(N=1)$ if bit seven of the accumulator is logic '1' after an arithmetic or logical operation (in many microprocessors this is known as the *sign* flag).

The operation of several of the status flags is illustrated in the following addition sequence:

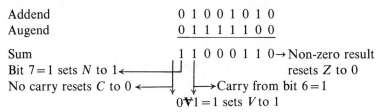

| Addend | 0 1 0 0 1 0 1 0 |
| Augend | 0 1 1 1 1 1 0 0 |

Sum   1 1 0 0 0 1 1 0 → Non-zero result
Bit 7 = 1 sets *N* to 1 ←   resets *Z* to 0
No carry resets *C* to 0 ←   → Carry from bit 6 = 1
                          0 ⊻ 1 = 1 sets *V* to 1

8.7.2 Intel 8080A and 8085 register structure (Fig. 8.7)

The 8080 family of CPUs has an eight-bit accumulator, A, and six eight-bit secondary registers, B, C, D, E, H, and L. Registers A, B, C, D, and E are intended to be used independently, but for special purposes they can be regarded as 16-bit register pairs as follows:

1. Register A and the *flag register* (FR)* form a register pair known as the *processor status word* (PSW).

2. Registers B and C can be used as a register pair.

3. Registers D and E can form a register pair.

The register pair HL is intended to be used as a single 16-bit register to store a 16-bit address; i.e., register pair HL forms a 'pointer' register which points at a location M in memory.

The stack pointer, SP, is a 16-bit register which allows a 'stack' to be located at any point in the memory. The program counter, PC, is a dedicated 16-bit register whose function has already been described. The flag register, FR,

---

* The FR in the 8080A/8085 family is generally similar to the processor status register, P, in the 6502.

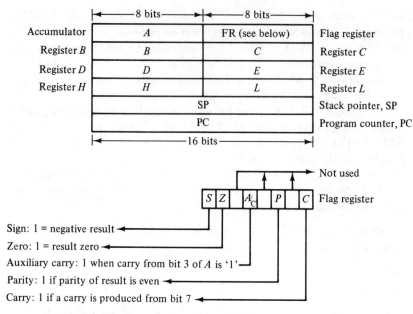

Fig. 8.7   Register structure of the 8080A and the 8085 CPUs

stores five status bits, S, Z, A_C, P, and C, as follows:

1. *Carry status flag, C.*   This flag 'saves' the 'carry' or 'borrow' produced in an arithmetic operation.
2. *Parity status flag, P.*   This flag is set ($P = 1$) when an arithmetic or logical operation results in an even number of '1' bits in the accumulator.
3. *Auxiliary carry flag, A_C.*   This flag is set ($A_C = 1$) when the carry from bit three of the accumulator to bit four is '1'.
4. *Zero flag, Z.*   This flag is set ($Z = 1$) when any arithmetic or logical operation has zero result.
5. *Sign flag, S.*   This flag is set ($S = 1$) if bit seven of the accumulator is '1' (similar to flag N in the 6502).

The operation of several of the status flags is illustrated in the following addition sequence:

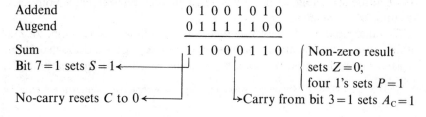

8.8   Types of instruction and programming language

A microprocessor can only accept and execute instructions in a binary format. If the instruction is written in binary, it is said to be in *machine code*. For example, a 6502 CPU interprets the binary word 10100000 (or $A0_{16}$) as 'load register Y' with data; the format of the instruction also tells the CPU where the data are to be found. Many microprocessors have a routine in the monitor program called a *hexadecimal loader*, which allows the operator to present the instruction to the computer in hexadecimal rather than in pure binary; the hexadecimal loader then converts the hex instruction into its pure binary version. Once the program has been produced in a form which is capable of being executed directly by the microcomputer, it is known as an *object program*.

Another form of low-level language is an *assembly lanugage*. In this language, each machine code instruction is represented by a combination of alphabetical and numerical characters (and, in some cases, some other characters) which are relatively easy to remember. That is, an assembly language instruction is in the form of a mnemonic. The hexadecimal version, $A0_{16}$, of the instruction mentioned above is equivalent to the assembly language instruction LDY # , where LDY means 'LoaD index register Y' and the symbol # indicates that the data to be loaded into register Y is to be found in the next byte in the program.

The assembly language program must be translated into the machine code of the microcomputer before it can be executed. One method of doing this is by writing down each assembly language instruction in its binary (or hex) form. This is known as *hand assembly*. An alternative method is to use an *assembler program* which is stored in ROM (see also Figs 8.3 and 8.5); the assembler accepts the assembly language program and converts it into the object code. The relationship between the *source program* (which is a program written by the programmer in a language other than machine code) and the object program is shown in Fig. 8.8.

In general, an assembly language can only be used on one type of CPU* and is not suitable for other types of CPU. Thus an assembly language program written for a 6502 CPU-based system cannot be directly used with an 8080- or 8085-based system.

The 'length' of a microcomputer instruction has been mentioned earlier (see Sec. 8.4), where it was stated that it may be either one, two, three, or four bytes. The first byte of the instruction is the *operation code* (usually abbreviated to *opcode*) which specifies the operation to be performed. For example, the 6502 opcode $A0_{16}$ means 'load index register Y with the next byte of data in the program', which is a two-byte instruction. The instruction with the opcode

---

* A *cross-assembler program* on a large computer enables microprocessor programs to be assembled on a large computer.

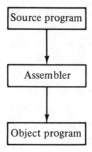

Fig. 8.8   The function of an assembler

AC_{16} means 'load index register Y with the data stored at the address specified in the next two bytes of the program', which is a three-byte instruction. Thus opcodes $A0$ and AC have the same result, i.e., index register Y is loaded with data, but each achieves the object in a different way.

8.9   Typical CPU connections

The external connections made to the 40-pin DIP encapsulation used by micrprocessors are many and varied (some 16-bit CPUs are housed in a 64-pin DIP). The connections shown in Fig. 8.9 for the 6502 and 8085 CPUs respectively are typical. Depending on the design philosophy, the 40 connecting pins on the chip may either be in excess of the system requirements (pins 5, 35, and 36 on the 6502 CPU are not connected to any chip circuitry) or there may not be enough connecting pins. In the latter case, some of the pins are multiplexed and have different uses at different points in time (in the 8085 chip, pins 12 to 19, inclusive, are multiplexed).

All 16 address bus lines are available on the 6502 chip, as are the eight data bus lines. In the 8085 chip, the data bus is multiplexed with the low-order address bus lines. Thus connection AD_0 (pin 12) acts as address bus line A_0 at one moment and data bus line D_0 at some other time; the signals on the control bus tell the external circuit which function AD_0 performs at any given time.

Both chips in Fig. 8.9 need a single 5-V power supply. The 6502 is used with an externally generated clock signal; the 8085 has its own internal clock generator which uses an external crystal connected between terminals X_1 and X_2 (pins 1 and 2) to provide an accurate timing mechanism.

Both CPUs in Fig. 8.9 have a $\overline{\text{RESET}}$ input terminal (pin 40 on the 6502 and pin 36 on the 8085); when a logic '0' is applied to this terminal, the system is 'reset' to its initial operating condition. This signal is frequently obtained from a manually operated switch which allows the operator to reset the operation of the microcomputer at any instant of time. When the system is reset, the program counter has an initial address forced into it, and this causes the CPU

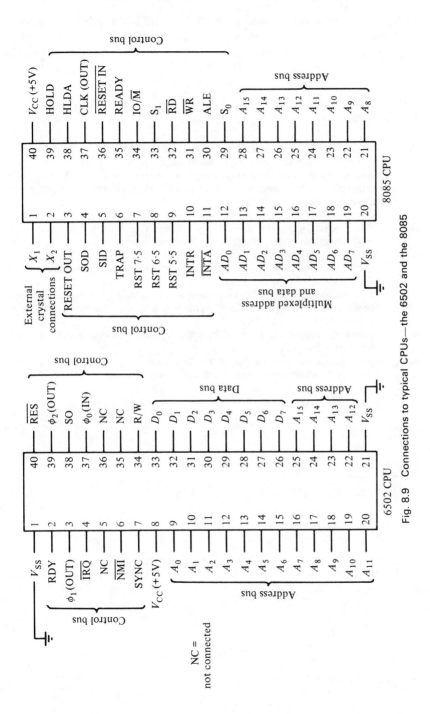

Fig. 8.9 Connections to typical CPUs—the 6502 and the 8085

to begin operating instructions from a basic 'start' address. In the case of the 8085 the program counter contents are reset to 0000_{16} and in the 6502 the program counter has the contents of locations $FFFC_{16}$ and $FFFD_{16}$ loaded into it.

Problems

8.1 What is meant by (a) hardware, (b) software, (c) firmware? Describe the relationship between them in a microprocessor-based system.

8.2 Describe the need for (a) read-only memory, (b) random-access memory, (c) the arithmetic and logic unit, (d) the control unit, and (e) the program counter in a microprocessor-based system.

8.3 Describe the microcomputer instruction cycle and outline its component parts.

8.4 What advantages are gained by using a standard bus system for microprocessor-based systems? What possible disadvantages can you suggest?

8.5 What is the purpose of the memory map of a microcomputer? Draw a memory map for an eight-bit microcomputer and explain how you have dedicated each area on the map.

8.6 Describe the need for address decoding in a microcomputer and explain, with the aid of a block diagram of the hardware, how the areas of the memory map in problem 8.5 have been decoded.

8.7 Discuss the register structure of three types of microprocessor and explain the philosophy behind each structure.

8.8 Compare the relative merits of machine code programming and assembly language programming. Write down and describe an instruction in each of the two forms of low-level language.

9. Instruction classification, addressing modes, and an instruction set

9.1 Classification of instructions

There are many ways in which instructions can be classified, and the instructions described in this chapter are divided into four categories as follows:

1. Data manipulation instructions (see also Sec. 9.15).
2. Data transfer instructions (see also Sec. 9.16).
3. Program manipulation instructions (see also Sec. 9.17).
4. Status management instructions (see also Sec. 9.18).

Data manipulation instructions include arithmetic and logic instructions together with increment instructions and also shift and rotate instructions.

Instructions in the **data transfer** group move data from one part of the microcomputer to another and include load and store instructions, register transfer instructions, and stack instructions.

Program manipulation instructions include instructions relating to the transfer of control from one part of the program to another and include jump and branch instructions together with subroutine call and return instructions.

Instructions in the **status management** group affect the state of the CPU, and include status register control instructions, maskable interrupt instructions, together with the break (BRK) instruction and the no-operation (NOP) instruction.

Each instruction in the *instruction set* may have several methods of implementation. For example, in the 6502 the assembly language instruction ADC (ADd memory, with Carry, to the contents of the accumulator) has, depending on the *addressing mode* (see Sec. 9.2), any one of eight methods of use, each method having its own opcode (these are 61, 65, 69, 6D, 71, 75, 79, and 7D respectively). The instruction set summary of the 6502 CPU is given in Appendix A.

9.2   Addressing modes

A list of the addressing modes used by a microprocessor is an indication of the versatility of the CPU in accessing data in a storage location. Addressing modes are many and varied and the following list is typical. The reader should note that an addressing mode may be implemented differently in different CPUs, and is advised to consult the manufacturers' technical literature for details. Moreover, not all addressing modes are available on every CPU; some CPUs have as few as four addressing modes while others have as many as 13 or more.

1. Absolute addressing (Sec. 9.3)
2. Page zero addressing (Sec. 9.4)
3. Immediate addressing (Sec. 9.5)
4. Implied addressing or inherent addressing (Sec. 9.6)
5. Accumulator addressing (Sec. 9.7)
6. Relative addressing (Sec. 9.8)
7. Indexed addressing (Sec. 9.9)
8. Indirect addressing (Sec. 9.10)
9. Register addressing (Sec. 9.11)
10. Register indirect addressing (Sec. 9.12)

Programmers using 6502-based and 6800-based systems can use any of methods 1 to 8, inclusive, although not all addressing modes are available for every instruction. Systems using 8080 or 8085 CPUs can use methods 1, 3, 4, 5, 9, and 10, while Z80 systems can use all methods except method 8.

9.3   Absolute addressing or direct addressing

In this form of addressing, the instruction completely specifies the location of the operand. Each instruction of this type is a three-byte instruction, the opcode (the first byte) specifies the operation to be carried out, while the second and third bytes specify the 16-bit address where the operand is to be found.

The execution of the 6502 CPU ADC instruction (ADd memory, with Carry, to the contents of the accumulator) using absolute addressing is shown in Fig. 9.1. The opcode ($6D$) is found in address $aaaa$ (each a representing a hexadecimal character). The opcode is transferred to the instruction register (IR), and the control unit of the CPU interprets it as a three-byte instruction; the contents of the program counter (PC) are therefore incremented by three during the course of the instruction. The second byte of the instruction in location $aaaa + 1$ contains the low byte, ll, of the address at which the data are located, and the third byte (at address $aaaa + 2$) contains the high byte hh of the required address.* The data are therefore stored at address $hhll$.

---

* It is the usual practice for the low byte of an address to be given before the high byte.

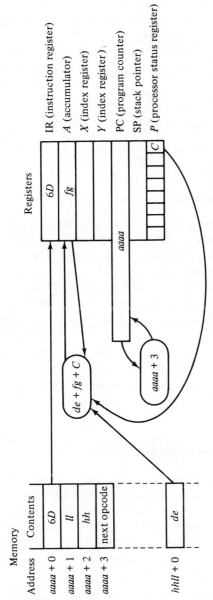

Fig. 9.1   Execution of the 6502 CPU ADC instruction using absolute or direct addressing

When the CPU has fetched all three bytes, the instruction is executed. The net result is that the contents, fg, of the accumulator are added to the contents, de, of location $hhll$ together with the carry bit, C, of the processor status register P. The result of this addition is left in the accumulator.

If $ll = 50$, $hh = 02$, $de = 1A$, $fg = 2C$, $C = 1$, then after the instruction the contents of location $hhll = 0250$ (which is $de = 1A$) is added not only to the contents of the accumulator but also to the contents of the carry flag as follows:

Contents of location 0250	$= 1A$
Original contents of the accumulator	$= 2C$
Content of the carry flag	$= 1$
Result (left in the accumulator)	$= 47$

9.4 Page zero addressing

This technique is generally the same as for absolute addressing with the exception that, since the operand is to be found in *page zero* of the memory, it is not necessary to specify the high byte of the address (which is the hex value 00).

The 6502 CPU page zero ADC instruction (opcode 65) is a two-byte instruction (remember, the high byte of the operand address is not specified in this addressing mode), so that Fig. 9.1 is modified as follows. Address $aaaa$ contains the opcode 65 and address $aaaa + 1$ contains the address of the operand on page zero. This instruction therefore adds the contents of location $00ll$ to the contents of the accumulator and also to the content of the carry flag, the result being left in the accumulator. Since this is a two-byte instruction, the contents of the program counter is therefore incremented by two during the instruction.

9.5 Immediate addressing

In this addressing mode, the operand is contained in the second byte of the instruction. Consider the execution of the 6502 CPU ADC instruction (opcode 69) in its immediate mode (see Fig. 9.2). The data, de, stored in address $aaaa + 1$ is added with the carry, C, to the contents of the accumulator, the result being left in the accumulator. The content of the PC is incremented by two.

9.6 Implied addressing or inherent addressing

Implied addressing mode instructions are one-byte instructions and require no operand; the instruction is executed with no other information than that given in the opcode. An example of this addressing mode is the 6502 CLC

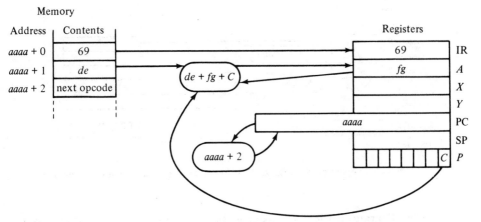

Fig. 9.2 Execution of the 6502 CPU ADC instruction using immediate addressing

instruction (CLear and Carry status flag) — opcode 18. The destination address — the carry flag of the status register — is implied by the instruction, and after its execution the carry flag is cleared or is reset to zero.

9.7 Accumulator addressing

This is another form of implied addressing, but in this case the instruction operates only on the accumulator. In the 6502 CPU, the one-byte accumulator addressing mode instructions are the ASL instruction (Arithmetic Shift Left the contents of the accumulator — see also Sec. 9.15), the LSR instruction (Logical Shift Right), the ROL instruction (ROtate Left through the carry flag the contents of the accumulator), and the ROR instruction (ROtate Right through the carry flag the contents of the accumulator).

9.8 Relative addressing

In the 6502 CPU, branch instructions (also known as conditional jump instructions) use relative addressing. An instruction of this kind causes control of the program to be transferred to a point in the program which is *offset* or is *displaced* by a given amount from the address stored in the program counter. Relative addressing allows programs to be easily relocated in the event that the complete program has to be moved or relocated in the memory; such programs are said to be *relocatable*. Relative addressing instructions are two-byte instructions, the second byte being the offset or displacement mentioned above (this is shown as *dd*, corresponding to two hex characters, in Fig. 9.3).

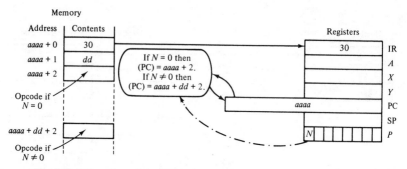

Fig. 9.3 Execution of the 6502 CPU BMI instruction using relative addressing

The diagram in Fig. 9.3 illustrates the execution of the 6502 CPU BMI instruction (Branch on MInus result) — opcode 30. When the opcode is transferred to the instruction register of the CPU, the control unit interrogates the state of the Negative (N) flag, and if $N = 0$ (result *not* minus) then the contents of the PC are incremented by two and the next opcode is fetched from address $aaaa + 2$. If $N = 1$ (result minus), then the contents of the PC are incremented by $2 + dd$, where dd is a signed eight-bit displacement expressed as two hex characters. If dd has a value in the range 00_{16} to $7F_{16}$, the displacement is positive. If $N = 1$, the next opcode is fetched from location $aaaa + 2 + dd$.

Since an eight-bit 2's complement value is limited to the range -128_{10} to $+127_{10}$, the maximum forward (positive) branch is to address $aaaa + 129_{10}$. The maximum backward (negative) branch is to address $aaaa - 126_{10}$.

The displacement associated with a relative addressing instruction can be calculated as follows. If the *transfer address* (TA) is the address to which program control must be transferred, the *base address* (BA) is the address of the location which stores the displacement for the branch instruction, i.e., it is the address of the second byte of the branch instruction, and the *effective address* (EA) is given by

$$\text{Effective address (EA)} = \text{transfer address (TA)} - 1$$

then the displacement in a relative addressing instruction is calculated as follows:

$$
\begin{aligned}
\text{Displacement} &= \text{effective address} - \text{base address} \\
&= \text{transfer address} - \text{base address} - 1 \\
&= \text{TA} - \text{BA} - 1
\end{aligned}
$$

Consider the following program (see also Table 10.7 in Chapter 10):

Memory address (hex)	Byte 1	Byte 2	Label	Instruction mnemonic
0205	46	30_{16}	NXMUL	LSR 30_{16}
0207	0E	dd_1		BCC ROTAT
020C	6A		ROTAT	ROR A
0210	D0	dd_2		BNE NXMUL

The instruction in location 0207 calls for a 'branch' to be made to the address of the 'label' ROTAT if the carry flag is 'cleared', i.e., a positive displacement relative to the contents of the program counter at that point. The instruction in location 0210 calls for a branch to be made to the address of the label NXMUL if the contents of the accumulator are not equal to zero, i.e., a negative displacement relative to the contents of the program counter at that point. The displacements are calculated as follows.

9.8.1 Displacement dd_1

Transfer address $TA = 020C_{16}$, base address $BA = 0208_{16}$. Then

$$TA - BA = 020C - 0208 = 0004_{16}$$

Hence

$$\text{Displacement, } dd_1 = TA - BA - 1 = 0004 - 0001 = 0003_{16}$$

However, since the displacement is represented by two hex characters in the program, then

$$\text{Displacement, } dd_1 = 03_{16}$$

The reader will note that this is a positive displacement of 03_{16}.

9.8.2 Displacement dd_2

Transfer address $TA = 0205_{16}$, base address $BA = 0211_{16}$. Since the base address is greater than the transfer address, the displacement dd_2 will be negative. It is therefore necessary to determine the 16's complement of the base address as follows:

$$\text{16's complement of } BA = FDEF_{16}$$

and

$$TA - BA = TA + \text{16's complement of } BA$$
$$= 0205 + FDEF = FFF4_{16}$$

Hence

$$Displacement,\ dd_2 = TA - BA - 1 = FFF4 - 1 = FFF4 + FFFF$$
$$= 00F3_{16}$$

Since the displacement is represented by the two least significant hex characters, then

$$Displacement,\ dd_2 = F3_{16}$$

This is equivalent to a decimal displacement of -13_{10}. The reader will find the displacement values given above in the multiplication program in Table 10.7 of Chapter 10.

9.9   Indexed addressing

In indexed addressing the 6502 CPU takes one of two forms, namely absolute indexed addressing (three-byte instructions) and page zero indexed addressing (two-byte instructions). Either the X-index register or the Y-index register may be involved.

The execution of the ADC instruction using *absolute indexed addressing with the X-register* (opcode 7D) is shown in Fig. 9.4. The opcode is stored in

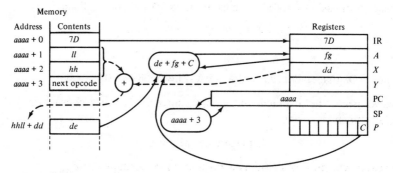

Fig. 9.4   Execution of the ADC instruction using absolute indexed addressing, indexed with the X register

address *aaaa*, and the high and low bytes of the base address are stored in the second and third bytes of the instruction. Since this is a three-byte instruction, the contents of the PC are incremented by three. Since the base address of the data to be accessed is indexed by the contents of the X-register (the latter is a one-byte signed binary number giving either a positive or negative displacement, dd), the data to be accessed are located at address $hhll + dd$. On completion of the instruction, the accumulator stores the sum of $de + fg + C$.

The ADC absolute addressed indexed instruction can also be executed using the Y-register—opcode 79—to store the displacement. The net result is the same, that is, the accumulator stores the result of the sum $de + fg + C$.

The ADC instruction can also be executed using a two-byte *zero page indexed instruction*, indexed with the *X-register*. The second byte of the instruction stores the location, *ll*, on page zero; the data to be accessed, *de*, is found at address $00ll + dd$. Once again, on completion of the instruction, the sum of $de + fg + C$ is left in the accumulator.

9.10 Indirect addressing

In the 6502 CPU, indirect addressing is implemented in one of three ways, namely absolute indirect addressing (or true indirect addressing), indexed indirect addressing (or pre-indexed indirect addressing), and indirect indexed addressing (or post-indexed indirect addressing). In indirect addressing modes, the address of the location where the data are stored, rather than the data themselves, is in the memory location specified by the instruction.

9.10.1 Absolute indirect addressing

The opcode (6C) of the JMP (JuMP to a new location) in the absolute indexed mode is stored in address $aaaa + 0$ (see Fig. 9.5); the second and third bytes of

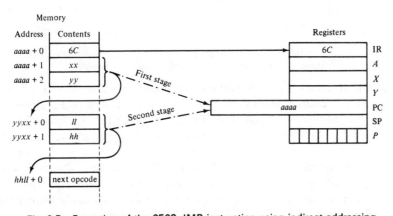

Fig. 9.5 Execution of the 6502 JMP instruction using indirect addressing

the instruction contain the low byte and high byte respectively of the address at which the low byte of the effective address of the data is stored. Thus the content of address *yyxx* is the low byte (*ll*) of the effective address where the data can be found. The high byte (*hh*) of the effective address of the data is stored in location $yyxx + 1$. Consequently, the next opcode is fetched from address $hhll + 0$.

9.10.2   Indexed indirect addressing or pre-indexed indirect addressing

In the 6502 CPU, this mode of addressing is used to access a memory location on page zero, i.e., a location in the first 256 bytes of memory where the indirect address is to be found. Moreover, *this mode of operation only uses index register X.*

The execution of the two-byte ADC instruction using indexed indirect addressing is shown in Fig. 9.6. The opcode (61) of the instruction is stored in

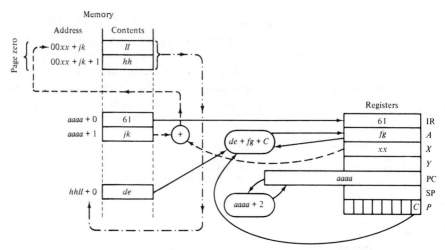

Fig. 9.6   Execution of the 6502 ADC instruction using indexed indirect addressing or pre-indexed indirect addressing using the X-index register

memory location *aaaa* + 0. The content of the second byte of the instruction is added to the content of index register X to give the low byte of the address on page zero of memory (i.e., address $00xx + jk$) at which the low byte (ll) of the effective address is found. The reader should note that any carry formed by the addition $xx + jk$ is discarded. The next byte on page zero (i.e., address $00xx + jk + 1$) stores the high byte (hh) of the effective address. The data, de, in the effective address ($hhll + 0$) are added not only to the contents, fg, of the accumulator but also to the bit stored in the carry flag, the result being left in the accumulator.

9.10.3   Indirect indexed addressing or post-indexed indirect addressing

The second byte of this range of two-byte instructions contains the low byte of the address at which the base address of the required data is to be found. In the 6502 CPU, this is a two-byte instruction *which used the contents of the Y*

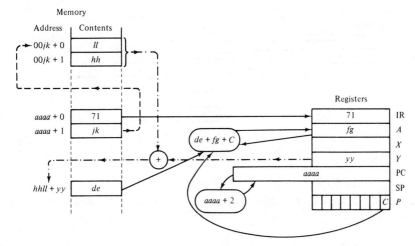

Fig. 9.7   Execution of the 6502 ADC instruction using indirect indexed addressing or post-indexed addressing using the Y-index register

register to index the base address, which is stored in page zero of the memory.

Figure 9.7 illustrates the execution of the indirect indexed ADC instruction. The instruction opcode (71) is stored in location *aaaa* + 0, and the second byte of the instruction contains the low byte of the address in page zero of memory at the low byte (*ll*) of the base address where the data are stored. Location 00*xx* + *jk* + 1 stores the high byte of the base address. The content, *yy*, of index register *Y* is added to the base address to give address *hhll* + *yy* where the data, *de*, are stored. On completion of the instruction the accumulator stores the sum *de* + *fg* + *C*.

9.11   Register addressing

This type of addressing is used in the 8080/8085/Z80 family, and in an instruction of this type the operand is contained in one of the general purpose registers.

The execution of the ADC *D* instruction (ADd register contents, with Carry, using register *D*) — opcode 8*A* — is shown in Fig. 9.8. This is a one-byte instruction and during the execution of the instruction the content of the program counter is incremented by unity. This instruction causes the byte of data, *fg*, in the accumulator to be added not only to the byte, *jk*, in register *D* but also to the bit stored in the carry flag, *C*, of the flag register. The result is left in the accumulator.

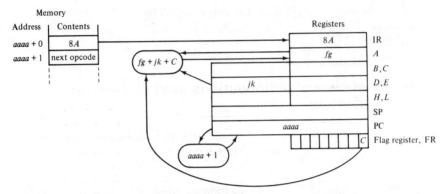

Fig. 9.8   Execution of the 8080/8085/Z80 family ADC *D* instruction using register addressing

9.12   Register indirect addressing

This addressing mode is also used by the 8080/8085/Z80 family. The instruction specifies a register pair (i.e., pair *BC*, or pair *DE*, or pair *HL*) which contains the 16-bit address where the data are located (the high-order byte of the address is stored in the first register of the pair, i.e., registers *B*, *D*, or *H*, and the low-order byte of the address is stored in the second register of the pair, i.e., registers *C*, *E*, or *L*).

The execution of the ADC *M* instruction (ADd with Carry the contents of the Memory location whose address is given by the contents of the register pair *HL*) is illustrated in Fig. 9.9. This one-byte instruction causes the contents of the program counter to be incremented by unity. The net result of this instruction is that the contents, *fg*, of the accumulator are added not only to the contents of the memory location, *hhll*, specified by the 16-bit value in register

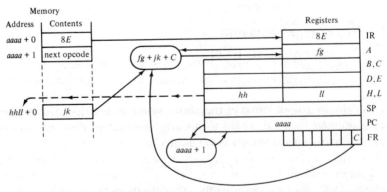

Fig. 9.9   Execution of the 8080/8085/Z80 family ADC *M* instruction using register indirect addressing

pair *HL* but also to the bit in the carry flag. The result is stored in the accumulator.

9.13 Symbols and abbreviations used to describe instructions

The following symbols are used to describe the instructions used in the remainder of this chapter and also in Chapter 10.

A	accumulator
b_n	the *n*th bit of a memory location or register (the 'first' bit is bit zero and the final bit of an eight-bit location is bit seven)
B	break command flag
C	the bit stored in the carry flag
D	the bit stored in the decimal mode flag
I	the bit stored in the interrupt disable flag
M	contents of a memory location
M_n	*n*th bit of a memory location
N	bit stored in the negative status flag
P	contents of the processor status register
PC	contents of the program counter
SP	contents of the stack pointer register
V	bit stored in the overflow flag
X	contents of the *X* register
Y	contents of the *Y* register
Z	bit stored in the zero status flag
( )	'the contents of' a memory location or register
→or←	'is transferred to'
↑	'pull' from the stack
↓	'push' onto the stack
∧	logical AND
∨	logical OR
∀	logical EXCLUSIVE-OR
+	addition
−	subtraction

To illustrate the use of some of the above symbols, consider the symbolic representation of the ADC (ADd with Carry) instruction described in some earlier examples. This is shown symbolically as

$$(A)+(M)+(C)\rightarrow A,C$$

This is interpreted as 'the sum of the contents of the accumulator, *A*, and memory location, *M*, and the carry flag, *C*, is stored in the accumulator, *A*; the contents of the carry flag, C, may also be changed by the result'. Alternatively, the instruction may be represented in the form

$$C,A \leftarrow (A) + (M) + (C)$$

The symbolic representation of the instruction is unchanged by the addressing mode used, since the latter does not alter the function carried out by the instruction, i.e., add with carry.

9.14   Assembly language instructions

It has already been shown that an instruction may have many methods of implementation. The machine code and assembly language instruction representations are designed to incorporate some information about the addressing mode used. For example, in the 6502 assembly language, all immediate addressing mode operands are prefixed by a # symbol, which identifies them from other types. The type of operand may also be indicated by an additional symbol as follows:

$$\begin{array}{rl} \$ & \text{hexadecimal operand} \\ @ & \text{octal operand} \\ \% & \text{binary operand} \\ \text{none} & \text{decimal operand} \end{array}$$

Thus the instructions LDA # $52, LDA # @122, LDA # %01010010, LDA # 82 are identical, and result in the binary value 01010010 being loaded into the accumulator 'immediate', i.e., from the second byte of the instruction. The symbols listed above are used in the remainder of the book, and the expression $52 should be read as 'the hexadecimal value 52'.

9.15   Data manipulation instructions

These instructions result in data being modified and include:

1. Arithmetic instructions.
2. Logical instructions.
3. Modify, shift, and rotate instructions.
4. Compare and bit test instructions.

9.15.1   Arithmetic instructions

In the 6502 these are limited to the following two instructions:

ADC: ADd memory contents to accumulator with Carry
$$(A)+(M)+(C)\rightarrow A; \; N, \; V, \; Z, \; C$$
Example: ADC # $B2
SBC: SuBtraCt memory contents from accumulator with borrow
$$(A)-(M)-(\bar{C})\rightarrow A; \; N, \; V, \; Z, \; C$$
Example: SBC # $B2

The notation adopted above gives the mnemonic for the instruction together with an explanation of the mnemonic. The operation carried out is given in the second line of the description, together with a list of the flags affected. Thus the ADC instruction adds together the contents of the accumulator (A) to the contents (M) of the specified memory and the contents (C) of the carry flag. The result is stored in the accumulator, and the negative flag (N), overflow flag (V), zero flag (Z), and the carry flag (C) may be affected.

9.15.2 Logical instructions

These instructions perform a logical function between the contents of a memory location and the accumulator, leaving the result in the accumulator:

AND: AND memory contents with accumulator
$$(A)\wedge(M)\rightarrow A; \; N, \; Z$$
Example: AND # $AA
ORA: OR memory contents with accumulator
$$(A)\vee(M)\rightarrow A; \; N, \; Z$$
Example: ORA # $AA
EOR: EXCLUSIVE-OR memory contents with accumulator
$$(A)\forall(M)\rightarrow A; \; N, \; Z$$
Example: EOR # $OF

Logical functions are carried out on a bit-by-bit basis throughout the two binary words involved. For example, in the case of the AND instruction, b_0 of the memory is ANDed with b_0 of the accumulator, b_1 of memory is ANDed with b_1 of the accumulator, etc. If the accumulator contains $3D, then the execution of an AND = $AA instruction results in the following:

Initial value in the accumulator = 00111101
$AA = 10101010

Result in the accumulator = 00101000 $\rightarrow Z$ flag = 0
N flag = 0 ⟵────────┘

With reference to the EXCLUSIVE-OR function, the reader will recall that when a bit is EXCLUSIVE-ORed with logic '0' it is unchanged and when EXCLUSIVE-ORed with a logic '1' it is inverted (i.e., a '1' can be regarded as an invert operation). If the accumulator contains $3D, then the execution of an EOR = $OF instruction results in the following:

Initial value in the accumulator $= 00111101$

$\$OF = \underline{00001111}$

Result in the accumulator $= 0011\underline{0010} \rightarrow Z$ flag $= 0$

N flag $= 0 \longleftarrow\hspace{2cm}\rfloor$

Inverted bits in the result

9.15.3 Modify, shift, and rotate instructions

Decrement and increment instructions respectively decrease and increase by unity the contents of either a memory or a register. The execution of the shift (ASL and LSR) and rotate (ROL and ROR) instructions are illustrated in Fig. 9.10.

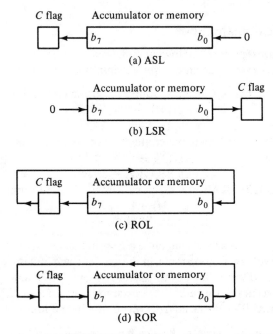

Fig. 9.10 Execution of the 6502 CPU accumulator addressing instructions: (a) ASL, (b) LSR, (c) ROL, (d) ROR

DEC: DECrement memory contents by unity

$(M) - 1 \rightarrow M$; N, Z

Example: DEC $010A

INC: INCrement memory contents by unity

$(M) + 1 \rightarrow M$; N, Z

Example: INC $010A

DEX: DEcrement X register by unity
$(X)-1 \rightarrow X$; N, Z
Example: DEX

INX: INcrement X register by unity
$(X)+1 \rightarrow X$; N, Z
Example: INX

DEY: DEcrement Y register by unity
$(Y)-1 \rightarrow Y$; N, Z
Example: DEY

INY: INcrement Y register by unity
$(Y)+1 \rightarrow Y$; N, Z
Example: INY

ASL: Arithmetic Shift Left (accumulator) or (memory) one bit
$C \leftarrow b_7$; $b_{n+1} \leftarrow b_n$; $b_0 \leftarrow 0$; N, Z, C
Example: ASL A

LSR: Logical Shift Right (accumulator) or (memory)
$0 \rightarrow b_7$; $b_{n+1} \rightarrow b_n$; $b_0 \rightarrow C$; $N=0$, Z, C
Example: LSR \$07AF

ROL: ROtate (accumulator) or (memory) Left through carry one bit
$C \leftarrow b_7$; $b_{n+1} \leftarrow b_n$; $b_0 \leftarrow C$; N, Z, C
Example: ROL A

ROR: ROtate (accumulator) or (memory) Right through carry one bit
$C \rightarrow b_7$; $b_{n+1} \rightarrow b_n$; $b_0 \rightarrow C$; N, Z, C
Example: ROR \$12AF,X

9.15.4 Compare and bit test instructions

Compare instructions subtract the contents of a memory location either from the contents of the accumulator (CMP instruction) or from a register (CPX and CPY instructions). The result of the subtraction is discarded, and the instruction does not alter the contents of either the memory location or of the accumulator or the register. However, the result of the subtraction may alter the contents of the N, Z, and C flags.

The bit test instruction (BIT) logically ANDs the contents of the accumulator with those of a selected memory location, the result of the ANDing operation being discarded. However, the contents of the N, V, and Z flags may be altered as follows: bit seven of the memory is copied into the N flag, bit six of the memory is copied into the V flag, and the Z flag is set to '1' if $(A) \wedge (M) = 0$, otherwise $Z = 0$.

CMP: CoMPare memory and accumulator
$(A)-(M)$; N, Z, C

CPX: ComPare memory and index register X
$(X)-(M)$; N, Z, C
CPY: ComPare memory and index register Y
$(Y)-(M)$; N, Z, C
BIT: test BITs in memory with accumulator
$(A)\wedge(M)$; $N = M_7$, $V = M_6$, $Z = \overline{A \wedge M}$

9.16 Data transfer instructions

These instructions result in data being transferred from one point in the computer to another and include:

1. Load, store, and register transfer instructions.
2. Stack instructions.

9.16.1 Load, store and register transfer instructions

The load instructions enable data to be loaded either into the accumulator or into a register from a memory location; the store instructions enable data to be stored in a memory location either from the accumulator or from a register. Register transfer instructions enable data to be transferred between the accumulator and one of the two index registers.

LDA: LoaD the Accumulator from memory
$(M) \rightarrow A$; N, Z
Example: LDA $AB,X
STA: STore Accumulator contents in memory
$(A) \rightarrow M$;
Example: STY $05
LDX: LoaD the X register from memory
$(M) \rightarrow X$; N, Z
Example: LDX $OF21
STX: STore the contents of the X register in memory
$(X) \rightarrow M$;
Example: STX $05,Y
LDY: LoaD the Y register from memory
(address) $\rightarrow Y$; N, Z
Example: LDY # OF
STY: STore the contents of the Y register in memory
$(Y) \rightarrow M$;
Example: STY $05,X
TAX: Transfer Accumulator contents to register X
$(A) \rightarrow X$; N, Z
Example: TAX

TXA: Transfer the contents of the X register to the Accumulator
$(X) \rightarrow A$; N, Z
Example: TXA

TAY: Transfer Accumulator contents to register Y
$(A) \rightarrow Y$; N, Z
Example: TAY

TYA: Transfer the contents of the Y register to the Accumulator
$(Y) \rightarrow A$; N, Z
Example: TYA

9.16.2 Stack instructions

A *stack* is a group of successive memory locations which are reserved for special functions such as subroutines (see Sec. 10.17) and interrupts (see Sec. 10.21). The majority of stacks are operated on a *last-in-first-out* (LIFO) basis; i.e., the last item of data stored in the stack *must be* the first to be retrieved. A simple analogy of this type of memory is a pile of books on a shelf; the last book to be placed on the top of the pile (analagous to the 'top' of the stack) is the first one to be taken off. A register known as the *stack pointer* (see also Figs 8.6, 8.7, 10.27, and 10.28) holds the address of the '*top*' *of the stack*, the address in this register being altered each time a byte of data is either added to or taken away from the stack. Depending on the design of the CPU, the stack pointer may either hold the absolute 16-bit address of the top of the stack (as it does in the 8080, 8085, and Z80 CPUs) or it may hold only the least significant byte of the address of the top of the stack (as it does in the 6502 CPU).

Stack instructions relate either to *pushing* data onto the stack or to *pulling* (or *popping*) data from the stack. In the following, the expression SP refers to the address of the top of the stack stored in the stack pointer, and S or (S) refers to the contents of that address.

PHA: PusH Accumulator contents onto stack
$(A) \rightarrow S$; $(SP - 1) \rightarrow SP$

PLA: PulL data from the top of the stack and store in Accumulator
$(S) \rightarrow A$; $(SP + 1) \rightarrow SP$

PHP: PusH Processor status register onto the stack
$(P) \rightarrow S$; $(SP - 1) \rightarrow SP$

PLP: PulL data from the stack and store in Processor status register
$(S) \rightarrow P$; $(SP + 1) \rightarrow SP$

TXS: Transfer the contents of the X register to the Stack pointer
$(X) \rightarrow SP$

TSX: Transfer the contents of the Stack pointer to index register X
$(SP) \rightarrow X$; N, Z

9.17 Program manipulation instructions

These instructions involve the transfer of control either conditionally or unconditionally as follows:

1. Branch or conditional jump instructions.
2. Unconditional jump instructions.

9.17.1 Branch instructions

These instructions cause the CPU to test the condition of one of the processor status flags and, depending on the condition of the flag, either transfers program control to a point some distance away from the address in the program counter or continues with the next instruction in the program. In the 6502 CPU, branch instructions use only relative addressing and the flags are unaffected.

> BCC: Branch on Carry Clear
> If $C=0$ then (PC)+displacement→PC
> Example: BCC $09
> BCS: Branch on Carry Set
> If $C=1$ then (PC)+displacement→PC
> Example: BCS $19
> BEQ: Branch if result is EQual to zero
> If $Z=1$ then (PC)+displacement→PC
> Example: BEQ $29
> BNE: Branch if result Not Equal to zero
> If $Z=0$ then (PC)+displacement→PC
> Example: BNE $39
> BMI: Branch if result MInus
> If $N=1$ then (PC)+displacement→PC
> Example: BMI $49
> BPL: Branch if result PLus
> If $N=0$ then (PC)+displacement→PC
> Example: BPL $59
> BVC: Branch if oVerflow flag Clear
> If $V=0$ then (PC)+displacement→PC
> Example: BVC $69
> BVS: Branch of oVerflow flag Set
> If $V=1$ then (PC)+displacement→PC
> Example: BVS $79

9.17.2 Jump instructions

These instructions cause program control to depart unconditionally from the normal sequence of events. Jump instructions in the 6502 differ from branch instructions in that they do not use relative addressing.

JMP: JuMP to a new location
New address→PC
Example: JMP THREE
JSR: Jump to Sub-Routine
PC(hi)→SP; PC(lo)→(SP − 1); SP − 2→SP
Sub-routine address→PC
Example: JSR $AB10
RTS: ReTurn from Sub-routine
(SP + 1)→PC(lo); (SP + 2)→PC(hi); SP + 2→SP; PC + 1→PC
Example: RTS
BRK: force BReaK (software interrupt)
PC(hi)→SP; PC(lo)→SP − 1; (P)→(SP − 2); SP − 3→SP; B = 1, I = 1
Example: BRK
RTI: ReTurn from Interrupt
(SP + 1)→P; (SP + 2)→PC(lo); (SP + 3)→PC(hi);
SP + 4→SP; PC + 1→PC; N, V, D, I, Z, C
Example: RTI

9.18 Status management instructions

These instructions enable the programmer to set or to clear various status register flags. To complete the instruction set, the no-operation instruction (NOP) has been included.

CLC: CLear Carry flag
$0 \rightarrow C$
SEC: SEt Carry flag
$1 \rightarrow C$
CLD: CLear Decimal mode flag
$0 \rightarrow D$
SED: SEt Decimal mode flag
$1 \rightarrow D$
CLI: CLear Interrupt disable mask (enable interrupts)
$0 \rightarrow I$
SEI: SEt Interrupt disable mask (disable maskable interrupts)
$1 \rightarrow I$
CLV: CLear oVerflow flag
$0 \rightarrow V$
NOP: No OPeration ('do nothing' instruction)

The status management instructions (also the NOP instruction) are one-byte instructions and all use the implied addressing mode. The assembly language instruction is therefore the same as the three-letter group which describes the instruction, i.e., CLC, SEC, CLD, etc.

Problems

9.1 Discuss methods of classifying instructions other than that described in Sec. 9.1.

9.2 With the aid of a diagram showing the flow of data between the registers and memory, describe the execution of the instruction

AND $0040

using (a) zero page addressing and (b) absolute addressing. Which, if any, status flags are affected, and why should this occur?

9.3 With the aid of a diagram, show how the logical AND function is executed using (a) immediate addressing, (b) absolute indexed addressing with the X register, (c) absolute indexed addressing with the Y register, and (d) zero page addressing.

9.4 Suppose that you are responsible for designing a CPU which uses relative addressing for logical instructions and arithmetic instructions. With the aid of a diagram showing the flow of data between the registers and memory, describe the operation of the following instructions: (a) AND memory with accumulator and (b) ADD memory with carry to accumulator.

10. Microprocessor programming and applications

10.1 Algorithms, flowcharts, and structured programs

When using a computer to solve a problem, it is important to define clearly what steps are to be carried out by the computer. A set of unambiguous steps or instructions designed to produce a solution of a problem is known as an *algorithm*. For example, an algorithm for evaluating the formula

$$f(x) = a_3 x^3 + a_2 x^2 + a_1 x + a_0$$

can be written in the form

$$f(x) = \{[(a_3)x + a_2]x + a_1\}x + a_0 \qquad (10.1)$$

The algorithm indicates that the formula can be evaluated by repeating a multiply-and-add routine three times.

The algorithm can be represented in a graphical form known as a *flowchart*, which uses a number of the symbols in Fig. 10.1. Each process or flowchart has a 'start' and a 'finish' or 'end', the start and the end being linked by a sequence of the symbols in Fig. 10.1. A flowchart for the algorithm in Eq. (10.1) is shown in Fig. 10.2. When writing a program which is equivalent to the flowchart in Fig. 10.2, the block marked START is replaced in the program by a number of instructions which establish the operating conditions within several hardware devices such as input/output ports (see also Sec. 10.6).

In block A of the flowchart a 'counter', n, is established; in our case the value of n is three (this is equal to the highest suffix associated with variable a). The value of the coefficients a_3, a_2, a_1, and a_0 are stored in a table, and the value of n (initially three) is used to access the nth coefficient in the table (a_3 initially) — see block B. This is multiplied by x in block C and in block D the contents of the counter are decremented (reduced by unity); this function is expressed in the form

$$n = n - 1$$

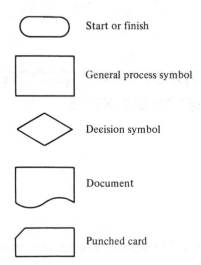

Start or finish

General process symbol

Decision symbol

Document

Punched card

Fig. 10.1   Some flowchart symbols

The 'equals' sign in the above expression is simply read as 'becomes'. That is, block E should be read as 'the value n stored in the counter is reduced by unity and becomes $(n-1)$'.

In block E, the next value of a_n (which is a_2 at the end of the first pass of path CDE of Fig. 10.2) is added to the value calculated in block C. Thus at the end of the first pass the value $a_3x + a_2$ is determined.

At point F in the flowchart, the value of n is tested to see if it has zero value. This test is carried out by means of a branch instruction or a conditional jump instruction (see also Secs 9.8 and 9.17); when testing for zero value in a 6502 CPU, a BEQ instruction would be used (or a JZ instruction in an 8080 or 8085 CPU). On completing the first traverse of the path $CDEF$, the value of n is nonzero, so that program control is transferred to point W and the path $CDEF$ is repeated. The computer program repeats the add and multiply loop until $n = 0$. When this occurs the program is allowed to continue to block G, which causes the result to be stored in a location in the memory of the computer.

Every program must have an orderly END to it (block H), otherwise the CPU would continue fetching and executing instructions continuously. Methods of terminating programs are discussed in this chapter.

A problem which frequently arises when writing computer programs is 'how can sections of a large program be kept distinct from one another so that errors can be isolated?'. One solution, known as *structured programming*, is widely used to prevent involved and unstructured programs getting out of hand. Structured programming involves the process of reducing each major section to one of three basic forms, namely:

1. A *linear structure* in which a series of statements is executed consecutively.

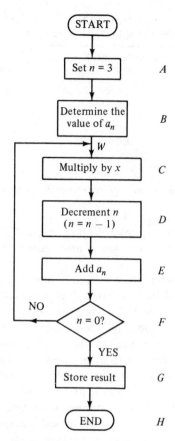

Fig. 10.2 Flowchart for a simple problem

2. A *conditional structure* in which the program branches into two paths, the branch selected depending on a particular condition in the CPU; this could, for example, be a 'branch' instruction following a mathematical or logical function. The two branches of the conditional structure meet again at a later point, so that the structure has a single exit point.
3. A *loop structure*; a typical loop structure is the 'do-until' structure of the type in Fig. 10.2. In the case of Fig. 10.2, the structure has a single entry point (at START) and a single exit point (at END), and the loop is executed until $n = 0$.

10.2 Terminating a low-level microcomputer program

Many computer programs have a linear structure, i.e., they have a simple function to perform, e.g., a simple addition. In order to terminate the program,

Table 10.1
One method of terminating a program

Memory address (hex)	Memory contents (hex)	Instruction mnemonic
0000	A9	LDA #00
0001	00	
⋮	⋮	⋮
000E	4C	JMP $000E
000F	0E	
0010	00	
0011	XX	

Note: XX=any two hexadecimal characters (and could either be a valid opcode or merely binary 'garbage').

simple methods have to be devised to prevent the CPU from attempting to fetch and execute instructions which are beyond the normal end of the program.

A simple method which may be used to terminate any linear program is to put the CPU into an endless loop from which it cannot escape until the CPU has been reset (which, in most cases, is done when the user presses the reset button of the CPU; see also Sec. 8.9). This is illustrated in the program in Table 10.1 which employs an instruction which causes program control to be transferred to location 000E as soon as it has executed the three-byte JMP (JuMP instruction) which commences at address 000E.

The first instruction in the program (the two bytes in locations $0000 and $0001) call for the CPU to load the accumulator immediately with the data in location 0001 — this instruction is irrelevant so far as terminating the program is concerned, but has been included to illustrate the fact that the program must begin at some point. The program continues (shown by the dots in the program) until it reaches the opcode of the final instruction in address $000E. This is the three-byte JMP $000E instruction occupying locations $000E to 0010. When this instruction is executed, it simply causes program control to jump back to address $000E, at which point it finds the JMP instruction once more. It continues to execute this loop until the reset button is pressed by the

Table 10.2
An alternative method of program termination (6502 CPU)

Memory address (hex)	Memory contents (hex)	Instruction mnemonic
0000	A9	LDA #00
0001	00	
⋮	⋮	⋮
000E	00	BRK
000F	XX	

Table 10.3
Simple data transfer

| Address | Byte (hex) | | | Instruction | |
(hex)	1	2	3	mnemonic	Comment
0000	A5	20		LDA $20	($0020)→accumulator
0002	8D	23	02	STA $0223	(Accumulator)→($0223)
0005	00			BRK	Terminate program

operator. The opcode in address $0011 is never 'read' since the computer cannot escape from the endless loop which terminates the program.

An alternative method is to terminate the program by returning control to the monitor program. Microcomputers provide this facility in one form or another, and in the 6502 CPU it is generally achieved by inserting a BReaK instruction (mnemonic BRK — opcode $00, which is a one-byte instruction). When the CPU receives this instruction the program is interrupted. This is illustrated in Table 10.2.

In Table 10.2, the program is terminated at address $000E, and the opcode in location $000F is never fetched. This method is used to terminate programs in this book which have a linear structure.

10.3 Simple data transfer and arithmetic operations

Many programs call for data in one memory location to be moved to another location. A simple program showing how the data in location $0020 are moved to $0223 is given in Table 10.3. Since the data are stored in page zero, the two-byte zero page 'LoaD the Accumulator' instruction LDA $20 copies the contents of address $0020 into the accumulator. The next instruction, whose opcode is stored in location $0002, uses the three-byte absolute addressing mode 'STore the contents of the Accumulator' instruction to store the data in address $0223. (*Note*: the low byte of the destination address is entered in the program before the high byte.)

A simple eight-bit addition program is described in Table 10.4. In this case, the data stored in location $0020 are added to the data contained in the program (in location $0004), the result being stored in location $0223. The first instruction in the program clears the carry flag (CLC), since it is quite possible that the flag may have been set to logic '1' by an earlier operation. The second instruction loads the contents of address $0020 into the accumulator. This is followed by an add-with-carry instruction in the immediate mode (ADC — opcode 69), which adds the data in the second byte of the ADC instruction to the contents of the accumulator. The final instruction transfers the result to address $0223.

Table 10.4
Single-byte addition

Address	Byte (hex)			Instruction	
(hex)	1	2	3	mnemonic	Comment
0000	18			CLC	Clear carry flag
0001	A5	20		LDA $20	($0020) →accumulator
0003	69	3F		ADC #$3F	(Accumulator) + $3F + accumulator
0005	8D	23	02	STA $0223	(Accumulator) →($0223)
0008	00			BRK	Terminate program

The addition process described above deals with values in the range zero to $FF. Larger numbers can be added using a similar routine, but the reader should note that the addition of the two low-byte values may produce a carry bit which must be added to the two high bytes. It is therefore necessary to clear the carry flag when the first byte is added, but the contents of the carry flag must be unchanged for any high-byte additions. Suppose that a 16-bit word whose low byte is stored in address $0040 and whose high byte is stored in address $0041 is to be added to a 16-bit word whose low byte is in location $0042 and whose high byte is in address $0043. The result is to be stored in locations $0044 (low byte) and $0045 (high byte). Sixteen-bit addition is sometimes known as *double-precision addition*, and a typical program is listed in Table 10.5.

The 'length' of the number that can be handled is increased in units of eight bits by repeating the LDA, ADC, STA sequence several times.

Subtraction is carried out in the 6502 CPU using the subtract instruction SBC as follows. Suppose that we need to subtract the contents of location $0041 from the contents of location $0040, the result being stored in location $0042. The program is listed in Table 10.6.

Table 10.5
Double-precision addition

Address	Byte (hex)			Instruction	
(hex)	1	2	3	mnemonic	Comment
0000	18			CLC	Clear carry flag for low byte
0001	A5	40		LDA $40	Low byte of addend →accumulator
0003	65	42		ADC $42	Add low byte of augend
0005	85	44		STA $44	Store low byte of result
0007	A5	41		LDA $41	High byte of addend →accumulator
0009	65	43		ADC $43	Add high byte of augend
000B	85	45		STA $45	Store high byte of result
000D	00			BRK	Terminate program

Table 10.6
Subtraction routine

Address (hex)	Byte (hex) 1	2	3	Instruction mnemonic	Comment
0000	38			SEC	Set carry flag for subtraction
0001	A5	40		LDA $40	Minuend→accumulator
0003	E5	41		SBC $41	(Accumulator)−subtrahend→accumulator
0005	85	42		STA $42	Result→($0042)
0007	00			BRK	

10.4 A binary multiplication routine

The mathematical instructions in the instruction set of a typical CPU are usually limited to add (and/or add with carry) and subtract (and/or subtract with borrow). Other mathematical functions such as multiply and divide must be generated from these and other basic instructions. In this section we study a program which multiplies two unsigned eight-bit binary numbers.

The basis of one method of binary multiplication was described in Sec. 7.12, where it was shown that a 16-bit register is needed to store the product of two eight-bit numbers. When two N-bit numbers are multiplied by a machine method, it is completed in N add-and-shift steps. In this case we use eight-bit numbers, so that the calculation is complete after eight add-and-shift steps. Each add-and-shift step follows the sequence below:

1. If the multiplier bit (LSB of the multiplier word) is zero, add zero to the high byte of the partial product.
2. If the multiplier bit is '1', add the multiplicand to the high byte of the partial product.
3. When either step 1 or step 2 is complete, shift the high byte and the low byte of the partial product one place right.
4. Repeat steps 1 and 3 or 2 and 3 eight times.

Suppose that the multiplier (MR) is stored in location $0030, the multiplicand (MD) is in location $0031, and the low byte of the 16-bit product is to be stored in location $0032 and the high byte in $0033. During the calculation, the high byte of the partial product (PP high) is stored in the accumulator (A) and the low byte of the partial product (PP low) is stored in location $0032. A diagram representing the basic add-and-shift mechanism is shown in Fig. 10.3.

The first step is to test the state of the multiplier bit (the least significant bit, b_0, of MR). This is achieved by a logical shift right (LSR instruction) of the contents of location $0030, which shifts bit b_0 into the carry flag (stage V of Fig. 10.3). In stage W of the figure, the bit stored in the C flag is tested by means of a BCC instruction (Branch on $C=0$); *if $C=0$*, a branch is made to the point marked **ROTAT** in stage Y of the routine. *If $C = 1$*, the MD is added to the high byte of the partial product (PP high). However, the addition instruction of the 6502 (ADC instruction — ADd memory with Carry) calls for the contents of the carry flag to be added as well. It is therefore necessary to clear the carry flag (CLC instruction) before executing the ADC instruction (stage X of the figure). The result of the operation in section X leaves the high byte of the partial

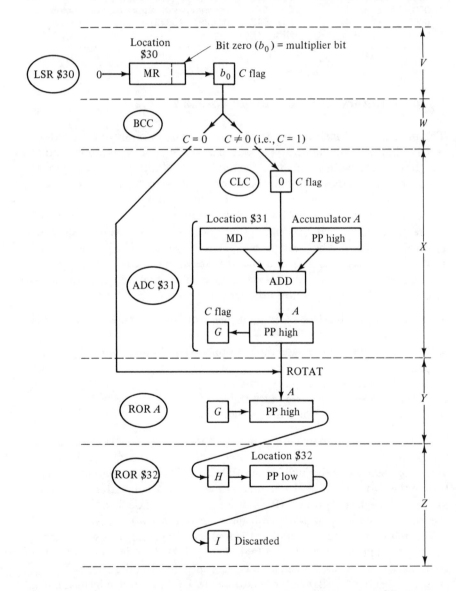

Fig. 10.3 Add and shift routine used in an eight-bit unsigned binary multiplication program

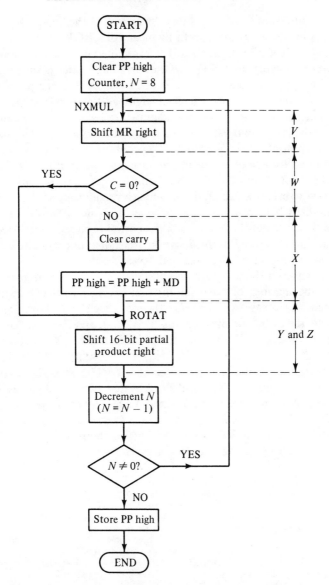

Fig. 10.4   Flowchart for an eight-bit × eight-bit unsigned binary multiplication program

product in the accumulator, together with any carry, G, generated by the ADC instruction.

Both routes of the BCC instruction in stage W rejoin in stage Y, where the high byte of the partial product is rotated right (ROR A instruction). This results in the carry, G, produced in stage X being transferred into bit seven of the accumulator; at the same time b_0 of the accumulator, shown as H in the figure, is transferred to the carry flag. In stage Z of the figure, the low byte of the partial product is rotated right by means of a ROR $32 instruction. This results in b_0 (H) of PP high at stage Y being shifted into b_7 of PP low; b_0 of PP low is, at this stage, transferred into the carry flag — this is shown as I in the figure. The latter is redundant and is discarded by a later operation.

The computer must then check if eight add-and-shift steps have been executed. If not, the routine is repeated until they have. When the calculation is complete, the program must either continue with the next step in the program or, if only multiplication is needed, the program is terminated.

A flowchart for a multiplication program is shown in Fig. 10.4, the position of stages V, W, X, Y, and Z of Fig. 10.3 being indicated on the figure. Initially it is necessary to clear the accumulator, which is used throughout the program to store the high byte of the partial product. It is not necessary to clear the location which stores the low byte of the partial product, i.e., $0032, since the eight bits initially stored in this location are shifted out and discarded by the operation in stage Z of Figs 10.3 and 10.4.

At the outset of the program it is necessary to set up a counter, N, which contains the number of times (eight) that the add-and-shift loop is to be completed. In our case, we store N in the index register X. Once this has been completed, the CPU executes sections V, W, X, Y, and Z of the flowchart. On completion of section Z, the contents of index register X is decremented by unity ($N = N - 1$), and register X is tested for the condition $(X) = 0$, i.e., $N = 0$. If $N \neq 0$, program control is returned to point $NXMUL$, when the next multiplier bit is tested and path V, W, X, Y, and Z is repeated. After eight passes of the loop the value of N is zero; when this occurs, the high byte of the partial product (which is now the high byte of the product) is stored in the accumulator, and is transferred to location $0033; the low byte of the product is in $0032. The program corresponding to Fig. 10.4 is given in Table 10.7.

Table 10.7
Multiplication routine

Address (hex)	Byte (hex) 1	2	3	Label	Instruction mnemonic	Comment
0200	D8			MULT	CLD	Clear decimal mode
0201	A9	00			LDA #$00	Clear PP high
0203	A2	08			LDX #$08	Load counter with N=8
0205	46	30		NXMUL	LSR $30	Shift multiplier bit into C flag
0207	90	03			BCC ROTAT	Branch to ROTAT if C=0
0209	18				CLC	Otherwise clear carry
020A	65	31			ADC $37	Add MD
020C	6A			ROTAT	ROR A	Rotate PP high
020D	66	32			ROR $32	Rotate PP low
020F	CA				DEX	N=N-1
0210	D0	F3			BNE NXMUL	Branch to NXMUL if $N \neq 0$
0212	85	33			STA $33	Store PP high
0214	00				BRK	

10.5 Simple input/output (I/O) ports

The function of an I/O port is to allow the CPU to communicate with a peripheral in the 'outside world'. The basis of a simple input port and a simple output port is shown in Fig. 10.5.

An *input port* allows data to be 'input' to the CPU from an external peripheral such as a keyboard. The switches in bank S1 inside the input port are closed when a logic '1' is applied to the chip select line CS1 (which is active 'high'); switches S1 are open-circuit when CS1 = 0. The switches in bank S2 are closed when $\overline{CS2}$ = 0 (active 'low') and are open when $\overline{CS2}$ = 1. The peripheral is given access to the data bus when the address of the input port has been applied to the address bus by the CPU (when this occurs, CS1 = 1) AND the $\overline{READ}$ control line has a logic '0' on it, i.e., $\overline{CS2}$ = 0. When an individual input port is given access to the data bus, all other ports are disabled by opening either or both banks of switches inside the port. These switches are, in reality, three-state logic gates.

An *output port* allows data to be 'output' from the CPU to a selected peripheral such as a video display unit. When chip select line CS1 on the output port in Fig. 10.5 has a logic '1' applied to it, the switches in bank S3 are closed; when $\overline{CS2}$ has a logic '0' applied to it, the switches in bank S4 are closed. When the output port has been correctly addressed, the data placed on the data bus by the CPU are transmitted to the output peripheral via the output port and its memory register or data latches. The reason for the need for these latches is that the CPU gives the output port access to the data bus for only about 0·5 μs, and it is usually necessary to 'latch' these data in the output port; otherwise the data will be lost.

10.6 Programmable I/O ports

Each port in Fig. 10.5 is dedicated to a single function, i.e., the port is either an input port or it is an output port. However, many applications require I/O ports which need to have a few input lines and a few output lines. It is for this reason that a variety of *programmable input/output ports* (PIO) are in widespread use in microcomputer systems. A variety of names are applied to these devices including PIO, peripheral interface adaptor (PIA), and versatile interface adaptor (VIA). Each has its own specialized features, most having two eight-bit programmable I/O ports, others having three eight-bit programmable ports, some having built-in timers, some having a small amount of RAM in them, and yet others having a small amount of ROM. More complex PIOs are sometimes given exotic names, and a chip which combines ROM (or RAM) with I/O and timers may be referred to as a RIOT.

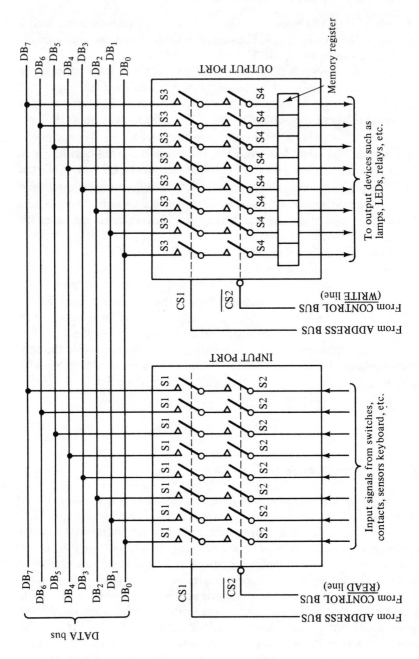

Fig. 10.5 Simplified operation of an input port and an output port

In our case we limit ourselves to the treatment of a simplified PIO which is loosely based on the 6522 versatile interface adaptor* (VIA).

A block diagram of a simplified programmable I/O port is shown in Fig. 10.6. The PIO has several internal registers in which data can be stored, each register having its own address. The PIO in Fig. 10.6 enables the user to control two eight-bit I/O ports (port A and port B respectively), giving control over 16 I/O lines.

When using a PIO it is necessary to *configure* the device by means of instructions, i.e., it has to be instructed which lines are to be used as input lines and which as output lines. When the microcomputer is initially reset (as occurs at start-up or switch-on), all internal registers in the PIO are cleared, resulting in both ports acting as input ports. If only one of the two eight-bit ports is used in a given application, the remaining port need not be configured since the CPU ensures that it is in a known state, namely it is an input port. In the case of the 6522 chip, the outputs from port A are not buffered and can only be lightly loaded;† the output from port B is buffered and can be used to drive larger loads such as relays.

Each port is configured by means of an eight-bit word which is sent from the CPU to the appropriate *data direction register*, which is described as DDRA for port A and DDRB for port B, the addresses for these being $A003 and $A002 respectively (see Fig. 10.6). A *logic '1'* positioned in a particular bit in the data direction register, say bit zero, results in the associated line, line zero, being an *outptut line*. A *logic '0'* positioned in another bit in the data direction register, say bit one, results in the associated line, line number one, being an *input line*. Thus if the binary word 00001111 is stored in DDRA and binary 11110000 is stored in DDRB, then port A lines PA_7 to PA_4, inclusive, are input lines and lines PA_3 to PA_0 are output lines; in the case of port B, lines PB_7 to PB_4, inclusive, are output lines and PB_3 to PB_0 are input lines. The PIO is usually configured at the beginning of the program, and it is usually not necessary to change the function of the I/O lines during the remainder of the program.

Once the port is configured, the *effective address of each port* so far as data transfer is concerned is given by the address of the *output register* associated with that port. The address of port A is therefore the address of the input/output register A(IORA) which is $A001 (see Fig. 10.6) and for port B the address of the input/output register B (IORB) is $A000.

---

* A full treatment of this device is given in the technical literature (see, for example, the Rockwell R6500 Hardware Manual).

† Port A can be used to drive loads if its output lines are buffered by external circuitry such as logic gates.

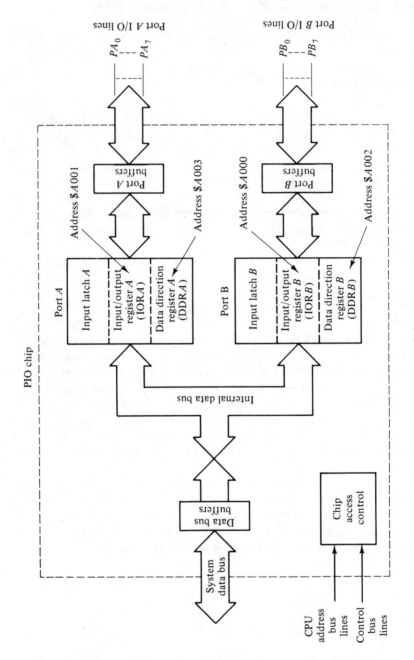

Fig. 10.6 Diagram of a simplified programmable input/output port (PIO)

10.7   Data transfer using a programmable I/O port

A block diagram showing how a PIO is used to transfer data from eight switches S0, S1, S2, ..., S7 to control eight lamps L0, L1, L2, ..., L7 is illustrated in Fig. 10.7. A program which controls the data transfer between the PIO ports via the central processor is given in Table 10.8; the function of the program is to enable switch S0 to control lamp L0, switch S1 to control lamp L1, etc.

The first two instructions cause all the lines from port A to act as input lines (this is as a result of storing $00 in DDR$A$). The next two instructions result in all the lines from port B being output lines (arising from the fact that FF is stored in DDRB). This completes the PIO configuration, and the program proper can begin. The program simply consists of loading the data in IORA

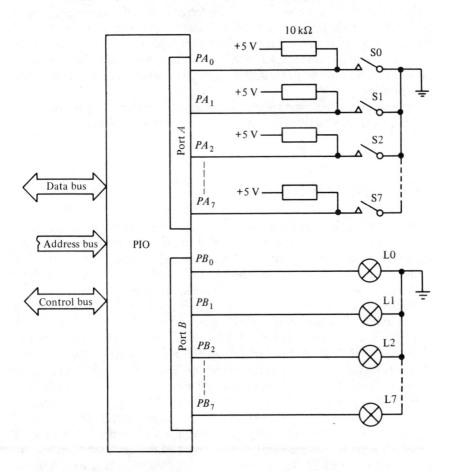

Fig. 10.7   Data transfer using a PIO

Table 10.8
Simple I/O routine

Address (hex)	Byte 1	Byte 2	Byte 3	Label	Instruction mnemonic	Comment
0000	A9	00			LDA #$00	
0002	8D	03	A0		STA DDRA	Make port A inputs
0005	A9	FF			LDA #$FF	
0007	8D	02	A0		STA DDRB	Make port B outputs
000A	AD	01	A0	REPEAT	LDA IORA	Fetch data from port A
000D	8D	00	A0		STA IORB	Store data in port B
0010	4C	0A	00		JMP REPEAT	Repeat fetch-store sequence

— corresponding to the signals from the eight switches (at address $A001) — into the accumulator. These data are transferred to IOR B — corresponding to the address of the lamps (i.e., $A000)—resulting in a switch in the logic '1' position illuminating a lamp and a switch in the logic '0' position extinguishing a lamp. The three-byte JMP REPEAT instruction causes program control to be handed back to the LDA IOR A instruction, when the FETCH-STORE sequence is repeated.

In this way, the logic state of the switches is transmitted to the lamps, and it appears as though each switch is connected directly to a single lamp.

10.8 Light-emitting diodes

LEDs are semiconductor p-n junction devices which emit optical radiation when forward biased. The wavelength of the radiated energy depends on the forbidden band-gap of the semiconductor; the most useful range of semiconductor materials includes those based on gallium arsenide and gallium arsenide phosphide. Using these materials, a range of colours can be generated, the most popular being red, green, yellow, and amber. The life expectancy of these devices is typically greater than 10^5 hours and, in general, they do not fail unpredictably but degrade slowly. The power supply requirements depend on the material used in the construction of the diode (and therefore on the colour radiated), and are typically 2–2·5 V at 5–40 mA. These values of p.d. and current are known as the *forward voltage*, V_F, and the *forward current*, I_F, respectively. The reverse breakdown voltage of LEDs is typically 3–10 V. When used with a.c. supplies it is usual to protect the diode from reverse breakdown by connecting a conventional p-n junction diode either in series with or in inverse-parallel with the LED; these modifications are illustrated in insets (i) and (ii) respectively in Fig. 10.8. When the LED is conducting, the p.d. across it falls to V_F; the current through the diode is limited

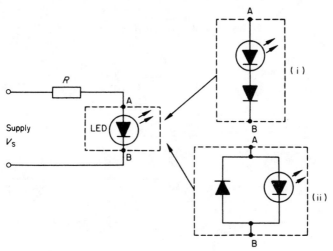

Fig. 10.8   Simple LED circuit

in value to a safe value, I_F, by resistor R, whose value is estimated from the equation

$$R = \frac{V_S - V_F}{I_F}$$

where V_S is the value of the supply voltage. This resistor, in the case of a conventional LED, is a discrete component which is connected externally to the LED. Certain types of LEDs, known as *resistor LEDs*, contain an integral current limiting resistor, and can be connected directly to the voltage specified for the diode; this voltage may, for example, be 5 V for use with TTL networks.

LEDs may either be used individually in the form of indicator lamps, or may be used in groups to provide either numerical or alphabetical character displays, or a combination of the two types of display (*alphanumeric displays*).

10.8.1   Segmented displays

The *seven-segment display* in Fig. 10.9(a) is widely used in numerical display systems, such as those found in instruments and in calculators. By illuminating combinations of segments, it is possible either to generate any one of the ten decimal digits (see Fig. 10.9b) or to generate one of a limited range of alphabetical characters (see Fig. 10.9c).

A block diagram of a seven-segment display system is illustrated in Fig. 10.10. The input pulses to be counted and displayed are applied serially to the system. These pulses are counted in a decade counter, the final value of the count being transferred to a 'data latch' unit containing D flip-flops. The function of the data latch is to provide a 'non-blinking' display in the time interval during which the incoming pulses are being counted by the counter

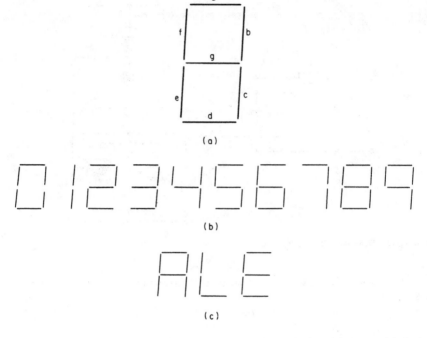

Fig. 10.9   (a) Seven-segment display, (b) numerical characters, (c) some alphabetical characters that the display can generate

module. When the counting sequence has been completed a 'latch strobe' pulse is generated by the logic circuitry, which causes the logic states in the counter to be transferred to the data latch element. If the incoming data are presented in a parallel form, then the decade counter module is redundant; if a 'non-blinking' display is not required, then the data latch is also surplus to requirements.

The signals on the output lines of the data latch are applied to a decoder, which provides signals on seven output lines which activate the segments of the seven-segment display. The design of a decoder for this purpose can be carried out using the principles outlined in Chapter 7. To provide the LEDs in the display with the correct value of current, driver circuits are interposed between the decoder and the display elements. The LED driver block in Fig. 10.10 has an additional input marked 'blanking input'; when a signal is applied to this line, it causes the display to be completely blanked out, i.e., it is not illuminated. This facility is used to blank out non-significant zeros in the display. In addition to the seven segments used to display both numerical and alphabetical characters, decimal point indication can also be provided in one of the two alternative positions shown in Fig. 10.10.

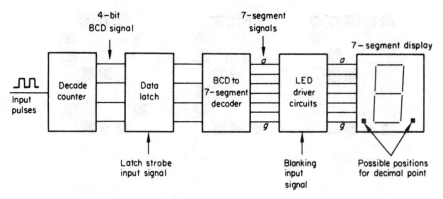

Fig. 10.10 A block diagram of a seven-segment display system

An alternative form of segmented display is the 16-segment pattern in Fig. 10.11(a). This type of display can generate all alphabetic and decimal characters, in addition to which other patterns can be generated. Several of the characters which can be displayed are illustrated in Fig. 10.11(b). Displays of this kind are frequently generated via a ROM character generator.

10.8.2 Matrix displays

Multidot matrix displays are widely used, the 5×7 dot matrix display (Fig. 10.12a) being very popular; the 4×7 dot matrix display in Fig. 10.12(b) is an alternative type. Characters specified by the ASCII code (American Standard Code for Information Interface) can be displayed on a 5×7 alphanumeric matrix display. The 5×7 display in Fig. 10.12(c) is a simplified version of that in Fig. 10.12(a), and is capable of generating the 10 decimal digits together with a limited range of alphabetical characters. Physically large displays can be produced using a matrix of LED lamps.

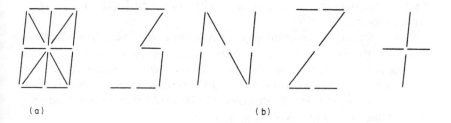

(a)   (b)

Fig. 10.11 (a) A 16-segment display and (b) some of the characters it can generate

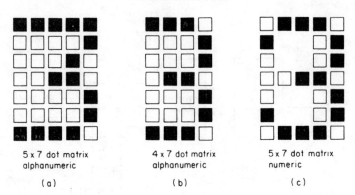

Fig. 10.12   Dot matrix displays: (a) 5×7 alphanumeric, (b) 4×7 alphanumeric, (c) 5×7 numeric

10.9   Microprocessor-driven displays

When a seven-segment LED display is operated from a microprocessor, each segment can be driven from one of the data bus lines, and the remaining data bus line (usually line seven) can be used to illuminate the decimal point segment (see also Fig. 10.10).

Some seven-segment LED displays have a common cathode connection, and require a drive circuit of the type shown for display A in Fig. 10.13. In this case a logic '1' applied to, for example, data bus line D_3, illuminates segment d of display A. Other seven-segment displays have a common-anode connection (see display B in Fig. 10.13). In this case a logic '1' applied to data bus D_3 applies a logic '0' via an inverting buffer to the cathode of segment d of display B, illuminating that segment. When the hex word $76 is applied to the data bus, both displays illuminate the letter 'H', and when $87 is applied, the combination '7.' is illuminated. (*Note*: it is assumed here that the decimal point LED is to the right of the seven-segment display.)

If the inverting buffers are omitted in the display B circuit, a logic '0' applied to one of the data bus lines illuminates the associated LED, and a logic '1' extinguishes it.

Where a message must be displayed, a number of LEDs can be multiplexed. That is, each LED is given access to the data bus for a short period of time which is long enough to cause the displayed character to be illuminated. Using a group of seven-segment display elements, a relatively 'long' message can be displayed by multiplexing the displays. The basis of a multiplexed 10-display circuit is shown in Fig. 10.14.

The address of the display circuit is the same as that of the four-bit data latch chip, and is deduced as follows. The data latch chip is enabled when EN = 1.

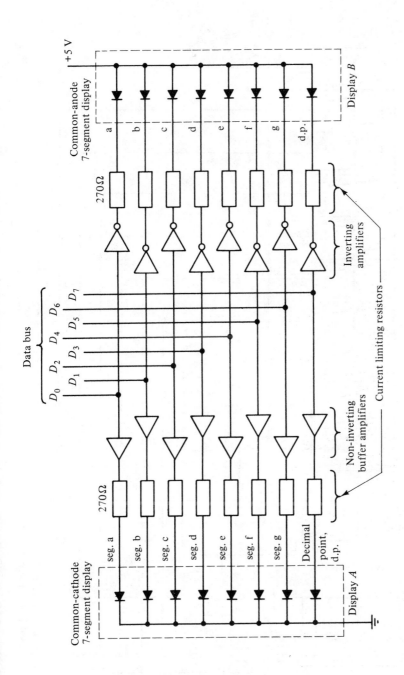

Fig. 10.13 Typical seven-segment LED display drive circuit

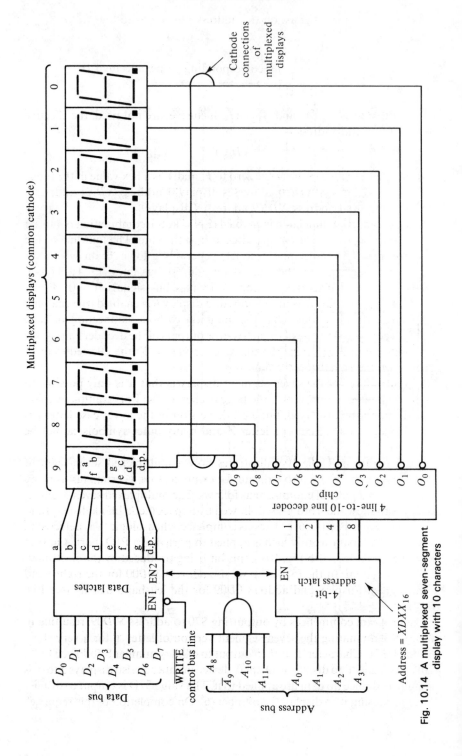

Fig. 10.14 A multiplexed seven-segment display with 10 characters

This occurs when the signals on the address bus are as follows:

$$\left.\begin{array}{l} A_8 = 1 \\ A_9 = 0 \\ A_{10} = 1 \\ A_{11} = 1 \end{array}\right\} \quad \text{corresponding to hexadecimal } D$$

Since address lines A_4–A_7 and A_{12}–A_{15}, inclusive, are not used, the effective hex version of the address is

$$XDXY$$

where X is a hex value in the range zero to F, and Y is a hex value in the range zero to 9. The address $XDX0$ addresses display 0, address $XDX1$ addresses display 1, etc., and address $XDX9$ addresses display 9.

When the four-bit data latch is enabled (EN = 1), the combination of bits on address lines A_0–A_3, inclusive, are latched into the chip. The four line-to-ten line decoder (BCD-to-decimal decoder) generates a logic '0' on whichever output line is selected by the address on address bus lines A_0–A_3. Thus if address 6 is selected (corresponding to address bus signals $A_3 = 0$, $A_2 = 1$, $A_1 = 1$, $A_0 = 0$), output O_6 is driven low, and display 6 is enabled (the enabling action arises from the fact that the common cathode connection of each display is connected to one of the active-low outputs of the decoder chip — see also display A in Fig. 10.13). The character displayed on the selected element depends on the signals on the data bus.

A disadvantage of the seven-segment display is that it is only possible to display a limited number of alphabetical characters. For example, capital letter T cannot be displayed, but a crude version of the lower case letter t is possible (segments e, f, and g); letter Z and many other symbols cannot be displayed.

The program in Table 10.9 illustrates how a multiplexed seven-segment display device can be used to indicate, for example, that a certain test is being performed on a piece of equipment as follows. The multiplexed seven-segment display is to show the word 'tESt' followed by a space (i.e., a blank display) and then the test number, i.e., 6. The test is completed when a logic '1' is detected in bit seven of a binary word which is applied to port A of a PIO (port A having address $A4001$—see also Fig. 10.6), this bit being produced by the electronics of the test system. In the following we use address $0D00$ for the right-hand seven-segment display and address 0D09 for the left-hand display (see Fig. 10.14).

The program commences by outputting $70 to address $0D09, resulting in display 9 illuminating the seven-segment version of letter 't' for a very short period of time. Character 'E' is then output to display number 8, followed by 'S' to display 7 and 't' to display 6. Display device number 5 (also displays 3 to 0) is extinguished since no data are applied to it. The value $7D is output to display device 4, causing it to display the number '6'. On completion of this sequence

Table 10.9
Multiplexed display routine

Address (hex)	Byte 1	Byte 2	Byte 3	Label	Instruction mnemonic	Comment
⋮	⋮	⋮	⋮		⋮	
0410	A9	70		START	LDA #$70	
0412	8D	09	0D		STA DISP9	t→display 9
0415	A9	79			LDA #$79	
0417	8D	08	0D		STA DISP8	E→display 8
041A	A9	6D			LDA #$6D	
041C	8D	07	0D		STA DISP7	S→display 7
041F	A9	70			LDA #$70	
0421	8D	06	0D		STA DISP6	t→display 6
0424	A9	7D			LDA #$7D	
0426	8D	04	0D		STA DISP4	6→display 4
0429	A9	00			LDA #$00	
042B	8D	04	0D		STA DISP4	Clear display 4
042E	AD	01	A0		LDA IORA	
0431	2A				ROL A	Test complete?
0432	90	DC			BCC START	NO, return to START
0434	XX	XX	XX			YES, continue program

bit seven of port A is tested, and if $b_7 = 0$ the display sequence is repeated.

The reader will note that the instructions in locations $0429 and $042B are used to extinguish the number '6' illuminated on display number 4; the reason is as follows. In the absence of these two instructions, and in the event of b_7 of port A being logic '1', the CPU does not branch to address $0410 but continues with the next instruction in the main program in location $0434 (not shown). Since both the display address and the data are latched (see Fig. 10.14) then, unless an instruction has been given to extinguish the last character displayed (number '6' in display 4), it will remain illuminated. It is therefore necessary to include these two instructions within the loop.

The use of a slightly more complex programming technique enables a 'continuously moving' message to be displayed on the multiplexed device.

The basis of a 20-character alphanumeric display system is shown in Fig. 10.15. Each display module has four 16-segment LED display devices, allowing four alphanumeric displays to be illuminated on each module. In the case considered, five display modules (modules DM_0 to DM_4) are controlled by a PIO having two output ports (port A and port B). To load data into module DM_0, its $\overline{CE}$ pin must be held low by the signal on PIO line PA_2 (module DM_1 is enabled by the signal on line PA_3, module DM_2 by PA_4, etc.). The code to produce the desired display is placed on PIO lines PB_0 to PB_6, inclusive, and this is latched into the data latch of DM_0 by holding the $\overline{W}$ line low (i.e., the $\overline{\text{WRITE LINE}}$); the $\overline{W}$ line on all the chips is energized by the signal on PIO line PA_7. The binary word stored in the data latch is converted to the pattern to give the desired display by means of a character generator

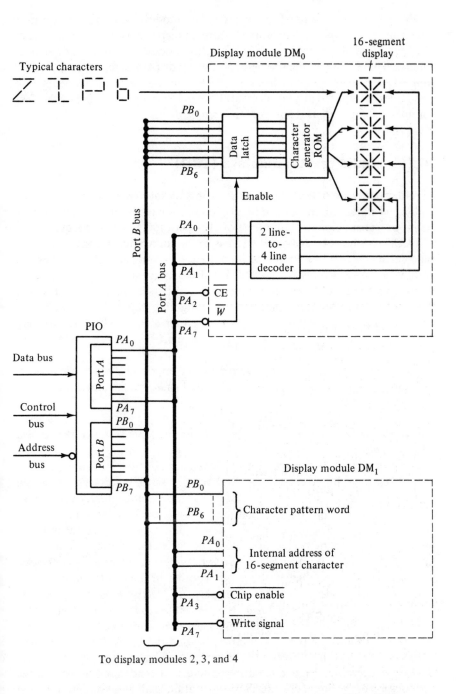

Fig. 10.15 A multiplexed 16-segment alphanumeric microprocessor-driven display

ROM which is contained in the display module, and this pattern is simultaneously applied to all four 16-segment displays. However, only one of the four 16-segment displays in the display module will be illuminated as follows. The address of the selected 16-segment display is placed on lines PA_0 and PA_1, the resulting signal from the two line-to-four line decoder being used to enable the required display element. Thus the character specified by the data on lines PB_0 to PB_6 is displayed on a single display element.

10.10   Liquid crystal displays (LCD)

Liquid crystals are organic fluids existing in a mesophase between their solid and liquid states. Unlike LEDs, LCDs do not radiate illumination, but either reflect or transmit incident illumination. In operation, the power requirement of a LCD is minute, being typically 15 μW or less for a 5 mm (0·2 in) high seven-segment display. If the source of illumination is ambient lighting, then no additional power supply is required, but if the ambient illumination is zero, then a light source is required. Since the display brilliance of LCDs is a function of the incident illumination, direct lighting improves the display. In general, where a principal requirement is either a physically large display together with a low power consumption, then LCDs are superior to other types.

There are many hundreds of liquid crystal compounds, which are divided into three groups, namely *nematic*, *smetic*, and *cholestric*, the former being of most interest here.

There are two types of nematic liquid crystal displays: one is the *dynamic scattering* type which causes light to be reflected, the other being known as *field effect* or *twisted nematic* type which allows light to be transmitted.

The general form of construction of a seven-segment display is illustrated in Fig. 10.16(a). The liquid crystal is sealed between two glass surfaces (one which may have a mirror finish), the surfaces having transparent conductive coatings on them. A typical spacing between the front and back plates is 10 μm. Any shape of display can be obtained using this method, and Fig. 10.16(b) and (c) is for a seven-segment numerical indicator. The lower electrode (b) is common to all segments, while the upper segments (c) are energized independently; the two sets of electrodes are aligned above one another in the display unit.

In order to produce the desired display, an electric field of about 0·5–1 MV/m (say 5–10 V across a 10-μm film) is applied to the liquid crystal. This causes the crystal molecules to rearrange their orientation (see below). There is very little spreading of the reorientation beyond the edges of the electrodes.

Electrolyte ions are an essential ingredient of liquid crystals and, if the display is energized by a d.c. supply, there is a tendency for electrolytic dissociation of the liquid crystal. This dissociation leads to a low deterioration in the display; LCDs do not fail catastrophically from this cause. Considerably

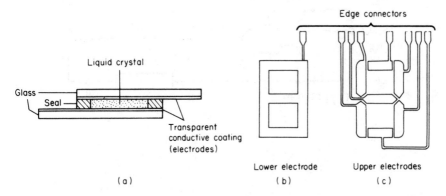

Fig. 10.16 Liquid crystal display: (a) section through the display, (b) the lower electrode for a seven-segment display, and (c) one form of arrangement of the upper electrodes

extended lifetimes (> 10 000 h) are obtained by exciting the LCD by a.c. signals in the frequency range 30–100 Hz. A typical LCD drive circuit for a single segment is shown in Fig. 10.17(a); in this circuit the common electrode (A) is connected to the clock source, while the 'displayed' electrode is driven by the EXCLUSIVE-OR gate G1. When the signal on the 'select' line is logic '0', the p.d. across the LCD element is zero and the display remains transparent. When a logic '1' is applied to the 'select' line, an a.c. signal is applied across the element and it becomes visible. Typical waveforms in the circuit are illustrated in Fig. 10.17. One EXCLUSIVE-OR gate per segment is required. A list of the more important characteristics of the two types of LCD are given in Table 10.10.

10.10.1 Dynamic scattering LCDs

The molecules in dynamic scattering displays are thread-like in form, and in the absence of an electric field the molecules align with one another under the influence of the molecular forces. In the unenergized state, light is transmitted through the liquid crystal and the display is transparent.

The application of a potential across the LCD causes turbulence domains to form within the film, and the molecules beneath the energized segments in these domains become very efficient scatterers of white light, causing the segment to have a white colour. The contrast ratio of this type of display increases with the value of the applied voltage, and rises to a maximum of about 20:1.

10.10.2 Field effect LCDs

In field effect or twisted nematic displays, the liquid crystal is sandwiched between two polarizing surfaces whose planes of polarization are at right

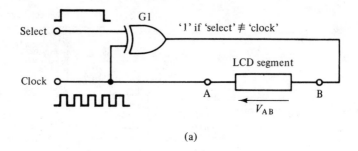

(a)

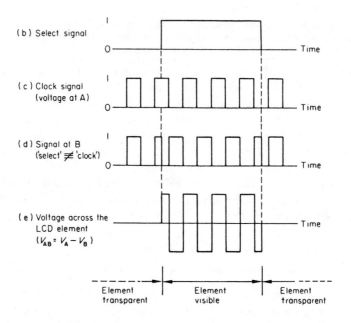

Fig. 10.17 (a) Drive circuit for an LCD element; (b) to (e) show typical waveforms

Table 10.10
Characteristics of LCDs

	Dynamic scattering	Field effect
Voltage	15–25	1·5–10
Current/cm²	1 μA	0·4 μA
Viewing angle	160°	90°–120°
Switching time	0·3 s	0·1–0·3 s
Life	10 000 h	10 000 h
Temperature range	0–80 °C	0–70 °C

angles to one another. In the unexcited state, the molecular structure of the LCD causes the plane of polarization of the incident light to be twisted through 90° so that it is transmitted through the second polarizing surface. If the lower glass surface has a mirror finish, the light is reflected back through the liquid crystal, where the plane of polarization is given a reverse 90° phase shift, so that it arrives at the upper polarizer in the correct plane to pass through it. In the unexcited mode, the display is therefore completely transparent.

The application of a potential between the LCD electrodes causes the molecules to align, and the incident light is transmitted without its plane of polarization being twisted. In this mode of operation, the planes of polarization of the light and that of the lower polarizer are at 90° to one another, and the incident light is completely absorbed by the lower polarizer. The result is a dark character which contrasts with the brighter surroundings. Contrast ratios in the range 25:1 to 35:1 are obtained from field effect LCDs.

Transmittive field effect displays do not have an internal mirror, and transmit light rather than reflect it. Hence it is possible either to have displays which have dark characters on a light background or light characters on a dark background.

10.11 A digital-to-analogue convertor (DAC)

Analogue control systems used in industry frequently have input signals derived from digital sources such as paper tapes, magnetic tapes, computers, etc., and a digital-to-analogue convertor is an essential part of the interface between the digital and analogue elements of the system.

A very popular type of DAC is the R-$2R$ ladder network in Fig. 10.18. This type of network uses only two values of resistance and is readily available in film integrated circuit form. The output voltage from the circuit in Fig. 10.18 is given by the expression

$$V_0 = V_{ref}(8A + 4B + 2C + D)/16$$

where $A, B, C,$ and D have either unity or zero logic value, corresponding to the positions of the switches.

10.12 A microprocessor-based waveform generator

When a DAC is interfaced to a microprocessor via an I/O port, the combination can be used as a waveform generator. The binary pattern corresponding to an instantaneous analogue voltage is generated by the CPU and this is converted by the DAC into the reauired analogue voltage. This process is repeated so that the desired waveshape is generated. In the

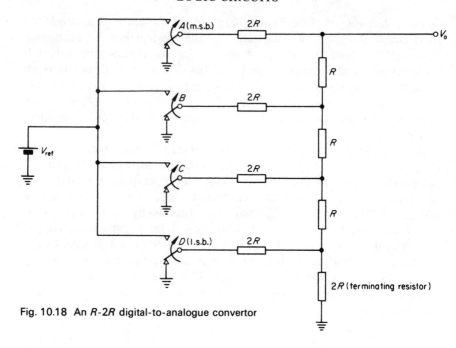

Fig. 10.18 An R-2R digital-to-analogue convertor

following, a program is developed which generates a sawtooth waveform or ramp waveform.

A block diagram of one form of waveform generator using a DAC is shown in Fig. 10.19(a), the DAC being interfaced to the CPU by a PIO. The effective address of the DAC is the same as that of port A of the PIO; using the addressing in Fig. 10.5, the effective address of port A is that of its input/output register ($A001) and the address of its data direction register is $A003.

In the program in Table 10.11, port A is configured as an output port; to do this, FF is loaded into DDRA. Then, simply as a matter of convenience, the same value is loaded into IORA and is automatically transmitted to the DAC to give the maximum possible output voltage. The CPU then enters a loop from which it cannot escape and in which it increments the contents of I/O register A every time it passes round the loop. This causes the digital signal from port A to 'ramp' up from zero to FF in a continuous pattern. This causes the output voltage from the DAC to have the ramp waveform shown in Fig. 10.19(b). If the time taken for each execution of the program loop is t_1 seconds, the periodic time of the waveform is $256t_1$. The frequency of the ramp waveform can be altered by modifying the program so that t_1 is altered.

More complex waveforms than the ramp waveform may be generated either by using the CPU to evaluate the solution of the equation of the waveform or, alternatively, by storing the waveform as a series of values in a 'table' in the memory of the computer; in the latter case, successive values in the table are 'output' to the DAC to give the desired waveform.

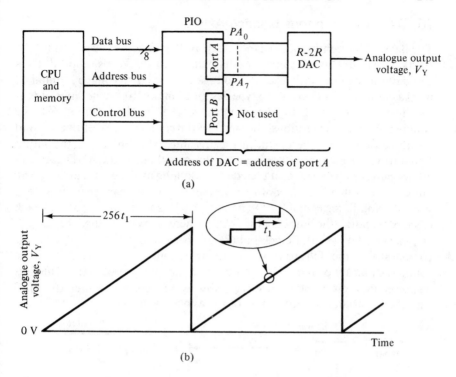

Fig. 10.19 (a) Block diagram of a microprocessor-driven DAC system and (b) ramp waveform produced by the DAC using the program in the text

10.13 Analogue-to-digital convertors (ADC)

Digital systems and data loggers must be capable of accepting analogue signals from transducers and instruments, leading to a need for analogue-to-digital convertors in interface units.

Table 10.11
Ramp waveform generator program

Address (hex)	Byte 1	2	3	Label	Instruction mnemonic	Comment
0200	A9	FF			LDA $FF	
0202	8D	03	A0		STA DDRA	Make port A outputs
0205	8D	01	A0		STA IORA	Store FF in IORA
0208	EE	01	A0	RAMP	INC IORA	Increment (IORA)
020B	4C	08	02		JMP RAMP	Repeat loop

10.13.1 A continuous balance ADC

The basis of the continuous balance ADC is illustrated by the circuit in Fig. 10.20(a). An unknown value of analogue voltage, V_X, is applied to a comparator together with a second voltage V_Y. The latter voltage is obtained from a counter via a DAC of the type described in Sec. 10.11; the value of V_Y is therefore proportional to the number stored in the counter. At the commencement of operations, the states of the counter are reset to zero, and the initial value of V_Y is zero. During the time interval when $V_X > V_Y$, the output signal from the comparator is logic '1'; this signal opens the AND gate and allows pulses to be applied to the counter. So long as the gate remains open, pulses are counted and V_Y continues to increase in the manner illustrated in Fig. 10.20(b). If, for example, a voltage of 1·1 V is to be measured and each clock pulse causes the output of the DAC to increase by 0·1 V, then the value of V_Y reaches 1·1 V when 11 clock pulses have been counted. When $V_Y \geqslant V_X$, the comparator output falls to zero and no further pulses are transmitted to the counter. By means of a suitable scaling factor, the value stored in the counter is displayed in terms of the value of V_X. By using a reversible counter, the ADC can 'track' variations in the value of the applied voltage.

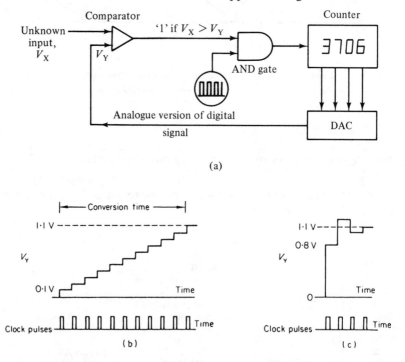

Fig. 10.20   (a) The basis of a continuous balance ADC; (b) shows how an input of 1·1 V may be encoded and (c) illustrates how 1·1 V is encoded using a successive approximation technique

This type of counter is relatively simple to construct, but the conversion time is relatively long if a large value of voltage is to be measured.

10.13.2 A successive approximation ADC

The *successive approximation ADC* is a variation of the continuous balance type, the difference between the two being in the sequence of trial voltages used to obtain the final balance. The successive approximation ADC commences by incrementing the most significant bit, and then progressively either adds or discards less significant bits until balance is reached. Assuming that the counter operates the 8421 BCD code, and that the least significant '1' causes the DAC to generate 0·1 V, then the following sequence of events occurs when balancing an input of 1·1 V. This sequence of events is illustrated in Fig. 10.20(c).

8 (0·8 V) tried and retained
an additional 4 (0·4 V) tried and rejected
an additional 2 (0·2 V) tried and retained
an additional 1 (0·1 V) tried and retained

As illustrated in the above description, the successive approximation ADC reaches balance in far fewer steps than does the continuous balance type, but requires more complex logic circuitry.

Both of the above types of convertors are capable of converting voltages to an accuracy of 0·01 per cent. They suffer from the disadvantage that their speed of conversion is so fast that they can give false readings if electrical noise is superimposed on the input signal. The effects of noise voltage can be reduced by filtering the input signal, but only at the expense of increasing the data conversion time. The successive approximation type is used where speed of conversion is important, such as in data acquisition systems.

A typical conversion rate for an eight-bit successive approximation ADC is 500 ns, and is 2 μs for a 12-bit conversion.

10.14 A microprocessor-based ADC

A basic software-driven ADC is shown in Fig. 10.21. The system can operate using either the continuous balance mode or the successive approximation mode (see also Sec. 10.13). The difference between the two modes of operation lies in the program which sends out the sequence of signals to the DAC part of the system. The basis of operation of either method of operation is as follows.

Initially, port B is defined as an input port (only line PB_7 is used in this case) and port A is defined as an output port. A given binary word is applied to the DAC via port A of the PIO and the analogue voltage V_Y produced by the DAC

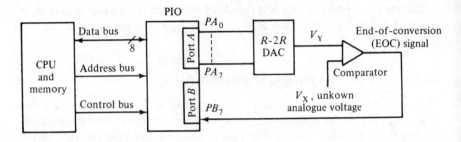

Fig. 10.21 Block diagram of a software-driven ADC

is compared with the unknown analogue voltage V_X. If V_Y is less than V_X, the output from the comparator is logic '0'; if V_Y is either equal to or is greater than V_X, the output from the comparator is logic '1'. The output line from the comparator is described as an *end-of-conversion* (EOC) line, since it has a logic '1' on it when the conversion process is complete or is ended.

Each time that a binary word is applied to the DAC, the CPU tests the state of the EOC line. If line PB_7 has a logic '0' on it, the conversion is not complete and the next binary test combination is applied to the DAC. If line PB_7 has a logic '1' on it, the conversion is complete and the digital equivalent of V_X can either be stored in the memory of the computer or it can be used in the next stage of the program.

A program for the *continuous balance* (ramp) mode of operation is given in Table 10.12. The voltage ramp which appears at V_Y is generally similar to that produced by the program in Table 10.11 with the exception that the ramp is terminated when $V_Y \geqslant V_X$. The addresses used in the program are as follows:

$0000 counter for the ramp signal
$020C start of ramp program
$A000 input/output register B of the PIO
$A001 input/output register A of the PIO
$A002 data direction register B of the PIO
$A003 data direction register A of the PIO

A software-driven successive approximation DAC uses the same hardware as the continuous balance convertor (see Fig. 10.21), but the software takes a different form. A flowchart for a *successive approximation* program is given in Fig. 10.22. In the case of this type of ADC, we need to make only as many sample trials as there are bits in the word length of the ADC. If the word length is eight bits, a counter (N) is established with the value eight in it; this counter is decremented each time that a pass of the program is made, so that after eight passes the conversion is complete.

In many cases the complete ADC together with its own successive approximation logic is available as a single chip, and is addressed by the CPU

Table 10.12
Program for a continuous balance ADC

Address (hex)	Byte 1	2	3	Label	Instruction mnemonic	Comment
0200	A9	FF			LDA #$FF	
0202	8D	03	A0		STA DDRA	Make port A outputs
0205	A9	00			LDA #$00	
0207	8D	02	A0		STA DDRB	Make port B inputs
020A	85	00			STA COUNT	Initialize ramp counter
020C	A5	00		STEP	LDA COUNT	Load from ramp counter
020E	8D	01	A0		STA IORA	Begin ramp
0211	AD	00	A0		LDA IORB	Get comparator output
0214	30	05			BMI DONE	Branch if DONE
0216	E6	00			INC COUNT	Otherwise increment counter
0218	4C	0C	02		JMP STEP	And return to STEP
021B	00			DONE	BRK	

in the same way that it addresses any other peripheral. A block diagram of a typical ADC chip is shown in Fig. 10.23. The conversion commences when the CPU sends a signal along the *start-of-conversion* (SOC) line; the ADC signals that the conversion is complete by sending a signal along the EOC line to the CPU. When the CPU is ready to receive data from the ADC, it sends a signal along the output enable line which enables the output buffers and gives the ADC access to the data bus.

10.15 Other types of analogue-to-digital convertor

A wide range of ADCs is available, each type being designed to satisfy a particular requirement. Brief notes are given below on three other types of ADC.

10.15.1 Voltage-to-frequency ADC

In this type, the unknown analogue voltage is applied to a voltage-controlled oscillator (VCO) which generates a frequency proportional to the unknown voltage. The frequency is measured by means of an electronic counter, the frequency being displayed in the form of a voltage measurement. This type of instrument can also double as a counter/timer.

10.15.2 Dual-slope or dual-ramp ADC

This type of ADC is widely used in digital voltmeters and has a high degree of noise immunity. The unknown analogue voltage charges a capacitor at a constant rate for a fixed period of time. The voltage across the capacitor at the end of the charging period is therefore proportional to the unknown analogue

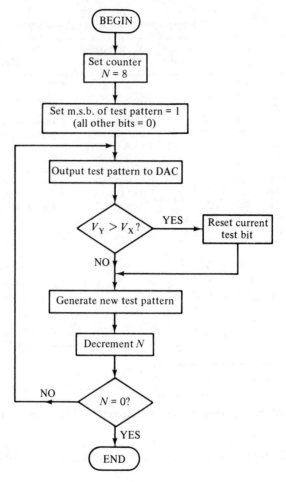

Fig. 10.22 Flowchart for a successive approximation ADC

voltage. The capacitor is discharged at a constant rate and, at the same time, pulses from an accurate timing source are applied to a counter. When the capacitor is discharged, the number of pulses counted by the counter is proportional to the analogue voltage.

10.15.3 Simultaneous convertor or flash convertor

In this type of convertor the unknown voltage, V_Y, is simultaneously compared with a number of preset reference voltages (see Fig. 10.24). For an n-bit conversion, there are $(2^n - 1)$ comparators; in a four-bit convertor there are 15 comparators, and in an eight-bit convertor there are 255 comparators. A single reference source, V_R, is used, this voltage being divided by means of a potential

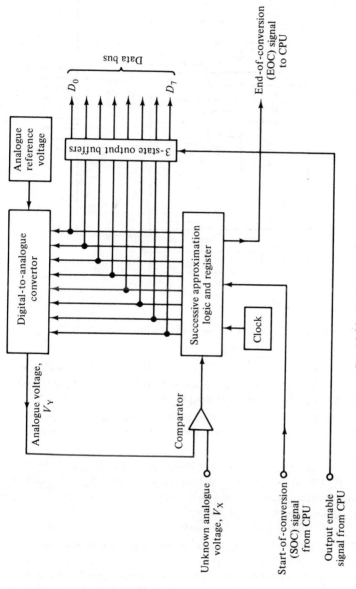

Fig. 10.23 An integrated circuit ADC

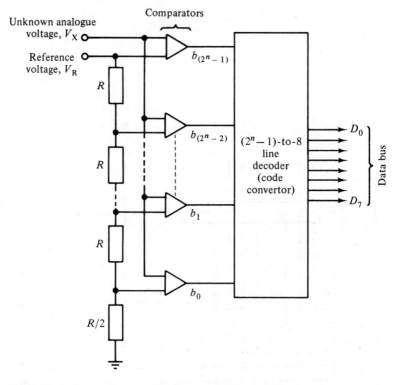

Fig. 10.24 Block diagram for an n-bit simultaneous ADC or 'flash' ADC

divider chain. The resistance associated with the least significant comparator in the chain is one-half that associated with other comparators to give a one-half step for the least significant comparator. Each of the other comparator threshold points is one voltage step above that of the less significant comparator.

If a four-bit convertor is used with an input voltage range of zero to one volt, the input signal is digitized to a resolution of four bits. This corresponds to 14 steps of $1/(2^4 - 1)$ volt $= 66.7$ mV and one step of $66.7/2 = 33.35$ mV; the first voltage comparison level is 33.35 mV and the final threshold level is $(14 \times 66.7$ mV$) + 33.35$ mV $= 967.15$ mV.

If the analogue voltage, V_X, is 450 mV, comparator outputs b_0 to b_6, inclusive, are at logic '1' and comparator outputs b_7 to b_{15} are at logic '0'. This type of output is sometimes known as a 'thermometer' type output. The function of the code convertor — see Fig. 10.24 — situated between the comparators and the convertor output is to convert the 'thermometer' type of output into a more suitable output such as pure binary. Since we are discussing a four-bit convertor, the code on the 16 lines b_0 to b_{15} is converted into a four-bit pure binary code which is applied to the data bus lines D_0 to D_3; data bus lines D_4 to D_7 are not used by this convertor.

A disadvantage of the flash convertor when compared with the successive approximation type is that a very large number of comparators are required, and there are difficulties in maintaining the accuracy of the resistor chain when the ambient temperature varies. Various techniques have been adopted to overcome this problem including (1) combining flash and successive approximation methods in one chip, (2) a serial-parallel method using flash convertors,* and (3) the use of multiple convertors in a time sequence.

10.16 Handshaking

The term *handshake* refers to a method of handling asynchronous transfer of data between the CPU and a peripheral. Peripherals frequently work at a different speed than the CPU, and it is vital to have some method of synchronizing the two. One method of doing this is to provide two 'handshake' lines between the CPU and the peripheral so that one device can 'tell' the other either that data are ready for transfer or that the data transferred have been received.

A handshake may be one of two kinds, namely an input handshake or an output handshake. In the following it is assumed that we need one I/O port to handle the signals transferred along the data bus between the CPU and the peripheral, and two I/O ports (one an input port and one an output port) each handling one handshake line (in practice, a single PIO satisfies all the needs of a handshake transfer).

10.16.1 Input handshake

A basic system for handling an input handshake is shown in Fig. 10.25. The data transfer is handled as follows:

1. The peripheral sends a DATA READY signal to input port B.

2. The CPU periodically interrogates port B to check if data are ready (the DATA READY signal may be held in a latch in port B).

3. If data are ready, the CPU reads the data from port A.

4. The CPU sends a DATA ACKNOWLEDGE signal to the peripheral via output port C to indicate that the data transfer has been completed.

---

* See, for example, 'New approaches to high-speed, high-resolution analogue-to-digital conversion', *Electronics and Power*, February 1982, by F. Shoreys.

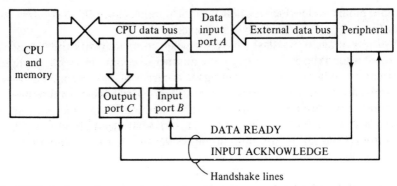

Fig. 10.25 An input data transfer using handshake logic

10.16.2 Output handshake

A basic system for handling an output handshake is shown in Fig. 10.26, and is described below:

1. The CPU sends an OUTPUT READY signal to the peripheral via output port C.
2. When the peripheral is ready to receive data, it sends a PERIPHERAL READY signal to the CPU via input port B.
3. The CPU sends the data to the peripheral via output port A.

10.17 Subroutines

A *subroutine* or subprogram is a short program that can be 'called' or reached from many points in the main program. The process of transferring control from the main program to the subroutine is known as a *subroutine call*. Many of the programs described so far can be used as subroutines.

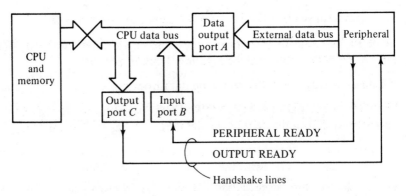

Fig. 10.26 An output data transfer using handshake logic

Suppose that the main program needs to use a multiplication routine (see Table 10.7) many times during its execution. It would be very uneconomic in terms of the amount of memory used if the multiplication routine was included in the main program each time it was needed. The method adopted to deal with this situation is to store the multiplication as a subroutine in memory locations not used by the main program; each time that the subroutine is needed, it is 'called' by the main program.

To understand the mechanics of calling a subroutine and returning from a subroutine, it is necessary to understand the operation and the use of a 'stack' in the memory. This is described in Sec. 10.18.

10.18 Stack operations

A *stack* is a sequence of memory locations used in a *last-in, first-out* (LIFO) manner in which the last item of data to be entered onto the stack is the first to be removed at a later time. In microcomputers the stack is part of the RAM area of memory and, depending on the design principles of the CPU, the stack may be located anywhere in RAM (as is the case, for example, in the 8080, 8085, or the Z80 family) or in a restricted area of RAM (as in the 6502; in 6502-based systems the stack is limited to the range of addresses \$0100 to \$01FF (this 256-byte depth of stack is adequate for most purposes).

An item of data is added to the stack by means of a *PUSH* operation and is removed from the stack by means of a *PULL* (or *POP*) operation. The 6502 CPU PUSH instructions are as follows, both being one-byte implied address instructions:

PHA (PusH Accumulator contents onto stack) — opcode \$48
PHP (PusH Processor status register contents onto stack) — opcode \$08

Thus, before the contents of any location (except the status register) can be transferred to the stack, it must first be transferred to the accumulator before being PUSHed. The execution of a PHA instruction is illustrated in Fig. 10.27, and is described below.

The *stack pointer*, SP (see Fig. 10.27), is loaded with the least significant byte of the address of the 'top' of the stack; this is shown as \$$ss$ in the figure. The most significant byte of the address of the top of the stack, i.e., \$01 in the 6502, is added automatically by the CPU. Thus the address of the 'top' of the stack is \$01ss; the initial value of \$$ss$ may be any hex number in the range \$00 to \$$FF$, but it is usual to load the stack pointer with \$$FF$ to give the stack its maximum range of 256 locations.

The opcode (\$48) of the PUSH instruction is stored in memory location \$$aaaa$ + 0, and is transferred to the instruction register where it is decoded; since this is a one-byte instruction, the content of the program counter is incremented by unity. The instruction calls for the contents (\$$fg$) of the

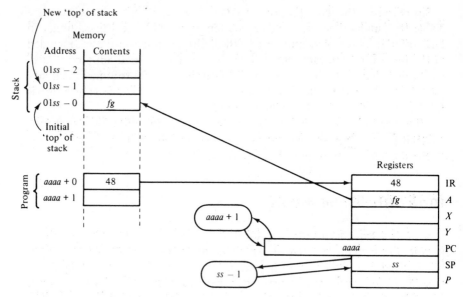

Fig. 10.27 Executing the 6502 CPU PHA instruction

accumulator to be PUSHed into the address given by the initial value of the top of the stack, i.e., into address $01ss. The content of the stack pointer is then *decremented* by unity, so that the SP register contains the value $ss − 1$; this is the new value of the 'top' of the stack and the address into which data are next PUSHed is $ss − 1$.

For example, if the accumulator contains $AB and the stack pointer initially contained $FF then, after a PHA instruction, location $01FF contains $AB and the SP contains $FE.

The 6502 CPU PULL instructions are the one-byte instructions below:

PLA (PulL a byte of data from the stack into the Accumulator) — opcode $68
PLP(PulL a byte of data from the stack into the Processor status register) — opcode $28

The execution of a PLP instruction is illustrated in Fig. 10.28. When a PLP instruction is encountered, the content of the PC is incremented by unity, and the content of the stack pointer is also *incremented* by unity. The CPU fetches the content of location $01ss + 1$ and transfers it to the processor status register. This instruction is used to restore the status register to its original condition on completion of a subroutine.

If the stack pointer contained $FD before the PLP instruction, after the execution of the instruction the SP contains $FE, and the contents of location $01FE have been copied into the status register.

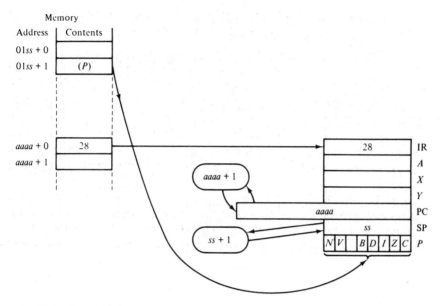

Fig. 10.28 Executing the 6502 CPU PLP instruction

10.19 Subroutine execution

The way in which a subroutine is called by the main program is illustrated in Fig. 10.29. When a three-byte JSR (Jump to SubRoutine) instruction (JSR$_1$ in Fig. 10.29) is encountered for the first time in the program, the CPU saves the two-byte contents of the program counter on the top of the stack, and replaces the contents of the PC with the two-byte address of the first instruction in the subroutine. Since the PC now contains the 'start address' of the subroutine, the next instruction executed is the first instruction in the subroutine. Each subroutine has four principal sections as follows:

1. A *save vital data* section in which the programmer must ensure that he 'saves' information on the stack which is vital to the operation of the system when control is transferred back to the main program on the completion of the subroutine. Typically, the user may wish to save the contents of the processor status register on the stack by means of a PHP instruction.

2. The *main body of the subroutine* which performs the function that the subroutine must carry out, e.g., multiplication of two numbers using the multiplication program MULT in Table 10.7.

3. The *restore vital data* routine; the programmer must ensure that the data saved on the stack during the 'save vital data' section are correctly restored. An example would be to restore the contents of the status register by means of a PLP instruction.

4. The subroutine must be terminated by means of a one-byte RTS instruction (ReTurn from Subroutine)—opcode $60—which is described below.

The RTS instruction restores the contents of the program counter to its value at the time of the subrouine call and then increments the contents of the program counter by unity; this ensures that the PC 'points' at the address of the opcode of the next instruction in the main program. Thus, if the JSR_1 instruction is stored at address $0270, the address ($0270 + 2) is transferred to the stack during the time that the subroutine is being executed. When the RTS instruction is encountered at the end of the first pass of the subroutine, the opcode at address ($0272 + 1) = $0273 in the main program is fetched and executed.

A little later in the main program the second Jump to SuBroutine instruction, JSR_2 in Fig. 10.29, is encountered. Once again, the (return address − 1) is pushed onto the stack and the subroutine start address is inserted into the PC. The subroutine is executed for the second time and, on completion of

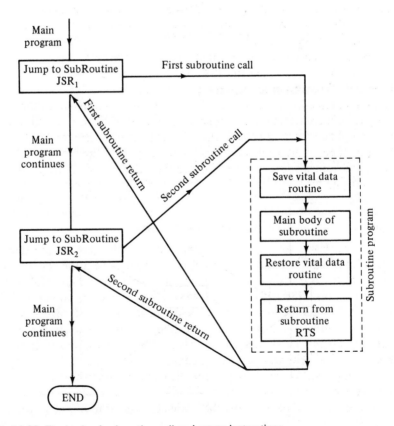

Fig. 10.29 The basis of subroutine call and return instructions

the subroutine, the (return address -1) for the main program is pulled from the stack and, after being incremented, is loaded into the program counter. The main program then continues as before.

10.20   Nested subroutines

There are many applications in which a subroutine may need to call a second subroutine, and even the second subroutine may need to call a third subroutine, and so on. In such cases, the subroutines are said to be *nested*. Two nested subroutines are illustrated in Fig. 10.30.

Figure 10.30 may, for example, represent the software operation of an electronic timer. Subroutine 2 could be a timing sequence to generate a 1-s time delay, subroutine 1 could be a 1-min time delay sequence (which involves calling for subroutine 2 sixty times), and the main program could be a 1-h time delay sequence. Using nested subroutines in this way allows both long and accurate time delay sequences to be built up.

The stack enables an orderly transfer to be made between the main program and each subroutine. When the JSR_1 instruction in Fig. 10.30 is executed, the address reached in the main program is pushed onto the top of the stack, the stack pointer then being decremented so that it 'points' to the next vacant location in the stack. When the JSR_2 instruction is reached, its address in subroutine 1 is pushed onto the stack, and the stack pointer decremented once more. On completion of subroutine 2, the RTS instruction causes the stack pointer to be incremented so that it points to the return address to subroutine 1. On completion of subroutine 1, the RTS instruction which terminates that subroutine once more causes the stack pointer to be incremented so that it points to the return address in the main program, allowing an orderly return to be made to it.

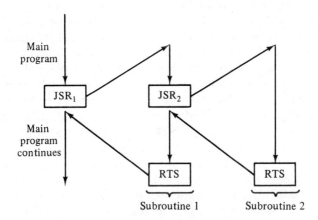

Fig. 10.30   Nested subroutines

10.21 Interrupts

Many microprocessor-based systems monitor a wide range of devices in a mode dictated by the main program. However, a number of transducers monitor events which are likely to be critical to the safe operation of the main system; clearly, a means must be devised to allow a signal from any one of these transducers to interrupt the operation of the main program so that precautionary action can be taken.

Where the signal from a sensor is vital to the safety of the system, it can be connected to a pin on the CPU chip known as an *interrupt* pin; when a suitable logic signal (sometimes logic '0') is applied to the pin, the main program is interrupted and program control is transferred to an *interrupt routine* (the address at which the interrupt occurred in the main program meanwhile being pushed onto the stack).

There are two types of interrupt, namely *maskable interrupts* and *nonmaskable interrupts*. The two types are illustrated by means of an analogy. Suppose that an executive is travelling between his office and a customer's works in his car, and that the car has a radio telephone and also, among other instruments, a low oil-pressure warning light. If, during the journey, his thoughts are interrupted when the telephone rings, he may either answer the telephone or he may choose to ignore it. That is, he may either *accept* the interrupt or he may *mask it out*. Such an interrupt is a maskable interrupt (in a microprocessor we may, by means of an instruction, either 'enable' a maskable interrupt — in which case it 'answers' the interrupt — or the interrupt may be 'disabled'—i.e., it is ignored). However, during the journey, the low oil-pressure warning light may suddenly be illuminated. This is clearly a non-maskable interrupt request which calls on him to stop the car and take appropriate action.

A typical function associated with a non-maskable interrupt in a microprocessor-based system is in the detection of power supply failure; if vital data are held in RAM, the CPU has only a few milliseconds in which to preserve the vital data before the system shuts down and the data are lost. In this situation the data are usually transferred into a RAM with battery back-up; this allows the data to be preserved until the power supply is reapplied.

It is useful to understand the general procedure followed by the CPU when executing an instruction, which is described in the following. The CPU fetches and executes the instruction and, on completing the instruction, it tests the interrupt flag to see if it has been set, i.e., it asks if the interrupts are enabled. If the interrupts are not enabled, the CPU fetches and executes the next instruction. If the interrupts are enabled, it proceeds to interrogate the logic signal on the interrupt pin; if the pin is not active (i.e., an interrupt has not occurred), the CPU fetches and executes the next instruction. If the interrupt pin is active, i.e., the interrupting device requires servicing, the CPU transfers program control in the interrupt routine by transferring the address of the first instruction in the interrupt routine to the program counter and, simultaneously, it saves the current contents of the program counter on the stack; this enables an orderly return to be made to the main program at a later time. (*Note*: in the 6502 CPU, an interrupt signal also results in the contents of the processor status register being saved on the stack.) Meanwhile, the CPU automatically disables maskable interrupts so that the 'interrupt' cannot itself be interrupted. On completion of the interrupt routine, the final instruction is a ReTurn from Interrupt (RTI—opcode $40 in the 6502) which simultaneously restores not only the return address in the main program to the program counter but also the contents of the status register to its pre-interrupt condition.

The simplest forms of CPU have a single maskable interrupt, allowing a single device to generate an interrupt signal. However, with such a CPU, more than one interrupting device can be used if the interrupt signals are gated together via a suitable logic circuit to drive the interrupt pin. When an interrupt signal is detected, the interrupt routine causes the interrupting sources to be sequentially *polled* or tested to detect which device has produced the interrupt signal. Interrupts can be given differing priority in the above system if the interrupt logic includes a priority encoder.

More sophisticated forms of CPU have both maskable and non-maskable interrupt pins on the chip and, in some cases, the maskable interrupts have a priority order. The latter enables the user to select the priority wiring different interrupting devices to different interrupt pins. Examples of the types of interrupt are given below.

The 6502 has an active-low non-maskable interrupt pin, $\overline{\text{NMI}}$ (pin 6), and an active-low maskable interrupt, $\overline{\text{IRQ}}$ (pin 4). The 8085 has a non-maskable interrupt, TRAP (pin 6), and four maskable interrupt pins, RST 7.5, RST 6.5, RST 5.5, and INTR (pins 7, 8, 9, and 10 respectively) in which RST 7.5 has the highest priority and INTR the lowest priority. The Z80 CPU has a single maskable interrupt, $\overline{\text{INT}}$ (pin 16), and a single non-maskable interrupt, $\overline{\text{NMI}}$ (pin 17). Many CPUs have a handshake facility which is used in connection with interrupt signals; e.g., the 8085 has an interrupt acknowledge pin — $\overline{\text{INTA}}$ — which is driven low when an interrupt occurs, this signal being used to activate the interrupting chip.

10.22 Direct memory access

Many peripheral devices such as high-speed analogue-to-digital convertors operate at a much higher speed than the CPU that controls them. A factor which limits the maximum throughput or 'update rate' of the central processor is the execution time of the instructions associated with processing the data from I/O ports. This includes the time taken to transfer the data to the accumulator, to process the data, and to store the result. Many processors

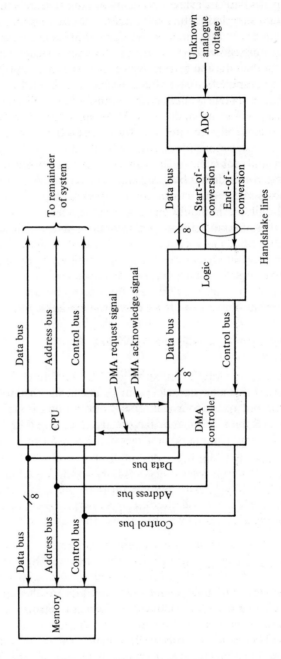

Fig. 10.31 The basis of direct memory access

require about 20 μs before they are ready to deal with the next item of data, giving an equivalent update rate of about 50 000 samples/s. A high-speed ADC can provide data samples at the rate of about 10^6 per second and, from the above, this is much faster than the rate at which the CPU can handle the data.

Direct memory access (DMA) is a method available to most microprocessors systems which allows data to be transferred directly from a peripheral to the memory of the computer without the intervention of the CPU (the CPU is, meanwhile, in a *hold* state while the data transfer takes place).

The basis of a DMA is shown in Fig. 10.31. When data are available from the ADC, the DMA controller initiates a DMA request signal. When the CPU has completed the instruction it is currently handling, it sends a DMA acknowledge signal to the controller (which is another form of handshake) and puts its own data bus, address bus, and control bus lines in a high impedance state; this allows the DMA controller to operate the system. The DMA controller then places not only the appropriate memory address on the address bus but also suitable signals on the control bus, and then transfers data from the ADC to the memory location. If further DMA transfers are necessary at this time, they are handled by the DMA controller. On completion of the DMA cycle, the controller ends the DMA request and allows the CPU to continue with its program. The reader will appreciate that different manufacturers may implement DMA operations in a slightly different way.

10.23 IEEE-488 and IEC-625 interface bus

The interconnections or interfacing between a microcomputer and peripherals such as electronic instruments present many problems which have largely been resolved by the use of 'standard' interface bus systems. One of the most popular of these is the IEEE-488 bus interface, which was first developed by the Hewlett-Packard Company of America in the form of the Hewlett-Packard Interface Bus (HPIB). Other names used to describe the system are the General Purpose Interface Bus (GPIB) and the IEC-625 bus interface (International Electrotechnical Commission).

The basis of the instrument interface is shown in Fig. 10.32. There are basically three types of device which may use the bus as follows:

1. A **listener**. This is an instrument which can receive data from other instruments or from a controller (see below). Examples include programmable power supplies, printers, and video display units.
2. A **talker**. This is an instrument which can send data to other instruments or to a controller. Examples include tape readers, electronic voltmeters, counters, data loggers, etc.
3. A **controller**. This device controls the flow of information and data along the bus lines. Examples include microcomputers and instruments with control functions.

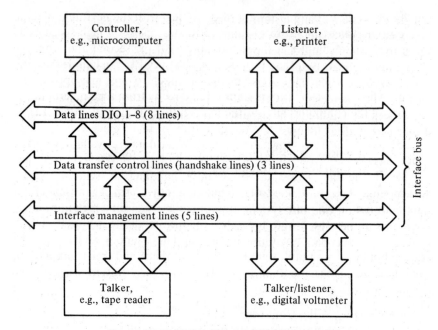

Fig. 10.32 The IEEE-488 and IEC-625 interface bus

Some instruments may combine two or more of the above features. For example, a digital voltmeter and a data logger may both be talker/listeners. A controller has both talking and listening capability, since it must not only talk to other instruments and listen to them, but must also control them. The controller must ensure that data is smoothly transferred between instruments; e.g., two talkers must not simultaneously be given access to the interface bus, otherwise chaos ensues! Data transfer is controlled by means of handshake functions; a talker must contain a 'source' handshake function and a listener must have an 'acceptor' handshake function.

A basic form of bus-organized test system may comprise the following:

1. A d.c. power supply (a listener) which applies a range of programmed voltages to a piece of equipment.
2. A digital voltmeter (which is both a talker and a listener) which measures voltages within the test equipment and reports the voltages back to the system.
3. A printer (a listener) which prints out the voltmeter readings.
4. A microcomputer (the controller).

In general, only one device can 'talk' over the bus while several devices can 'listen' to the bus at any one time, the bus handshake signals ensuring that the data transmission rate does not exceed the speed of the slowest listener.

A system may have a number of controllers, but only one of them actively controls the system at any instant of time. Yet other systems may not have a controller, and consist of one talker and one or more listeners; the instruments are set to 'talk only' and 'listen only' by local control.

The interface bus comprises 16 lines as follows. There are eight *data lines* (DIO 1–8) along which data, addresses, instructions, etc., can be transmitted, generally in the seven-bit ASCII or ISO code, the eighth bit being used for a parity check bit if desired. The signals are transmitted in *negative logic* having *positive potentials* as follows:

A voltage $\leqslant 0.8$ V ('low' state) is logic '1' (or *true*)

A voltage $\geqslant 2.0$ V ('high' state) is logic '0' (or *false*)

The maximum data transfer rate is one M byte/s. Up to 15 instruments can be interconnected on one bus system, and to ensure high-speed data transfer between them the cable length between each pair of instruments should not exceed 2 m, subject to a restriction on the total cable length of the bus not exceeding 20 m.

The function of the three *data transfer control lines* (*handshake lines*) is described below:

DAV—DAta Valid from source device
  DAV = 1 when valid data is on the data bus
NRFD — Not Ready For Data
  NRFD = 0 when *all* acceptor devices are ready for data
NDAC — Not Data ACcepted
  NDAC = 0 when *all* the listening devices have accepted the data

The NRFD lines and the NDAC lines of the instrument are connected in a WIRED-OR configutation, so that if any one device is not ready to accept data then NRFD = 1; also, NDAC = 1 if any listener has not accepted the data.

The five *interface management lines* are as follows:

ATN — ATentionN
  ATN = 0 when the bus is in the data mode
  ATN = 1 when the bus is in the command mode
IFC — InterFace Clear
  IFC = 1 sets the interface of all instruments to a predetermined state
REN — Remote ENable
  REN = 1 enables instruments with a local/remote control feature to be switched from local control to remote control
SRQ — Service ReQuest
  SRQ = 1 when an instrument with a service request function in its interface indicates the need for attention
EOI — End Or Identify
  When EOI = 1 AND ATN = 0, a talker instrument can use EOI to indicate the end of a multi-byte data transfer.

When EOI = 1 AND ATN = 1, a controller uses EOI for the execution of a polling sequence or testing sequence.

A simplified operating sequence of the interface bus signals is described below:

1. ATN = 1 (bus in command mode); the talker address followed by the listener address are placed on the DIO (data) lines.
2. ATN = 0 (bus in data mode); data are placed in the DIO lines by the talker. The talker sets DAV = 0 (DAta *not* Valid) and the listeners set NRFD = 1 (None Ready For Data) and NDAC = 1 (none have accepted data).
3. Only when all listeners are ready for data does NRFD = 0. The talker sets DAV = 1 to indicate that data are valid.
4. When all listeners have accepted the data, NDAC = 0 (data accepted by every listener).
5. The talker completes the handshake by making DAV = 0 (data no longer valid). The talker can then use the above procedure to put new data on the bus lines.

Problems

10.1 Data are stored in locations $0240 and $0241. After a mathematical operation, the result is to be stored in locations $0235 and $024F. Write a program which:
(a) adds the binary data in the specified locations,
(b) decimal adds the data in the specified locations (assume that decimal data are stored),
(c) subtracts the contents of $0241 from the contents of $0240.

10.2 Binary data are stored in locations $0260, $0263, and $0264. Write a program which satisfies the following specification:

Form the one's complement of ($0260) and store the result in location $0261. If bit seven of ($0260) is zero, terminate the program; otherwise add the contents of $0260 and $0261 and store the result in location $0262. If the content of $0262 is zero, terminate the program; otherwise form the EXCLUSIVE-OR function of ($0263) and ($0264) and store the result in location $0265.

10.3 Write a program commencing at location $0200 which satisfies the following specification:

Data are stored in locations $0240 and $0241. The contents of the two locations are added together and the result is stored in location $0241. The content of this location is to be displayed on a display device whose address is $0D00 for 0·1 s, after which the contents of location $0241 are to be incremented and the display routine repeated. The 'increment and display' sequence is to be repeated until the value stored in location $0241 is zero.

10.4 Modify the program in problem 10.3 to incorporate a subroutine which causes the character to be displayed for 0·1 s, after which it is extinguished for 0·1 s so that each character displayed appears to flash on and off once.

10.5   Write a program commencing at address $0200 which satisfies the following specification:

Eight switches are connected to port A of a programmable I/O port, and eight LEDs are connected to port B in the manner shown in Fig. 10.7. The internal addresses of registers of the port are:

> Input/output register B $A000
> Input/output register A $A001
> Data direction register B $A002
> Data direction register A $A003

The switch connected to line PA_n is to control the LED connected to line PB_n; i.e., switch PA_0 controls the LED connected to PB_0, switch PA_1 controls LED PB_1, etc. When a switch is in the logic '0' position, the corresponding LED is to be extinguished. When the switch is in the logic '1' position, the LED is to flash on and off with a periodic time of 0·2 s.

10.6   Using a PIO with the addresses listed in problem 10.5, write a program satisfying the following specification:

On switch-on (with all switches in the logic '0' position), LED PB_7 is illuminated for 0·1 s, the remaining LEDs being extinguished. LED PB_7 is then extinguished and LED PB_6 is illuminated for 0·1 s. Provided that all the switches connected to port B remain at logic '0', each LED connected to port B is to be illuminated in sequence for 0·1 s until, finally, LED PB_0 is illuminated; after this LED has been extinguished, LED PB_7 is illuminated once more and the sequence repeated.

During each LED illumination sequence, the switches connected to port A are to be tested to check if any one of them produces a logic '1' signal. If switch PA_n provides a logic '1', the LED flashing sequence is to be terminated and the LED PB_n must be illuminated so long as $PA_n = 1$. When PA_n returns to zero, the LED flashing sequence *continues from the point where switch PA_n became logic '1'*.

10.7   Write a program for a successive approximation analogue-to-digital convertor using an eight-bit ADC chip.

Appendix A

6502 Instruction Set

Mnemonic	Operation	Immediate (2 byte)	Absolute (3 byte)	Zero page (2 byte)	Accumulator (1 byte)	Implied (1 byte)	(Indexed, X) (2 byte)	(Indexed), Y 2 byte	Zero page, X (2 byte)	Absolute, X (3 byte)	Absolute, Y (3 byte)	Relative (2 byte)	Indirect (3 byte)	Zero page, Y (2 byte)	N	V	B	D	I	Z	C	Mnemonic
ADC	$A+M+C \rightarrow A$	69	6D	65			61	71	75	7D	79				N	V				Z	C	ADC
AND	$A \wedge M \rightarrow A$	29	2D	25			21	31	35	3D	39				N					Z	C	AND
ASL	$C \leftarrow \boxed{7 \quad 0} \leftarrow 0$		0E	06	0A				16	1E					N					Z	C	ASL
BCC	Branch on $C=0$											90										BCC
BCS	Branch on $C=1$											B0										BCS
BEQ	Branch on $Z=1$											F0										BEQ
BIT	$A \wedge M$		2C	24											M_7	M_6				Z		BIT
BMI	Branch on $N=1$											30										BMI
BNE	Branch on $Z=0$											D0										BNE
BPL	Branch on $N=0$											10										BPL
BRK	Break					00													1			BRK
BVC	Branch on $V=0$											50						1				BVC
BVS	Branch on $V=1$											70										BVS
CLC	$0 \rightarrow C$					18															0	CLC
CLD	$0 \rightarrow D$					D8												0				CLD

Processor status register flags: N V · B D I Z C

264

Mnemonic	Operation	Immed.	Absolute	Zero Page	Accum.	Implied	(Ind, X)	(Ind), Y	Z Page, X	Abs, X	Abs, Y	Z Page, Y	Flags (N Z C)
CLI	$0 \to I$					58							0 (I)
CLV	$0 \to V$					B8							0 (V)
CMP	$A - M$	C9	CD	C5			C1	D1	D5	DD	D9		N Z C
CPX	$X - M$	E0	EC	E4									N Z C
CPY	$Y - M$	C0	CC	C4									N Z C
DEC	$M - 1 \to M$		CE	C6					D6	DE			N Z
DEX	$X - 1 \to X$					CA							N Z
DEY	$Y - 1 \to Y$					88							N Z
EOR	$A \veebar M \to A$	49	4D	45			41	51	55	5D	59		N Z
INC	$M + 1 \to M$		EE	E6					F6	FE			N Z
INX	$X + 1 \to X$					E8							N Z
INY	$Y + 1 \to Y$					C8							N Z
JMP	Jump to new location		4C										
JSR	Jump to subroutine		20										
LDA	$M \to A$	A9	AD	A5			A1	B1	B5	BD	B9		N Z
LDX	$M \to X$	A2	AE	A6							BE	B6	N Z
LDY	$M \to Y$	A0	AC	A4					B4	BC			N Z
LSR	$0 \to \boxed{7 \quad 0} \to C$		4E	46	4A				56	5E			0 Z C
NOP	No operation					EA							
ORA	$A \wedge M \to A$	09	0D	05			01	11	15	1D	19		N Z
PHA	$A \to M_s\; S - 1 \to S$					48							
PHP	$P \to M_s\; S - 1 \to S$					08							
PLA	$S + 1 \to S\; M_s \to A$					68							N Z
PLP	$S + 1 \to S\; M_s \to P$					28							(Restored)
ROL	$\boxed{\leftarrow 7 \quad 0 \leftarrow C \leftarrow}$		2E	26	2A				36	3E			N Z C

JMP (Indirect) = 6C

Mnem.	Operation	Imm	ZP	ZP,X	ZP,Y	Abs	Abs,X	Abs,Y	(Ind,X)	(Ind),Y	A	Impl	N	V	D	I	Z	C
ROR	→[7 0]→C→		66	76		6E	7E				6A		N				Z	C
RTI	Return from interpt.											40	(Restored)					
RTS	Return from subrtn.											60						
SBC	A−M−C̄→A	E9	E5	F5		ED	FD	F9	E1	F1			N	V			Z	(1)
SEC	1→C											38						1
SED	1→D											F8			1			
SEI	1→I											78				1		
STA	A→M		85	95		8D	9D	99	81	91								
STX	X→M		86		96	8E												
STY	Y→M		84	94		8C												
TAX	A→X											AA	N				Z	
TAY	A→Y											A8	N				Z	
TSX	S→X											BA	N				Z	
TXA	X→A											8A	N				Z	
TXS	X→S											9A						
TYA	Y→A											98	N				Z	

Notes:

(1) Carry not borrow
S: Stack pointer
A = Accumulator
M_s = Top of stack
X = X register
Y = Y register
∧ = AND
V = OR
∀ = EXCLUSIVE-OR

N = Negative flag
V = Overflow flag
B = Break flag
D = Decimal mode flag
I = Interrupt disable flag
Z = Zero flag
C = Carry flag

(Published by courtesy of Rockwell International)

Appendix B

To enable readers to interpret logic diagrams using standard symbols, a condensed list is given in the following table.

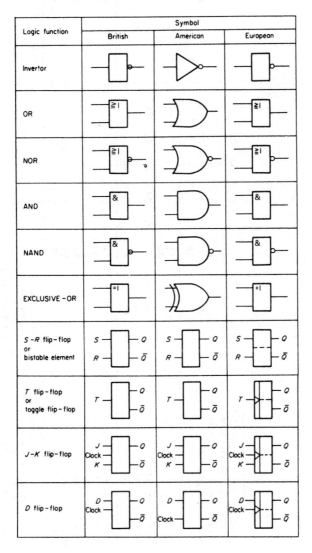

Logic function	Symbol		
	British	American	European
Invertor			
OR			
NOR			
AND			
NAND			
EXCLUSIVE – OR			
S – R flip – flop or bistable element			
T flip – flop or toggle flip – flop			
J – K flip – flop			
D flip – flop			

Bibliography

CLEARY, J. F., (Ed.), *General Electric Transistor Manual*, International General Electric Company, 1964.

FLEGG, H. C., *Boolean Algebra*, Blackie, 1972.

LEVENTHAL, L. A., *6502 Assembly Language Programming*, Osborne–McGraw-Hill, 1979.

LEWIN, D., *Logical Design of Switching Circuits*, Nelson, 1982.

MALEY, G. A., and J. EARLE, *The Logical Design of Transistor Digital Computers*, Prentice-Hall, 1963.

MILLMAN, J., and C. C. HALKIAS, *Integrated Electronics*, McGraw-Hill, 1972.

MORRIS, N. M., *Microprocessor and Microcomputer Technology*, Macmillan, 1982.

MORRIS, N. M., *Advanced Industrial Electronics*, McGraw-Hill, 1974.

MORRIS, N. M., *Semiconductor Devices*, Macmillan, 1976.

PEATMAN, J. B., *Microcomputer-Based Design*, McGraw-Hill, 1977.

WOOLONS, D. J., *Introduction to Digital Computer Design*, McGraw-Hill, 1973.

Index

Printed and bound in Great Britain at
The Camelot Press Ltd, Southampton